1-1 WORK TOGETHER, p. 11

Performing file maintenance activities; adding general ledger accounts   [4]

2120   Federal Income Tax Payable _____

2125   Social Security Tax Payable _____

2128   Medicare Tax Payable _____

2129   Unemployment Tax Payable—Federal _____

2130   Unemployment Tax Payable—State _____

_____

_____

_____

_____

_____

_____

_____

_____

_____

1-1 ON YOUR OWN, p. 11

Performing file maintenance activities; adding general ledger accounts   [5]

6205   Depreciation Expense—Office Equipment _____

6208   Payroll Taxes Expense _____

6210   Rent Expense _____

6213   Salary Expense—Administrative _____

6215   Supplies Expense—Office _____

6220   Utilities Expense _____

_____

_____

_____

_____

_____

_____

_____

_____

Extra form

1-2 WORK TOGETHER
ON YOUR OWN, p. 19

Journalizing and posting purchases on account and purchases returns and allowances **[3, 5]**

PURCHASES JOURNAL

PAGE 3

	DATE		ACCOUNT CREDITED	PURCH. NO.	POST. REF.	1 ACCOUNTS PAYABLE CREDIT	2 PURCHASES DEBIT COMPACT DISCS	3 PURCHASES DEBIT TAPES	
1	20-- Mar.	1	Raymond Wholesalers	283	280	1 3 5 0 00		1 3 5 0 00	1
2		2	Artex Music	284	210	9 6 5 00	9 6 5 00		2
3		18	Quality Tapes	288	270	2 6 8 00		2 6 8 00	3
4		23	Castle Records and Tapes	289	220	9 9 3 00		9 9 3 00	4
5		31	Totals			3 5 7 6 00	9 6 5 00	2 6 1 1 00	5
6						(2105)	(5105-1)	(5105-2)	6
7									7
8									8
9									9
10									10
11									11

[3, 5]

PURCHASES RETURNS AND ALLOWANCES JOURNAL

PAGE 3

	DATE		ACCOUNT DEBITED	DEBIT MEMO. NO.	POST. REF.	1 ACCOUNTS PAYABLE DEBIT	2 PURCHASES RETURNS AND ALLOWANCES CREDIT COMPACT DISCS	3 PURCHASES RETURNS AND ALLOWANCES CREDIT TAPES	
1	20-- Mar.	5	Dade, Inc.	36	230	1 6 5 00	1 6 5 00		1
2		6	Raymond Wholesalers	37	280	1 0 0 00		1 0 0 00	2
3		20	Artex Music	38	210	1 2 0 00	1 2 0 00		3
4		31	Castle Records and Tapes	39	220	1 5 0 00		1 5 0 00	4
5		31	Totals			5 3 5 00	2 8 5 00	2 5 0 00	5
6						(2105)	(5110-1)	(5110-2)	6
7									7
8									8
9									9
10									10
11									11
12									12
13									13
14									14
15									15

Name _____ Date _____ Class _____

1-2 WORK TOGETHER
ON YOUR OWN (continued)

[4, 6]

GENERAL LEDGER

ACCOUNT Accounts Payable   ACCOUNT NO. 2105

DATE		ITEM	POST. REF.	DEBIT	CREDIT	BALANCE	
						DEBIT	CREDIT
20-- Mar.	1	Balance	✓				2 1 7 0 00
	31		P3		3 5 7 6 00		5 7 4 6 00
	31		PR3	5 3 5 00			5 2 1 1 00

OYO 1-2

ACCOUNT Purchases—Compact Discs   ACCOUNT NO. 5105-1

DATE		ITEM	POST. REF.	DEBIT	CREDIT	BALANCE	
						DEBIT	CREDIT
20-- Mar.	31		P3	9 6 5 00		9 6 5 00	

OYO 1-2

ACCOUNT Purchases—Tapes   ACCOUNT NO. 5105-2

DATE		ITEM	POST. REF.	DEBIT	CREDIT	BALANCE	
						DEBIT	CREDIT
20-- Mar.	31		P3	2 6 1 1 00		2 6 1 1 00	

OYO 1-2

ACCOUNT Purchases Returns and Allowances—Compact Discs   ACCOUNT NO. 5110-1

DATE		ITEM	POST. REF.	DEBIT	CREDIT	BALANCE	
						DEBIT	CREDIT
20-- Mar.	31		PR3		2 8 5 00		2 8 5 00

OYO 1-2

ACCOUNT Purchases Returns and Allowances—Tapes   ACCOUNT NO. 5110-2

DATE		ITEM	POST. REF.	DEBIT	CREDIT	BALANCE	
						DEBIT	CREDIT
20-- Mar.	31		PR3		2 5 0 00		2 5 0 00

OYO 1-2

Name _____ Date _____ Class _____

1-2 WORK TOGETHER ON YOUR OWN (continued)

[4, 6]

ACCOUNTS PAYABLE LEDGER

VENDOR Artex Music **VENDOR NO.** 210

DATE		ITEM	POST. REF.	DEBIT	CREDIT	CREDIT BALANCE
20-- Mar.	1	Balance	✓			4 8 0 00
	2		P3		9 6 5 00	1 4 4 5 00
	20		PR3	1 2 0 00		1 3 2 5 00

VENDOR Castle Records and Tapes **VENDOR NO.** 220

DATE		ITEM	POST. REF.	DEBIT	CREDIT	CREDIT BALANCE
20-- Mar.	1	Balance	✓			7 6 0 00
	23		P3		9 9 3 00	1 7 5 3 00
	31		PR3	1 5 0 00		1 6 0 3 00

VENDOR Dade, Inc. **VENDOR NO.** 230

DATE		ITEM	POST. REF.	DEBIT	CREDIT	CREDIT BALANCE
20-- Mar.	1	Balance	✓			5 7 0 00
	5		PR3	1 6 5 00		4 0 5 00

VENDOR Park Recording Company **VENDOR NO.** 260

DATE		ITEM	POST. REF.	DEBIT	CREDIT	CREDIT BALANCE
20-- Mar.	1	Balance	✓			3 6 0 00

1-2 WORK TOGETHER
ON YOUR OWN (concluded)

[4, 6]

ACCOUNTS PAYABLE LEDGER

VENDOR Quality Tapes   **VENDOR NO.** 270

	DATE	ITEM	POST. REF.	DEBIT	CREDIT	CREDIT BALANCE	
	20-- Mar. 18		P3		2 6 8 00	2 6 8 00	OYO 1-2

VENDOR Raymond Wholesalers   **VENDOR NO.** 280

	DATE	ITEM	POST. REF.	DEBIT	CREDIT	CREDIT BALANCE	
	20-- Mar. 1		P3		1 3 5 0 00	1 3 5 0 00	WT 1-2
	6		PR3	1 0 0 00		1 2 5 0 00	

Extra forms

VENDOR _____   **VENDOR NO.** _____

	DATE	ITEM	POST. REF.	DEBIT	CREDIT	CREDIT BALANCE	

VENDOR _____   **VENDOR NO.** _____

	DATE	ITEM	POST. REF.	DEBIT	CREDIT	CREDIT BALANCE	

Journalizing and posting departmental cash payments [4, 6]

CASH PAYMENTS JOURNAL

PAGE 17

DATE	ACCOUNT TITLE	CK. NO.	POST. REF.	GENERAL DEBIT	GENERAL CREDIT	ACCOUNTS PAYABLE DEBIT	PURCH. DISCOUNT CR. GUITARS	PURCH. DISCOUNT CR. KEYBOARDS	CASH CREDIT
20-- Sept. 5	Peninsula Guitar	241	230			1150000			1150000
7	Supplies	242	1130	12000					12000
9	Magic Keyboards	243	220			200000		4000	196000
16	Magic Keyboards	244	220			180000		3600	176400
19	Peninsula Guitar	245	230			168000			168000
30	Supplies	246	1130	1500					6400
	Advertising Expense		6105	2200					
	Miscellaneous Expense		6220	2700					
30	Miscellaneous Expense	M54	6220	1000					1000
30	Credit Card Fee Expense	M55	6110	27800					27800
				47200		663000		7600	702600
				(✓)		(2105)		(5115-2)	(1105)

1-3 WORK TOGETHER
ON YOUR OWN (continued)

[5, 7]

GENERAL LEDGER

ACCOUNT Cash   ACCOUNT NO. 1105

DATE		ITEM	POST. REF.	DEBIT	CREDIT	BALANCE	
						DEBIT	CREDIT
20-- Sept.	1	Balance	✓			23 1 2 0 00	
	30		CP17		7 0 2 6 00	16 0 9 4 00	

ACCOUNT Petty Cash   ACCOUNT NO. 1110

DATE		ITEM	POST. REF.	DEBIT	CREDIT	BALANCE	
						DEBIT	CREDIT
20-- Sept.	1	Balance	✓			3 0 0 00	

ACCOUNT Supplies   ACCOUNT NO. 1130

DATE		ITEM	POST. REF.	DEBIT	CREDIT	BALANCE	
						DEBIT	CREDIT
20-- Sept.	1	Balance	✓			2 5 6 0 00	
	7		CP17	1 2 0 00		2 6 8 0 00	
	30		CP17	1 5 00		2 6 9 5 00	

ACCOUNT Accounts Payable   ACCOUNT NO. 2105

DATE		ITEM	POST. REF.	DEBIT	CREDIT	BALANCE	
						DEBIT	CREDIT
20-- Sept.	1	Balance	✓				1 9 6 3 00
	30		P14		6 6 3 0 00		8 5 9 3 00
	30		CP17	6 6 3 0 00			1 9 6 3 00

1-3 **WORK TOGETHER**
ON YOUR OWN (continued)

[5, 7]

GENERAL LEDGER

ACCOUNT Purchases Discount—Guitars   ACCOUNT NO. 5115-1

DATE	ITEM	POST. REF.	DEBIT	CREDIT	BALANCE DEBIT	BALANCE CREDIT

ACCOUNT Purchases Discount—Keyboards   ACCOUNT NO. 5115-2

DATE	ITEM	POST. REF.	DEBIT	CREDIT	BALANCE DEBIT	BALANCE CREDIT
20-- Sept. 30		CP17		7 6 00		7 6 00

ACCOUNT Advertising Expense   ACCOUNT NO. 6105

DATE	ITEM	POST. REF.	DEBIT	CREDIT	BALANCE DEBIT	BALANCE CREDIT
20-- Sept. 30		CP17	2 2 00		2 2 00	

ACCOUNT Credit Card Fee Expense   ACCOUNT NO. 6110

DATE	ITEM	POST. REF.	DEBIT	CREDIT	BALANCE DEBIT	BALANCE CREDIT
20-- Sept. 30		CP17	2 7 8 00		2 7 8 00	

1-3 WORK TOGETHER
ON YOUR OWN (concluded)

[5, 7]

ACCOUNT Miscellaneous Expense   ACCOUNT NO. 6220

DATE		ITEM	POST. REF.	DEBIT	CREDIT	BALANCE DEBIT	BALANCE CREDIT
20-- Sept.	30		CP17	2 7 00		2 7 00	
	30		CP17	1 0 00		3 7 00	

OYO 1-3

ACCOUNTS PAYABLE LEDGER

VENDOR Carmel Music   VENDOR NO. 210

DATE		ITEM	POST. REF.	DEBIT	CREDIT	CREDIT BALANCE
20-- Sept.	1	Balance	✓			1 9 6 3 00

VENDOR Magic Keyboards   VENDOR NO. 220

DATE		ITEM	POST. REF.	DEBIT	CREDIT	CREDIT BALANCE
20-- Sept.	2		P14		3 8 0 0 00	3 8 0 0 00
	9		CP17	2 0 0 0 00		1 8 0 0 00
	16		CP17	1 8 0 0 00		——

WT OYO 1-3 1-3

VENDOR Peninsula Guitar   VENDOR NO. 230

DATE		ITEM	POST. REF.	DEBIT	CREDIT	CREDIT BALANCE
20-- Sept.	2		P14		8 0 0 00	8 0 0 00
	3		P14		2 0 3 0 00	2 8 3 0 00
	5		CP17	1 1 5 0 00		1 6 8 0 00
	16		CP17	1 6 8 0 00		——

WT OYO 1-3 1-3

Name _____ Date _____ Class _____

Performing file maintenance activities; adding general ledger accounts

1110   Cash _____

1113   Petty Cash _____

1115   Accounts Receivable _____

1118   Allowance for Uncollectible Accounts _____

1120   Merchandise Inventory _____

1123   Supplies—Office _____

1125   Supplies—Store _____

1130   Prepaid Insurance _____

_____

_____

_____

_____

_____

_____

_____

_____

_____

_____

_____

_____

_____

_____

_____

_____

_____

_____

_____

_____

_____

_____

1-1 **APPLICATION PROBLEM**

Extra form

1-2 APPLICATION PROBLEM, p. 29

Journalizing and posting departmental purchases on account and purchases returns and allowances

[1, 2]

PURCHASES JOURNAL

PAGE 11

	DATE		ACCOUNT CREDITED	PURCH. NO.	POST. REF.	1 ACCOUNTS PAYABLE CREDIT	PURCHASES DEBIT 2 CELLULAR PHONES	PURCHASES DEBIT 3 PAGERS	
1	20-- Oct.	1	CarPhone Wholesalers	183	210	1 2 7 0 00	1 2 7 0 00		1
2		2	PageMax, Inc.	184	250	9 7 0 00		9 7 0 00	2
3		5	ExecuPhone	185	240	2 1 0 0 00	2 1 0 0 00		3
4		9	Cell Advantage, Inc.	186	220	9 4 5 00		9 4 5 00	4
5		13	ComSystems	187	230	2 2 4 0 00		2 2 4 0 00	5
6		19	Telecom Corporation	188	270	4 5 0 00	4 5 0 00		6
7		23	ExecuPhone	189	240	1 0 0 3 00	1 0 0 3 00		7
8		31	Totals			8 9 7 8 00	4 8 2 3 00	4 1 5 5 00	8
9						(2105)	(5105-1)	(5105-2)	9
10									10
11									11

[1, 3]

PURCHASES RETURNS AND ALLOWANCES JOURNAL

PAGE 3

	DATE		ACCOUNT DEBITED	DEBIT MEMO. NO.	POST. REF.	1 ACCOUNTS PAYABLE DEBIT	PURCHASES RETURNS AND ALLOWANCES CREDIT 2 CELLULAR PHONES	PURCHASES RETURNS AND ALLOWANCES CREDIT 3 PAGERS	
1	20-- Oct.	6	Western Distributors	40	280	2 0 5 00		2 0 5 00	1
2		17	CarPhone Wholesalers	41	210	1 2 0 00	1 2 0 00		2
3		20	PageMax, Inc.	42	250	9 0 00		9 0 00	3
4		30	Phone Solution	43	260	7 5 00	7 5 00		4
5		31	Totals			4 9 0 00	1 9 5 00	2 9 5 00	5
6						(2105)	(5110-1)	(5110-2)	6
7									7
8									8
9									9
10									10
11									11
12									12
13									13
14									14
15									15

1-2 APPLICATION PROBLEM (continued)

[2, 3]

GENERAL LEDGER

ACCOUNT Accounts Payable   **ACCOUNT NO.** 2105

DATE		ITEM	POST. REF.	DEBIT	CREDIT	BALANCE DEBIT	BALANCE CREDIT
20-- Oct.	1	Balance	✓				2 6 3 5 00
	31		P11		8 9 7 8 00		11 6 1 3 00
	31		PR3	4 9 0 00			11 1 2 3 00

ACCOUNT Purchases—Cellular Phones   **ACCOUNT NO.** 5105-1

DATE	ITEM	POST. REF.	DEBIT	CREDIT	BALANCE DEBIT	BALANCE CREDIT
20-- Oct. 31		P11	4 8 2 3 00		4 8 2 3 00	

ACCOUNT Purchases—Pagers   **ACCOUNT NO.** 5105-2

DATE	ITEM	POST. REF.	DEBIT	CREDIT	BALANCE DEBIT	BALANCE CREDIT
20-- Oct. 31		P11	4 1 5 5 00		4 1 5 5 00	

ACCOUNT Purchases Returns and Allowances—Cellular Phones   **ACCOUNT NO.** 5110-1

DATE	ITEM	POST. REF.	DEBIT	CREDIT	BALANCE DEBIT	BALANCE CREDIT
20-- Oct. 31		PR3		1 9 5 00		1 9 5 00

ACCOUNT Purchases Returns and Allowances—Pagers   **ACCOUNT NO.** 5110-2

DATE	ITEM	POST. REF.	DEBIT	CREDIT	BALANCE DEBIT	BALANCE CREDIT
20-- Oct. 31		PR3		2 9 5 00		2 9 5 00

1-2 APPLICATION PROBLEM (continued)

[2, 3]

ACCOUNTS PAYABLE LEDGER

VENDOR Car Phone Wholesalers   VENDOR NO. 210

DATE		ITEM	POST. REF.	DEBIT	CREDIT	CREDIT BALANCE
20-- Oct.	1	Balance	✓			6 5 0 00
	1		P11		1 2 7 0 00	1 9 2 0 00
	17		PR3	1 2 0 00		1 8 0 0 00

VENDOR Cell Advantage, Inc.   VENDOR NO. 220

DATE		ITEM	POST. REF.	DEBIT	CREDIT	CREDIT BALANCE
20-- Oct.	9		P11		9 4 5 00	9 4 5 00

VENDOR ComSystems   VENDOR NO. 230

DATE		ITEM	POST. REF.	DEBIT	CREDIT	CREDIT BALANCE
20-- Oct.	1	Balance	✓			4 3 0 00
	13		P11		2 2 4 0 00	2 6 7 0 00

VENDOR ExecuPhone   VENDOR NO. 240

DATE		ITEM	POST. REF.	DEBIT	CREDIT	CREDIT BALANCE
20-- Oct.	5		P11		2 1 0 0 00	2 1 0 0 00
	23		P11		1 0 0 3 00	3 1 0 3 00

1-2 APPLICATION PROBLEM (concluded)

[2, 3]

ACCOUNTS PAYABLE LEDGER

VENDOR PageMax, Inc.   VENDOR NO. 250

DATE		ITEM	POST. REF.	DEBIT	CREDIT	CREDIT BALANCE
20--Oct.	2		P11		9 7 0 00	9 7 0 00
	20		PR3	9 0 00		8 8 0 00

VENDOR Phone Solution   VENDOR NO. 260

DATE		ITEM	POST. REF.	DEBIT	CREDIT	CREDIT BALANCE
20--Oct.	1	Balance	✓			8 5 0 00
	30		PR3	7 5 00		7 7 5 00

VENDOR Telecom Corporation   VENDOR NO. 270

DATE		ITEM	POST. REF.	DEBIT	CREDIT	CREDIT BALANCE
20--Oct.	19		P11		4 5 0 00	4 5 0 00

VENDOR Western Distributors   VENDOR NO. 280

DATE		ITEM	POST. REF.	DEBIT	CREDIT	CREDIT BALANCE
20--Oct.	1	Balance	✓			7 0 5 00
	6		PR3	2 0 5 00		5 0 0 00

1-3 APPLICATION PROBLEM, p. 30

Journalizing and posting departmental cash payments [1, 2]

CASH PAYMENTS JOURNAL   PAGE 21

	DATE	ACCOUNT TITLE	CK. NO.	POST. REF.	GENERAL DEBIT	GENERAL CREDIT	ACCOUNTS PAYABLE DEBIT	PURCH. DISCOUNT CR. CRAFTS	PLANTS	CASH CREDIT	
1	Nov. 1	Miscellaneous Expense	303	6220	15000					15000	1
2	2	Rent Expense	304	6230	130000					130000	2
3	4	Wholesale Crafts, Inc.	305	240			88500	1770		86730	3
4	5	Advertising Expense	306	6105	8350					8350	4
5	8	Supplies	307	1130	9550					9550	5
6	10	Northtown Plants	308	230			125000		2500	122500	6
7	13	Century Crafts, Inc.	309	210			96300	1926		94374	7
8	15	Miscellaneous Expense	310	6220	3350					3350	8
9	21	Supplies	311	1130	5200					5200	9
10	23	Evergreen Trees & Shrubs	312	220			184000		3680	180320	10
11	27	Evergreen Trees & Shrubs	313	220			146000		2920	143080	11
12	30	Supplies	314	1130	8900					21200	12
13		Advertising Expense		6105	8340						13
14		Miscellaneous Expense		6220	3960						14
15	30	Miscellaneous Expense	M26	6220	1430					1430	15
16	30	Credit Card Fee Expense	M27	6110	48820					48820	16
17	30	Totals			242900		639800	3696	9100	869904	17
18					(✓)		(2105)	(5115-1)	(5115-2)	(1105)	18

1-3 APPLICATION PROBLEM (continued)

[1, 2]

GENERAL LEDGER

ACCOUNT Cash   ACCOUNT NO. 1105

DATE		ITEM	POST. REF.	DEBIT	CREDIT	BALANCE DEBIT	BALANCE CREDIT
20-- Nov.	1	Balance	✓			18 3 8 0 00	
	30		CP21		8 6 9 9 04	9 6 8 0 96	

ACCOUNT Petty Cash   ACCOUNT NO. 1110

DATE		ITEM	POST. REF.	DEBIT	CREDIT	BALANCE DEBIT	BALANCE CREDIT
20-- Nov.	1	Balance	✓			5 0 0 00	

ACCOUNT Supplies   ACCOUNT NO. 1130

DATE		ITEM	POST. REF.	DEBIT	CREDIT	BALANCE DEBIT	BALANCE CREDIT
20-- Nov.	1	Balance	✓			1 2 6 0 00	
	8		CP21	9 5 50		1 3 5 5 50	
	21		CP21	5 2 00		1 4 0 7 50	
	30		CP21	8 9 00		1 4 9 6 50	

ACCOUNT Accounts Payable   ACCOUNT NO. 2105

DATE		ITEM	POST. REF.	DEBIT	CREDIT	BALANCE DEBIT	BALANCE CREDIT
20-- Nov.	1	Balance	✓				8 8 5 00
	30		P11		5 5 1 3 00		6 3 9 8 00
	30		CP21	6 3 9 8 00		—	—

ACCOUNT Purchases Discount—Crafts   ACCOUNT NO. 5115-1

DATE		ITEM	POST. REF.	DEBIT	CREDIT	BALANCE DEBIT	BALANCE CREDIT
20-- Nov.	30		CP21		3 6 96		3 6 96

1-3 APPLICATION PROBLEM (continued)

[2]

GENERAL LEDGER

ACCOUNT Purchases Discount—Plants   ACCOUNT NO. 5115-2

DATE	ITEM	POST. REF.	DEBIT	CREDIT	BALANCE DEBIT	BALANCE CREDIT
20-- Nov. 30		CP21		9 1 00		9 1 00

ACCOUNT Advertising Expense   ACCOUNT NO. 6105

DATE	ITEM	POST. REF.	DEBIT	CREDIT	BALANCE DEBIT	BALANCE CREDIT
20-- Nov. 5		CP21	8 3 50		8 3 50	
30		CP21	8 3 40		1 6 6 90	

ACCOUNT Credit Card Fee Expense   ACCOUNT NO. 6110

DATE	ITEM	POST. REF.	DEBIT	CREDIT	BALANCE DEBIT	BALANCE CREDIT
20-- Nov. 30		CP21	4 8 8 20		4 8 8 20	

ACCOUNT Miscellaneous Expense   ACCOUNT NO. 6220

DATE	ITEM	POST. REF.	DEBIT	CREDIT	BALANCE DEBIT	BALANCE CREDIT
20-- Nov. 1		CP21	1 5 0 00		1 5 0 00	
15		CP21	3 3 50		1 8 3 50	
30		CP21	3 9 60		2 2 3 10	
30		CP21	1 4 30		2 3 7 40	

ACCOUNT Rent Expense   ACCOUNT NO. 6230

DATE	ITEM	POST. REF.	DEBIT	CREDIT	BALANCE DEBIT	BALANCE CREDIT
20-- Nov. 2		CP21	1 3 0 0 00		1 3 0 0 00	

1-3 **APPLICATION PROBLEM (concluded)**

ACCOUNTS PAYABLE LEDGER

VENDOR Century Crafts, Inc.   **VENDOR NO.** 210

DATE	ITEM	POST. REF.	DEBIT	CREDIT	CREDIT BALANCE
20-- Nov. 6		P11		9 6 3 00	9 6 3 00
13		CP21	9 6 3 00		——

VENDOR Evergreen Trees & Shrubs   **VENDOR NO.** 220

DATE	ITEM	POST. REF.	DEBIT	CREDIT	CREDIT BALANCE
20-- Nov. 16		P11		1 8 4 0 00	1 8 4 0 00
20		P11		1 4 6 0 00	3 3 0 0 00
23		CP21	1 8 4 0 00		1 4 6 0 00
27		CP21	1 4 6 0 00		——

VENDOR Northtown Plants   **VENDOR NO.** 230

DATE	ITEM	POST. REF.	DEBIT	CREDIT	CREDIT BALANCE
20-- Nov. 3		P11		1 2 5 0 00	1 2 5 0 00
10		CP21	1 2 5 0 00		——

VENDOR Wholesale Crafts, Inc.   **VENDOR NO.** 240

DATE	ITEM	POST. REF.	DEBIT	CREDIT	CREDIT BALANCE
20-- Nov. 1	Balance	✓			8 8 5 00
4		CP21	8 8 5 00		——

1-4 APPLICATION PROBLEM, p. 30

Reconciling a bank statement

RECONCILIATION OF BANK STATEMENT

Date _____10/31/--_____

1. Enter CHECKBOOK BALANCE as shown on check stub.
2. Enter and add bank charges to obtain TOTAL BANK CHARGES.
3. Deduct TOTAL BANK CHARGES from CHECKBOOK BALANCE to obtain ADJUSTED CHECKBOOK BALANCE.
4. Enter BANK BALANCE as shown on bank statement.
5. Enter and add the amounts of any outstanding deposits recorded on the check stubs but not listed on the bank statement to obtain TOTAL OUTSTANDING DEPOSITS.
6. Add TOTAL OUTSTANDING DEPOSITS to BANK BALANCE to obtain TOTAL.
7. Sort all checks included in the statement numerically or by date issued.
   a. Check off on the check stubs of the checkbook each of the checks paid by the bank.
   b. Enter the check numbers and amounts of checks still outstanding.
   c. Add the outstanding checks to obtain TOTAL OUTSTANDING CHECKS.
8. Deduct TOTAL OUTSTANDING CHECKS from TOTAL to obtain ADJUSTED BANK BALANCE.
9. The ADJUSTED CHECKBOOK BALANCE and the ADJUSTED BANK BALANCE should agree, proving that both the checkbook balance and the bank balance are correct.

(1) CHECKBOOK BALANCE .... $ _____37,757.00_____

BANK CHARGES

Description	Amount	
Service Charge	8	80
Credit Card Charge	325	20

(2) DEDUCT TOTAL BANK CHARGES .... $ _____334.00_____

(3) ADJUSTED CHECKBOOK BALANCE . $ _____37,423.00_____

(4) BANK BALANCE .... $ _____31,820.00_____

OUTSTANDING DEPOSITS

Date	Amount	
10/27	7,152	75

(5) ADD TOTAL OUTSTANDING DEPOSITS .... $ _____7,152.75_____

(6) TOTAL .... $ _____38,972.75_____

OUTSTANDING CHECKS

CK. NO.	Amount	
361	89	50
362	1,460	25

(7) DEDUCT TOTAL OUTSTANDING CHECKS .... $ _____1,549.75_____

(8) ADJUSTED BANK BALANCE .... $ _____37,423.00_____

Extra form

RECONCILIATION OF BANK STATEMENT

Date _____

1. Enter CHECKBOOK BALANCE as shown on check stub.
2. Enter and add bank charges to obtain TOTAL BANK CHARGES.
3. Deduct TOTAL BANK CHARGES from CHECKBOOK BALANCE to obtain ADJUSTED CHECKBOOK BALANCE.
4. Enter BANK BALANCE as shown on bank statement.
5. Enter and add the amounts of any outstanding deposits recorded on the check stubs but not listed on the bank statement to obtain TOTAL OUTSTANDING DEPOSITS.
6. Add TOTAL OUTSTANDING DEPOSITS to BANK BALANCE to obtain TOTAL.
7. Sort all checks included in the statement numerically or by date issued.
   a. Check off on the check stubs of the checkbook each of the checks paid by the bank.
   b. Enter the check numbers and amounts of checks still outstanding.
   c. Add the outstanding checks to obtain TOTAL OUTSTANDING CHECKS.
8. Deduct TOTAL OUTSTANDING CHECKS from TOTAL to obtain ADJUSTED BANK BALANCE.
9. The ADJUSTED CHECKBOOK BALANCE and the ADJUSTED BANK BALANCE should agree, proving that both the checkbook balance and the bank balance are correct.

(1) CHECKBOOK BALANCE................ $ _____

BANK CHARGES

Description	Amount	
Service Charge		

(2) DEDUCT TOTAL BANK CHARGES.... $ _____

(3) ADJUSTED CHECKBOOK BALANCE. $ _____

(4) BANK BALANCE........................... $ _____

OUTSTANDING DEPOSITS

Date	Amount	

(5) ADD TOTAL OUTSTANDING DEPOSITS................................... $ _____

(6) TOTAL .... $ _____

OUTSTANDING CHECKS

CK. NO.	Amount	

(7) DEDUCT TOTAL OUTSTANDING CHECKS .... $ _____

(8) ADJUSTED BANK BALANCE .... $ _____

1-5 MASTERY PROBLEM, p. 31

Performing file maintenance activities; journalizing departmental purchases and cash payments; reconciling a bank statement

[1]

6205   Depreciation Expense—Office Equipment _____

6208   Insurance Expense _____

6210   Miscellaneous Expense _____

6215   Rent Expense _____

6220   Supplies Expense—Office _____

6225   Supplies Expense—Store _____

6230   Uncollectible Accounts Expense _____

[2, 5]

PURCHASES JOURNAL
PAGE 11

	DATE		ACCOUNT CREDITED	PURCH. NO.	POST. REF.	ACCOUNTS PAYABLE CREDIT	PURCHASES DEBIT CAMERAS	PURCHASES DEBIT ACCESSORIES	
1	20-- Nov.	2	Standish Photo Supplies	262		8 0 0 00		8 0 0 00	1
2		3	Jens Wholesale Cameras	263		8 4 0 00	8 4 0 00		2
3		10	Focal Camera Distributors	264		3 8 8 00	3 8 8 00		3
4		17	Farmer Camera Supply, Inc.	265		5 5 0 00		5 5 0 00	4
5		19	Jens Wholesale Cameras	266		1 1 2 0 00	1 1 2 0 00		5
6		23	Quality Film Company	267		3 3 6 00		3 3 6 00	6
7		24	National Camera Outlet	268		6 2 6 40	6 2 6 40		7
8		30	Totals			4 6 6 0 40	2 9 7 4 40	1 6 8 6 00	8
9									9
10									10

[2, 5]

PURCHASES RETURNS AND ALLOWANCES JOURNAL
PAGE 11

	DATE		ACCOUNT DEBITED	DEBIT MEMO. NO.	POST. REF.	ACCOUNTS PAYABLE DEBIT	PURCHASES RETURNS AND ALLOWANCES CREDIT CAMERAS	PURCHASES RETURNS AND ALLOWANCES CREDIT ACCESSORIES	
1	20-- Nov.	7	Jens Wholesale Cameras	28		8 8 00	8 8 00		1
2		16	Quality Film Company	29		1 3 2 50		1 3 2 50	2
3		18	Farmer Camera Supply, Inc.	30		7 5 00		7 5 00	3
4		30	Totals			2 9 5 50	8 8 00	2 0 7 50	4
5									5
6									6

1-5 MASTERY PROBLEM (continued)

[2, 4, 5]

CASH PAYMENTS JOURNAL PAGE 21

DATE		ACCOUNT TITLE	CK. NO.	POST. REF.	GENERAL DEBIT	GENERAL CREDIT	ACCOUNTS PAYABLE DEBIT	PURCH. DISCOUNT CR. CAMERAS	PURCH. DISCOUNT CR. ACCESSORIES	CASH CREDIT
20— Nov.	1	Advertising Expense	273		9500					9500
	1	Rent Expense	274		125000					125000
	3	National Camera Outlet	275				50000	1000		49000
	5	Standish Photo Supplies	276				64500		1290	63210
	11	Supplies—Store	277		8250					8250
	14	Standish Photo Supplies	278				80000			80000
	17	Focal Camera Distributors	279				38800	776		38024
	18	Jens Wholesale Cameras	280				75200			75200
	21	Supplies—Office	281		6230					6230
	24	Farmer Camera Supply, Inc.	282				47500		950	46550
	26	Jens Wholesale Cameras	283				112000	2240		109760
	29	Supplies—Store	284		5300					5300
	30	Supplies—Office	285		5710					22100
		Advertising Expense			6250					
		Miscellaneous Expense			10140					
	30	Miscellaneous Expense	M31		2020					2020
	30	Credit Card Fee Expense	M32		38280					38280
	30	Totals			216680		468000	4016	2240	678424

Name _____ Date _____ Class _____

1-5 MASTERY PROBLEM (concluded)

[3]

RECONCILIATION OF BANK STATEMENT   Date ___11/30/--___

1. Enter CHECKBOOK BALANCE as shown on check stub.
2. Enter and add bank charges to obtain TOTAL BANK CHARGES.
3. Deduct TOTAL BANK CHARGES from CHECKBOOK BALANCE to obtain ADJUSTED CHECKBOOK BALANCE.
4. Enter BANK BALANCE as shown on bank statement.
5. Enter and add the amounts of any outstanding deposits recorded on the check stubs but not listed on the bank statement to obtain TOTAL OUTSTANDING DEPOSITS.
6. Add TOTAL OUTSTANDING DEPOSITS to BANK BALANCE to obtain TOTAL.
7. Sort all checks included in the statement numerically or by date issued.
    a. Check off on the check stubs of the checkbook each of the checks paid by the bank.
    b. Enter the check numbers and amounts of checks still outstanding.
    c. Add the outstanding checks to obtain TOTAL OUTSTANDING CHECKS.
8. Deduct TOTAL OUTSTANDING CHECKS from TOTAL to obtain ADJUSTED BANK BALANCE.
9. The ADJUSTED CHECKBOOK BALANCE and the ADJUSTED BANK BALANCE should agree, proving that both the checkbook balance and the bank balance are correct.

(1) CHECKBOOK BALANCE.............. $ __18,680.00__

BANK CHARGES

Description	Amount	
Service Charge	20	20
Credit Card Charge	382	80

(2) DEDUCT TOTAL BANK CHARGES.... $ ___403.00___

(3) ADJUSTED CHECKBOOK BALANCE . $ __18,277.00__

(4) BANK BALANCE......................... $ __16,578.00__

OUTSTANDING DEPOSITS

Date	Amount	
11/29	3,070	60

(5) ADD TOTAL OUTSTANDING DEPOSITS................. $ __3,070.60__

(6) TOTAL .... $ __19,648.60__

OUTSTANDING CHECKS

CK. NO.	Amount	
283	1,097	60
284	53	00
285	221	00

(7) DEDUCT TOTAL OUTSTANDING CHECKS .... $ __1,371.60__

(8) ADJUSTED BANK BALANCE.......... $ __18,277.00__

Extra form

RECONCILIATION OF BANK STATEMENT   Date _____

1. Enter CHECKBOOK BALANCE as shown on check stub.
2. Enter and add bank charges to obtain TOTAL BANK CHARGES.
3. Deduct TOTAL BANK CHARGES from CHECKBOOK BALANCE to obtain ADJUSTED CHECKBOOK BALANCE.
4. Enter BANK BALANCE as shown on bank statement.
5. Enter and add the amounts of any outstanding deposits recorded on the check stubs but not listed on the bank statement to obtain TOTAL OUTSTANDING DEPOSITS.
6. Add TOTAL OUTSTANDING DEPOSITS to BANK BALANCE to obtain TOTAL.
7. Sort all checks included in the statement numerically or by date issued.
   a. Check off on the check stubs of the checkbook each of the checks paid by the bank.
   b. Enter the check numbers and amounts of checks still outstanding.
   c. Add the outstanding checks to obtain TOTAL OUTSTANDING CHECKS.
8. Deduct TOTAL OUTSTANDING CHECKS from TOTAL to obtain ADJUSTED BANK BALANCE.
9. The ADJUSTED CHECKBOOK BALANCE and the ADJUSTED BANK BALANCE should agree, proving that both the checkbook balance and the bank balance are correct.

(1) CHECKBOOK BALANCE............... $ _____   **(4) BANK BALANCE**......................... $ _____

BANK CHARGES

Description	Amount	
Service Charge		

OUTSTANDING DEPOSITS

Date	Amount	

(5) ADD TOTAL OUTSTANDING DEPOSITS................................. $ _____

(6) TOTAL...................................... $ _____

OUTSTANDING CHECKS

CK. NO.	Amount	

(2) DEDUCT TOTAL BANK CHARGES.... $ _____

(7) DEDUCT TOTAL OUTSTANDING CHECKS .... $ _____

(3) ADJUSTED CHECKBOOK BALANCE . $ _____   **(8) ADJUSTED BANK BALANCE** .... $ _____

Name _____ Date _____ Class _____

1-6 CHALLENGE PROBLEM, p. 32

Journalizing purchases at net amount and using the account Discounts Lost　　　　　[1, 2]

PURCHASES JOURNAL　　　　PAGE 11

	DATE		ACCOUNT CREDITED	PURCH. NO.	POST. REF.	ACCOUNTS PAYABLE CREDIT (1)	PURCHASES DEBIT CAMERAS (2)	PURCHASES DEBIT ACCESSORIES (3)	
1	20-- Nov.	2	Standish Photo Supplies	262		784 00		784 00	1
2		3	Jens Wholesale Cameras	263		823 20	823 20		2
3		10	Focal Camera Distributors	264		380 24	380 24		3
4		17	Farmer Camera Supply, Inc.	265		539 00		539 00	4
5		19	Jens Wholesale Cameras	266		1097 60	1097 60		5
6		23	Quality Film Company	267		329 28		329 28	6
7		24	National Camera Outlet	268		613 87	613 87		7
8		30	Totals			4567 19	2914 91	1652 28	8
9									9
10									10
11									11

[1, 2]

PURCHASES RETURNS AND ALLOWANCES JOURNAL　　　　PAGE 11

	DATE		ACCOUNT DEBITED	DEBIT MEMO. NO.	POST. REF.	ACCOUNTS PAYABLE DEBIT (1)	PURCHASES RETURNS AND ALLOWANCES CREDIT CAMERAS (2)	PURCHASES RETURNS AND ALLOWANCES CREDIT ACCESSORIES (3)	
1	20-- Nov.	7	Jens Wholesale Cameras	28		86 24	86 24		1
2		16	Quality Film Company	29		129 85		129 85	2
3		18	Farmer Camera Supply, Inc.	30		73 50		73 50	3
4		30	Totals			289 59	86 24	203 35	4
5									5
6									6
7									7
8									8
9									9
10									10
11									11
12									12
13									13
14									14
15									15

1-6 CHALLENGE PROBLEM (concluded)

[1, 2]

CASH PAYMENTS JOURNAL   PAGE 21

	DATE	ACCOUNT TITLE	CK. NO.	POST. REF.	GENERAL DEBIT	GENERAL CREDIT	ACCOUNTS PAYABLE DEBIT	CASH CREDIT	
	20-- Nov.								
1	1	Advertising Expense	273		9500			9500	1
2	1	Rent Expense	274		125000			125000	2
3	3	National Camera Outlet	275				49000	49000	3
4	5	Standish Photo Supplies	276				63210	63210	4
5	11	Supplies—Store	277		8250			8250	5
6	14	Standish Photo Supplies	278				78400	80000	6
7		Discounts Lost				1600			7
8	17	Focal Camera Distributors	279				38024	38024	8
9	18	Jens Wholesale Cameras	280				73696	75200	9
10		Discounts Lost			1504				10
11	21	Supplies—Office	281		6230			6230	11
12	24	Farmer Camera Supply, Inc.	282				46550	46550	12
13	26	Jens Wholesale Cameras	283				109760	109760	13
14	28	Supplies—Store	284		5300			5300	14
15	30	Supplies—Office	285		5710			22100	15
16		Advertising Expense			6250				16
17		Miscellaneous Expense			10140				17
18	30	Miscellaneous Expense	M31		2020			2020	18
19	30	Credit Card Fee Expense	M32		38280			38280	19
20	30	Totals			219784		458640	678424	20
21									21
22									22
23									23
24									24
25									25

Name _____ Date _____ Class _____

2-1 WORK TOGETHER
ON YOUR OWN, p. 47

Journalizing and posting departmental sales on account and sales returns and allowances [3–7]

SALES JOURNAL   PAGE 9

	DATE		ACCOUNT DEBITED	SALE NO.	POST. REF.	ACCOUNTS RECEIVABLE DEBIT	SALES TAX PAYABLE CREDIT	SALES CREDIT SWIMWEAR	SALES CREDIT ACCESSORIES	
1	20-- Sept.	1	Dana Brein	012	110	31 80	1 80	30 00		1
2		10	Kim Lockhart	013	120	79 50	4 50		75 00	2
3		14	Western High School Swim Team	014	140	220 00		220 00		3
4		18	John Muller	015	130	12 72	72		12 00	4
5		24	Dana Brein	016	110	74 20	4 20		70 00	5
6		30	Totals			418 22	11 22	250 00	157 00	6
7						(1115)	(2130)	(4105-1)	(4105-2)	7
8										8
9										9
10										10
11										11

SALES RETURNS AND ALLOWANCES JOURNAL   PAGE 9

	DATE		ACCOUNT CREDITED	CREDIT MEMO. NO.	POST. REF.	ACCOUNTS RECEIVABLE CREDIT	SALES TAX PAYABLE DEBIT	SALES RETURNS AND ALLOWANCES DEBIT SWIMWEAR	SALES RETURNS AND ALLOWANCES DEBIT ACCESSORIES	
1	20-- Sept.	15	Kim Lockhart	23	120	79 50	4 50		75 00	1
2		30	John Muller	24	130	12 72	72		12 00	2
3		30	Totals			92 22	5 22	—	87 00	3
4						(1115)	(2130)		(4110-2)	4
5										5
6										6
7										7
8										8
9										9
10										10
11										11
12										12
13										13
14										14
15										15

2-1 WORK TOGETHER
ON YOUR OWN (continued)

[4, 6, 7]

GENERAL LEDGER

ACCOUNT Accounts Receivable   ACCOUNT NO. 1115

DATE		ITEM	POST. REF.	DEBIT	CREDIT	BALANCE DEBIT	BALANCE CREDIT
20-- Sept.	1	Balance	✓			2 3 9 50	
	30		S9	4 1 8 22		6 5 7 72	
	30		SR9		9 2 22	5 6 5 50	

ACCOUNT Sales Tax Payable   ACCOUNT NO. 2130

DATE		ITEM	POST. REF.	DEBIT	CREDIT	BALANCE DEBIT	BALANCE CREDIT
20-- Sept.	1	Balance	✓				1 2 3 20
	30		S9		1 1 22		1 3 4 42
	30		SR9	5 22			1 2 9 20

ACCOUNT Sales—Swimwear   ACCOUNT NO. 4105-1

DATE		ITEM	POST. REF.	DEBIT	CREDIT	BALANCE DEBIT	BALANCE CREDIT
20-- Sept.	30		S9		2 5 0 00		2 5 0 00

ACCOUNT Sales—Accessories   ACCOUNT NO. 4105-2

DATE		ITEM	POST. REF.	DEBIT	CREDIT	BALANCE DEBIT	BALANCE CREDIT
20-- Sept.	30		S9		1 5 7 00		1 5 7 00

ACCOUNT Sales Returns and Allowances—Swimwear   ACCOUNT NO. 4110-1

DATE		ITEM	POST. REF.	DEBIT	CREDIT	BALANCE DEBIT	BALANCE CREDIT

ACCOUNT Sales Returns and Allowances—Accessories   ACCOUNT NO. 4110-2

DATE		ITEM	POST. REF.	DEBIT	CREDIT	BALANCE DEBIT	BALANCE CREDIT
20-- Sept.	30		SR9	8 7 00		8 7 00	

2-1 WORK TOGETHER, ON YOUR OWN (continued)

[4, 6, 7]

ACCOUNTS RECEIVABLE LEDGER

CUSTOMER Dana Brein   CUSTOMER NO. 110

DATE		ITEM	POST. REF.	DEBIT	CREDIT	DEBIT BALANCE
20-- Sept.	1	Balance	✓			5 5 00
	1		S9	3 1 80		8 6 80
	24		S9	7 4 20		1 6 1 00

CUSTOMER Kim Lockhart   CUSTOMER NO. 120

DATE		ITEM	POST. REF.	DEBIT	CREDIT	DEBIT BALANCE
20-- Sept.	1	Balance	✓			1 3 6 00
	10		S9	7 9 50		2 1 5 50
	15		SR9		7 9 50	1 3 6 00

CUSTOMER John Muller   CUSTOMER NO. 130

DATE		ITEM	POST. REF.	DEBIT	CREDIT	DEBIT BALANCE
20-- Sept.	1	Balance	✓			4 8 50
	18		S9	1 2 72		6 1 22
	30		SR9		1 2 72	4 8 50

CUSTOMER Western High School Swim Team   CUSTOMER NO. 140

DATE		ITEM	POST. REF.	DEBIT	CREDIT	DEBIT BALANCE
20-- Sept.	14		S9	2 2 0 00		2 2 0 00

2-1 WORK TOGETHER ON YOUR OWN

Extra forms

CUSTOMER _____ CUSTOMER NO. _____

DATE	ITEM	POST. REF.	DEBIT	CREDIT	DEBIT BALANCE

CUSTOMER _____ CUSTOMER NO. _____

DATE	ITEM	POST. REF.	DEBIT	CREDIT	DEBIT BALANCE

CUSTOMER _____ CUSTOMER NO. _____

DATE	ITEM	POST. REF.	DEBIT	CREDIT	DEBIT BALANCE

CUSTOMER _____ CUSTOMER NO. _____

DATE	ITEM	POST. REF.	DEBIT	CREDIT	DEBIT BALANCE

CUSTOMER _____ CUSTOMER NO. _____

DATE	ITEM	POST. REF.	DEBIT	CREDIT	DEBIT BALANCE

2-2 WORK TOGETHER
ON YOUR OWN, p. 54

Journalizing and posting departmental cash receipts

[3, 5, 7]

CASH RECEIPTS JOURNAL

PAGE 21

DATE	ACCOUNT TITLE	DOC. NO.	POST. REF.	GENERAL DEBIT	GENERAL CREDIT	ACCOUNTS RECEIVABLE CREDIT	SALES TAX PAYABLE DEBIT	SALES TAX PAYABLE CREDIT	SALES CREDIT FURNITURE	SALES CREDIT CARPETING	SALES DISCOUNT DEBIT FURNITURE	SALES DISCOUNT DEBIT CARPETING	CASH DEBIT
20-- Feb. 1	Mona Andrews Design	R343	110			1929 20	2 18					36 40	1890 62
7		T7	✓					345 24	3286 00	2468 00			6099 24
12	Bob Smits	R344	130			636 00	72				12 00		623 28
14		T14	✓					285 90	2653 00	2112 00			5050 90
19	Joan Seymour	R345	120			742 00	84				14 00		727 16
21		T21	✓					354 48	3057 00	2851 00			6262 48
28		T28	✓					346 20	2803 00	2967 00			6116 20
28	Totals					3307 20	3 74	1331 82	11799 00	10398 00	26 00	36 40	26769 88
						(1115)	(2130)	(2130)	(4105-1)	(4105-2)	(4115-1)	(4115-2)	(1105)

2-2 WORK TOGETHER
ON YOUR OWN (continued)

[4, 6, 7]

GENERAL LEDGER

ACCOUNT Cash   ACCOUNT NO. 1105

DATE		ITEM	POST. REF.	DEBIT	CREDIT	BALANCE	
						DEBIT	CREDIT
20-- Feb.	1	Balance	✓			43 3 4 0 00	
	28		CR21	26 7 6 9 88		70 1 0 9 88	

ACCOUNT Accounts Receivable   ACCOUNT NO. 1115

DATE		ITEM	POST. REF.	DEBIT	CREDIT	BALANCE	
						DEBIT	CREDIT
20-- Feb.	1	Balance	✓			4 1 1 8 10	
	28		CR21		3 3 0 7 20	8 1 0 90	

ACCOUNT Sales Tax Payable   ACCOUNT NO. 2130

DATE		ITEM	POST. REF.	DEBIT	CREDIT	BALANCE	
						DEBIT	CREDIT
20-- Feb.	1	Balance	✓				3 8 7 0 00
	28		CR21	3 74			3 8 6 6 26
	28		CR21		1 3 3 1 82		5 1 9 8 08

ACCOUNT Sales—Furniture   ACCOUNT NO. 4105-1

DATE		ITEM	POST. REF.	DEBIT	CREDIT	BALANCE	
						DEBIT	CREDIT
20-- Feb.	28		CR21		11 7 9 9 00		11 7 9 9 00

2-2 WORK TOGETHER
ON YOUR OWN (continued)

[4, 6, 7]

GENERAL LEDGER

ACCOUNT Sales—Carpeting   ACCOUNT NO. 4105-2

DATE	ITEM	POST. REF.	DEBIT	CREDIT	BALANCE DEBIT	BALANCE CREDIT
20-- Feb. 28		CR21		10 3 9 8 00		10 3 9 8 00

ACCOUNT Sales Discount—Furniture   ACCOUNT NO. 4115-1

DATE	ITEM	POST. REF.	DEBIT	CREDIT	BALANCE DEBIT	BALANCE CREDIT
20-- Feb. 28		CR21	2 6 00		2 6 00	

ACCOUNT Sales Discount—Carpeting   ACCOUNT NO. 4115-2

DATE	ITEM	POST. REF.	DEBIT	CREDIT	BALANCE DEBIT	BALANCE CREDIT
20-- Feb. 28		CR21	3 6 40		3 6 40	

Extra form

ACCOUNT   ACCOUNT NO.

DATE	ITEM	POST. REF.	DEBIT	CREDIT	BALANCE DEBIT	BALANCE CREDIT

2-2 WORK TOGETHER
ON YOUR OWN (concluded)

[4, 6]

ACCOUNTS RECEIVABLE LEDGER

CUSTOMER Mona Andrews Design   CUSTOMER NO. 110

DATE		ITEM	POST. REF.	DEBIT	CREDIT	DEBIT BALANCE
20-- Feb.	1	Balance	✓			2 0 7 0 20
	1		CR21		1 9 2 9 20	1 4 1 00

CUSTOMER Joan Seymour   CUSTOMER NO. 120

DATE		ITEM	POST. REF.	DEBIT	CREDIT	DEBIT BALANCE
20-- Feb.	1	Balance	✓			7 4 2 00
	19		CR21		7 4 2 00	—

CUSTOMER Bob Smits   CUSTOMER NO. 130

DATE		ITEM	POST. REF.	DEBIT	CREDIT	DEBIT BALANCE
20-- Feb.	1	Balance	✓			8 5 3 20
	12		CR21		6 3 6 00	2 1 7 20

Extra form

CUSTOMER   CUSTOMER NO.

DATE		ITEM	POST. REF.	DEBIT	CREDIT	DEBIT BALANCE

Name _____ Date _____ Class _____

Journalizing and posting departmental sales on account and sales returns and allowances [1, 2]

SALES JOURNAL   PAGE 4

	DATE		ACCOUNT DEBITED	SALE NO.	POST. REF.	ACCOUNTS RECEIVABLE DEBIT (1)	SALES TAX PAYABLE CREDIT (2)	SALES CREDIT CLOTHING (3)	SALES CREDIT SHOES (4)	
1	20-- Apr.	1	Cherie Grecki	63	130	97 65	4 65		93 00	1
2		2	Wade Thomas	64	180	157 50	7 50	150 00		2
3		5	Phil Kellerman	65	140	77 70	3 70		74 00	3
4		5	Debbie Prosser	66	160	189 00	9 00		180 00	4
5		7	Wade Thomas	67	180	241 50	11 50	230 00		5
6		12	Carole Tate	68	170	288 75	13 75	275 00		6
7		17	Cherie Grecki	69	130	48 30	2 30		46 00	7
8		19	Archibald School District	70	110	463 00		463 00		8
9		27	Dana Eggers	71	120	102 90	4 90	98 00		9
10		30	Ben Nesbitt	72	150	130 20	6 20		124 00	10
11		30	Totals			1796 50	63 50	1216 00	517 00	11
12						(1115)	(2130)	(4105-1)	(4105-2)	12

[1, 3]

SALES RETURNS AND ALLOWANCES JOURNAL   PAGE 4

	DATE		ACCOUNT CREDITED	CREDIT MEMO. NO.	POST. REF.	ACCOUNTS RECEIVABLE CREDIT (1)	SALES TAX PAYABLE DEBIT (2)	SALES RETURNS AND ALLOWANCES DEBIT CLOTHING (3)	SALES RETURNS AND ALLOWANCES DEBIT SHOES (4)	
1	20-- Apr.	5	Cherie Grecki	12	130	97 65	4 65		93 00	1
2		10	Debbie Prosser	13	160	84 00	4 00		80 00	2
3		15	Wade Thomas	14	180	147 00	7 00	140 00		3
4		24	Carole Tate	15	170	60 90	2 90	58 00		4
5		30	Totals			389 55	18 55	198 00	173 00	5
6						(1115)	(2130)	(4110-1)	(4110-2)	6
7										7
8										8
9										9
10										10
11										11
12										12
13										13
14										14
15										15

2-1 APPLICATION PROBLEM (continued)

[2, 3]

GENERAL LEDGER

ACCOUNT Accounts Receivable   ACCOUNT NO. 1115

DATE		ITEM	POST. REF.	DEBIT	CREDIT	BALANCE DEBIT	BALANCE CREDIT
20-- Apr.	1	Balance	✓			1 5 5 8 75	
	30		S4	1 7 9 6 50		3 3 5 5 25	
	30		SR4		3 8 9 55	2 9 6 5 70	

ACCOUNT Sales Tax Payable   ACCOUNT NO. 2130

DATE		ITEM	POST. REF.	DEBIT	CREDIT	BALANCE DEBIT	BALANCE CREDIT
20-- Apr.	1	Balance	✓				1 5 8 70
	30		S4		6 3 50		2 2 2 20
	30		SR4	1 8 55			2 0 3 65

ACCOUNT Sales—Clothing   ACCOUNT NO. 4105-1

DATE	ITEM	POST. REF.	DEBIT	CREDIT	BALANCE DEBIT	BALANCE CREDIT
20-- Apr. 30		S4		1 2 1 6 00		1 2 1 6 00

ACCOUNT Sales—Shoes   ACCOUNT NO. 4105-2

DATE	ITEM	POST. REF.	DEBIT	CREDIT	BALANCE DEBIT	BALANCE CREDIT
20-- Apr. 30		S4		5 1 7 00		5 1 7 00

ACCOUNT Sales Returns and Allowances—Clothing   ACCOUNT NO. 4110-1

DATE	ITEM	POST. REF.	DEBIT	CREDIT	BALANCE DEBIT	BALANCE CREDIT
20-- Apr. 30		SR4	1 9 8 00		1 9 8 00	

ACCOUNT Sales Returns and Allowances—Shoes   ACCOUNT NO. 4110-2

DATE	ITEM	POST. REF.	DEBIT	CREDIT	BALANCE DEBIT	BALANCE CREDIT
20-- Apr. 30		SR4	1 7 3 00		1 7 3 00	

2-1 APPLICATION PROBLEM (continued)

[1]

ACCOUNTS RECEIVABLE LEDGER

CUSTOMER Archibald School District   CUSTOMER NO. 110

DATE		ITEM	POST. REF.	DEBIT	CREDIT	DEBIT BALANCE
20-- Apr.	1	Balance	✓			3 2 5 00
	19		S4	4 6 3 00		7 8 8 00

CUSTOMER Dana Eggers   CUSTOMER NO. 120

DATE		ITEM	POST. REF.	DEBIT	CREDIT	DEBIT BALANCE
20-- Apr.	1	Balance	✓			4 7 2 50
	27		S4	1 0 2 90		5 7 5 40

CUSTOMER Cherie Grecki   CUSTOMER NO. 130

DATE		ITEM	POST. REF.	DEBIT	CREDIT	DEBIT BALANCE
20-- Apr.	1	Balance	✓			2 9 9 25
	1		S4	9 7 65		3 9 6 90
	5		SR4		9 7 65	2 9 9 25
	17		S4	4 8 30		3 4 7 55

CUSTOMER Phil Kellerman   CUSTOMER NO. 140

DATE		ITEM	POST. REF.	DEBIT	CREDIT	DEBIT BALANCE
20-- Apr.	5		S4	7 7 70		7 7 70

CUSTOMER Ben Nesbitt   CUSTOMER NO. 150

DATE		ITEM	POST. REF.	DEBIT	CREDIT	DEBIT BALANCE
20-- Apr.	1	Balance	✓			2 7 3 00
	30		S4	1 3 0 20		4 0 3 20

2-1 APPLICATION PROBLEM (concluded)

[1]

ACCOUNTS RECEIVABLE LEDGER

CUSTOMER Debbie Prosser   CUSTOMER NO. 160

DATE		ITEM	POST. REF.	DEBIT	CREDIT	DEBIT BALANCE
20-- Apr.	5		S4	1 8 9 00		1 8 9 00
	10		SR4		8 4 00	1 0 5 00

CUSTOMER Carole Tate   CUSTOMER NO. 170

DATE		ITEM	POST. REF.	DEBIT	CREDIT	DEBIT BALANCE
20-- Apr.	1	Balance	✓			1 8 9 00
	12		S4	2 8 8 75		4 7 7 75
	24		SR4		6 0 90	4 1 6 85

CUSTOMER Wade Thomas   CUSTOMER NO. 180

DATE		ITEM	POST. REF.	DEBIT	CREDIT	DEBIT BALANCE
20-- Apr.	2		S4	1 5 7 50		1 5 7 50
	7		S4	2 4 1 50		3 9 9 00
	15		SR4		1 4 7 00	2 5 2 00

Extra form

CUSTOMER _____ CUSTOMER NO. _____

DATE	ITEM	POST. REF.	DEBIT	CREDIT	DEBIT BALANCE

2-2 APPLICATION PROBLEM, p. 56

Journalizing and posting departmental cash receipts

[1, 2]

CASH RECEIPTS JOURNAL

PAGE 18

	DATE	ACCOUNT TITLE	DOC. NO.	POST. REF.	GENERAL DEBIT	GENERAL CREDIT	ACCOUNTS RECEIVABLE CREDIT	SALES TAX PAYABLE DEBIT	SALES TAX PAYABLE CREDIT	SALES CREDIT TABLES	SALES CREDIT CHAIRS	SALES DISCOUNT DEBIT TABLES	SALES DISCOUNT DEBIT CHAIRS	CASH DEBIT	
1	June 1	Wayne Miller	R110	120			157 50	15						154 35	1
2	2	Amy Cannon	R111	110			388 50	37				7 40		380 73	2
3	6	Bob Witt	R112	160			210 00							210 00	3
4	6	✓	T6						565 00	6240 00	5060 00			11865 00	4
5	11	Dawn Sanzone	R113	150			525 00	50				10 00		514 50	5
6	13	✓	T13						460 50	5640 00	3570 00			9670 50	6
7	17	Amy Cannon	R114	110			336 00	32				6 40		329 28	7
8	18	Dave Ring	R115	140			451 50	43				8 60		442 47	8
9	20	✓	T20						598 00	7110 00	4850 00		6 00	12558 00	9
10	24	Joe Ricardo	R116	130			787 50	75				9 00		771 75	10
11	27	✓	T27						602 00	6890 00	5150 00			12642 00	11
12	30	✓	T30						309 00	3200 00	2980 00			6489 00	12
13	30	Totals					2856 00	2 52	2534 50	29080 00	21610 00	41 40	9 00	56027 58	13
14							(1115)	(2130)	(2130)	(4105.1)	(4105.2)	(4115.1)	(4115.2)	(1105)	14

2-2 APPLICATION PROBLEM (continued)

[2]

GENERAL LEDGER

ACCOUNT Cash   ACCOUNT NO. 1105

DATE		ITEM	POST. REF.	DEBIT	CREDIT	BALANCE DEBIT	BALANCE CREDIT
20-- June	1	Balance	✓			59 9 1 3 00	
	30		CR18	56 0 2 7 58		115 9 4 0 58	

ACCOUNT Accounts Receivable   ACCOUNT NO. 1115

DATE		ITEM	POST. REF.	DEBIT	CREDIT	BALANCE DEBIT	BALANCE CREDIT
20-- June	1	Balance	✓			3 5 4 1 20	
	30		CR18		2 8 5 6 00	6 8 5 20	

ACCOUNT Sales Tax Payable   ACCOUNT NO. 2130

DATE		ITEM	POST. REF.	DEBIT	CREDIT	BALANCE DEBIT	BALANCE CREDIT
20-- June	1	Balance	✓				4 4 6 00
	30		CR18	2 52			4 4 3 48
	30		CR18		2 5 3 4 50		2 9 7 7 98

ACCOUNT Sales—Tables   ACCOUNT NO. 4105-1

DATE	ITEM	POST. REF.	DEBIT	CREDIT	BALANCE DEBIT	BALANCE CREDIT
20-- June 30		CR18		29 0 8 0 00		29 0 8 0 00

ACCOUNT Sales—Chairs   ACCOUNT NO. 4105-2

DATE	ITEM	POST. REF.	DEBIT	CREDIT	BALANCE DEBIT	BALANCE CREDIT
20-- June 30		CR18		21 6 1 0 00		21 6 1 0 00

2-2 APPLICATION PROBLEM (continued)

[1, 2]

GENERAL LEDGER

ACCOUNT Sales Discount—Tables   ACCOUNT NO. 4115-1

DATE	ITEM	POST. REF.	DEBIT	CREDIT	BALANCE DEBIT	BALANCE CREDIT
20-- June 30		CR18	4 1 40		4 1 40	

ACCOUNT Sales Discount—Chairs   ACCOUNT NO. 4115-2

DATE	ITEM	POST. REF.	DEBIT	CREDIT	BALANCE DEBIT	BALANCE CREDIT
20-- June 30		CR18	9 00		9 00	

ACCOUNTS RECEIVABLE LEDGER

CUSTOMER Amy Cannon   CUSTOMER NO. 110

DATE	ITEM	POST. REF.	DEBIT	CREDIT	DEBIT BALANCE
20-- June 1	Balance	✓			8 2 3 70
2		CR18		3 8 8 50	4 3 5 20
17		CR18		3 3 6 00	9 9 20

CUSTOMER Wayne Miller   CUSTOMER NO. 120

DATE	ITEM	POST. REF.	DEBIT	CREDIT	DEBIT BALANCE
20-- June 1	Balance	✓			2 0 0 00
1		CR18		1 5 7 50	4 2 50

2-2 APPLICATION PROBLEM (concluded)

ACCOUNTS RECEIVABLE LEDGER

CUSTOMER Joe Ricardo   **CUSTOMER NO.** 130

DATE		ITEM	POST. REF.	DEBIT	CREDIT	DEBIT BALANCE
20-- June	1	Balance	✓			1 0 5 9 90
	24		CR18		7 8 7 50	2 7 2 40

CUSTOMER David Ring   **CUSTOMER NO.** 140

DATE		ITEM	POST. REF.	DEBIT	CREDIT	DEBIT BALANCE
20-- June	1	Balance	✓			4 5 1 50
	18		CR18		4 5 1 50	—

CUSTOMER Dawn Sanzone   **CUSTOMER NO.** 150

DATE		ITEM	POST. REF.	DEBIT	CREDIT	DEBIT BALANCE
20-- June	1	Balance	✓			5 2 5 00
	11		CR18		5 2 5 00	—

CUSTOMER Bob Witt   **CUSTOMER NO.** 160

DATE		ITEM	POST. REF.	DEBIT	CREDIT	DEBIT BALANCE
20-- June	1	Balance	✓			4 8 1 10
	6		CR18		2 1 0 00	2 7 1 10

2-3 MASTERY PROBLEM, p. 58

Journalizing departmental sales, sales returns and allowances, and cash receipts   [1, 2]

SALES JOURNAL   PAGE 6

	DATE		ACCOUNT DEBITED	SALE NO.	POST. REF.	ACCOUNTS RECEIVABLE DEBIT	SALES TAX PAYABLE CREDIT	SALES CREDIT MEN'S CLOTHING	SALES CREDIT WOMEN'S CLOTHING	
1	20-- June	1	Jason Gunn	134		693 00	33 00	660 00		1
2		3	Kara Wilder	135		451 50	21 50	430 00		2
3		11	Paul Reed	136		882 00	42 00	840 00		3
4		15	Linda Baron	137		449 40	21 40		428 00	4
5		17	Robin Vaughn	138		252 00	12 00	240 00		5
6		28	Royalton Schools	139		760 00			760 00	6
7		30	Totals			3487 90	129 90	2170 00	1188 00	7
8										8
9										9
10										10

[1, 2]

SALES RETURNS AND ALLOWANCES JOURNAL   PAGE 11

	DATE		ACCOUNT CREDITED	CREDIT MEMO. NO.	POST. REF.	ACCOUNTS RECEIVABLE CREDIT	SALES TAX PAYABLE DEBIT	SALES RETURNS AND ALLOWANCES DEBIT MEN'S CLOTHING	SALES RETURNS AND ALLOWANCES DEBIT WOMEN'S CLOTHING	
1	20-- June	8	Kara Wilder	28		99 75	4 75	95 00		1
2		21	Linda Baron	29		70 35	3 35		67 00	2
3		30	Totals			170 10	8 10	95 00	67 00	3
4										4
5										5
6										6
7										7
8										8
9										9
10										10
11										11
12										12
13										13
14										14
15										15

2-3 MASTERY PROBLEM (concluded)

[1, 3]

CASH RECEIPTS JOURNAL

PAGE 11

	DATE	ACCOUNT TITLE	DOC. NO.	POST. REF.	GENERAL DEBIT (1)	GENERAL CREDIT (2)	ACCOUNTS RECEIVABLE CREDIT (3)	SALES TAX PAYABLE DEBIT (4)	SALES TAX PAYABLE CREDIT (5)	SALES CREDIT MEN'S CLOTHING (6)	SALES CREDIT WOMEN'S CLOTHING (7)	SALES DISCOUNT DEBIT MEN'S CLOTHING (8)	SALES DISCOUNT DEBIT WOMEN'S CLOTHING (9)	CASH DEBIT (10)
1	20-- June 4	William Hodges	R83				3 7 8 00	36					7 20	3 7 0 44
2	4	✔	T4	✔					2 4 0 00	2 2 8 0 00	2 5 2 0 00			5 0 4 0 00
3	6	Robin Vaughn	R84				6 7 2 00	64				12 80		6 5 8 56
4	9	Kara Wilder	R85				4 1 8 95	40					7 98	4 1 0 57
5	11	Jason Gunn	R86				6 9 3 00	66				13 20		6 7 9 14
6	11	✔	T11	✔					4 8 7 50	4 7 2 0 00	5 0 3 0 00			1 0 2 3 7 50
7	13	Kara Wilder	R87				3 5 1 75	34				6 70		3 4 4 71
8	18	✔	T18	✔					5 0 5 50	5 1 3 0 00	4 9 8 0 00			1 0 6 1 5 50
9	21	Paul Reed	R88				8 8 2 00	84				16 80		8 6 4 36
10	25	✔	T25	✔					4 8 3 00	4 7 5 0 00	4 9 1 0 00			1 0 1 4 3 00
11	30	✔	T30	✔					3 0 4 50	2 9 8 0 00	3 1 1 0 00			6 3 9 4 50
12	30	Totals					3 3 9 5 70	3 24	2 0 2 0 50	1 9 8 6 0 00	2 0 5 5 0 00	49 50	15 18	5 7 5 8 28

2-4 CHALLENGE PROBLEM, p. 59

Journalizing departmental sales, sales returns and allowances, and cash receipts   [1, 2]

SALES JOURNAL   PAGE 6

	DATE		ACCOUNT DEBITED	SALE NO.	POST. REF.	1 ACCOUNTS RECEIVABLE DEBIT	2 SALES CREDIT MEN'S CLOTHING	3 SALES CREDIT WOMEN'S CLOTHING	
1	20-- June	1	Jason Gunn	134		660 00	660 00		1
2		3	Kara Wilder	135		430 00	430 00		2
3		11	Paul Reed	136		840 00	840 00		3
4		15	Linda Baron	137		428 00		428 00	4
5		17	Robin Vaughn	138		240 00	240 00		5
6		28	Royalton Schools	139		760 00		760 00	6
7		30	Totals			3358 00	2170 00	1188 00	7
8									8
9									9
10									10
11									11

[1, 2]

SALES RETURNS AND ALLOWANCES JOURNAL   PAGE 6

	DATE		ACCOUNT CREDITED	CREDIT MEMO. NO.	POST. REF.	1 ACCOUNTS RECEIVABLE CREDIT	2 SALES RETURNS AND ALLOWANCES DEBIT MEN'S CLOTHING	3 SALES RETURNS AND ALLOWANCES DEBIT WOMEN'S CLOTHING	
1	20-- June	8	Kara Wilder	28		95 00	95 00		1
2		21	Linda Baron	29		67 00		67 00	2
3		30	Totals			162 00	95 00	67 00	3
4									4
5									5
6									6
7									7
8									8
9									9
10									10
11									11
12									12
13									13
14									14
15									15

CASH RECEIPTS JOURNAL PAGE 11

DATE	ACCOUNT TITLE	DOC. NO.	POST. REF.	GENERAL DEBIT	GENERAL CREDIT	ACCOUNTS RECEIVABLE CREDIT	SALES CREDIT MEN'S CLOTHING	SALES CREDIT WOMEN'S CLOTHING	SALES DISCOUNT DEBIT MEN'S CLOTHING	SALES DISCOUNT DEBIT WOMEN'S CLOTHING	CASH DEBIT	
20-- June 4	William Hodges	R83				360 00				3 60	35 6 40	1
4	✓	T4	✓				2280 00	2520 00			4800 00	2
6	Robin Vaughn	R84				640 00			6 40		633 60	3
9	Kara Wilder	R85				399 00				3 99	395 01	4
11	Jason Gunn	R86				660 00			6 60		653 40	5
11	✓	T11	✓				4720 00	5030 00			9750 00	6
13	Kara Wilder	R87				335 00			3 35		331 65	7
18	✓	T18	✓				5130 00	4980 00			10110 00	8
21	Paul Reed	R88				840 00			8 40		831 60	9
25	✓	T25	✓				4750 00	4910 00			9660 00	10
30	✓	T30	✓				2980 00	3110 00			6090 00	11
30	Totals					3234 00	19860 00	20550 00	24 75	7 59	43611 66	12

3-1 WORK TOGETHER, p. 69

Preparing a benefits record; calculating employee earnings;
preparing a commissions record

[4]

BENEFITS RECORD

EMPLOYEE NO. __4__   EMPLOYEE NAME _Susan Fulton_   DEPARTMENT _Hardware_

DATE OF INITIAL EMPLOYMENT ___November 1, 20--___   YEAR _20--_

	PAY PERIOD ENDED	VACATION TIME				SICK LEAVE TIME				PERSONAL LEAVE TIME			
		BEGIN. HOURS AVAIL.	HOURS EARNED	HOURS USED	ACC. HOURS AVAIL.	BEGIN. HOURS AVAIL.	HOURS EARNED	HOURS USED	ACC. HOURS AVAIL.	BEGIN. HOURS AVAIL.	HOURS EARNED	HOURS USED	ACC. HOURS AVAIL.
1	1/2	96	4	16	84	90	2	0	92	15	1	2	14
2	1/16	84	4	8	80	92	2	4	90	14	1	0	15
3													
4													
5													
6													
7													
8													
9													
10													
11													
12													
13													
14													
15													

[5]

EMPLOYEE EARNINGS

Employee Number	Hours Worked		Regular Rate	Earnings		Total Earnings
	Regular	Overtime		Regular	Overtime	
1	80	5	8.75	700.00	65.63	765.63
2	80	4	7.00	560.00	42.00	602.00

3-1 WORK TOGETHER (concluded)

[6]

COMMISSIONS RECORD

EMPLOYEE NO. _2_   EMPLOYEE NAME _John Balderas_____

COMMISSION RATE _1%_____   MONTH _January_____   YEAR _20--_____

DEPT. _Hardware_____   REGULAR BIWEEKLY SALARY _$1,200.00_____

Sales

Sales on Account . . . . $ ____10,348.00

Cash and Credit Card Sales . . . . ____15,523.00

Total Sales . . . . $ ____25,871.00

Less: Sales Discounts . . . . $ ____179.00

Sales Returns
and Allowances . . . . ____2,039.00   ____2,218.00

Net Sales . . . . $ ____23,653.00

Commission on Net Sales . . . . $ ____236.53

Extra form

COMMISSIONS RECORD

EMPLOYEE NO. _____   EMPLOYEE NAME _____

COMMISSION RATE _____   MONTH _____   YEAR _____

DEPT. _____   REGULAR BIWEEKLY SALARY _____

Sales

Sales on Account . . . . $ _____

Cash and Credit Card Sales . . . . _____

Total Sales . . . . $ _____

Less: Sales Discounts . . . . $ _____

Sales Returns
and Allowances . . . . _____   _____

Net Sales . . . . $ _____

Commission on Net Sales . . . . $ _____

Name _____ Date _____ Class _____

3-1 ON YOUR OWN, p. 70

Preparing a benefits record; calculating employee earnings; preparing a commissions record

[7]

BENEFITS RECORD

EMPLOYEE NO. _12_   EMPLOYEE NAME _Keith Parker_   DEPARTMENT _Paint_

DATE OF INITIAL EMPLOYMENT _June 1, 19--_   YEAR _20--_

		1	2	3	4	5	6	7	8	9	10	11	12
	PAY PERIOD ENDED	VACATION TIME				SICK LEAVE TIME				PERSONAL LEAVE TIME			
		BEGIN. HOURS AVAIL.	HOURS EARNED	HOURS USED	ACC. HOURS AVAIL.	BEGIN. HOURS AVAIL.	HOURS EARNED	HOURS USED	ACC. HOURS AVAIL.	BEGIN. HOURS AVAIL.	HOURS EARNED	HOURS USED	ACC. HOURS AVAIL.
1	1/2	104	4	24	84	96	2	0	98	26	1	4	23
2	1/16	84	4	8	80	98	2	8	92	23	1	0	24
3													
4													
5													
6													
7													
8													
9													
10													
11													
12													
13													
14													
15													

[8]

EMPLOYEE EARNINGS

Employee Number	Hours Worked		Regular Rate	Earnings		Total Earnings
	Regular	Overtime		Regular	Overtime	
3	80	6	9.25	740.00	83.25	823.25
4	80	4	7.50	600.00	45.00	645.00

3-1 ON YOUR OWN (concluded)

[9]

COMMISSIONS RECORD

EMPLOYEE NO. _5_   EMPLOYEE NAME _Anna Paden_

COMMISSION RATE _1%_   MONTH _January_   YEAR _20--_

DEPT. _Paint_   REGULAR BIWEEKLY SALARY _$1,100.00_

Sales

Sales on Account	$	9,313.20
Cash and Credit Card Sales		13,970.80
Total Sales	$	23,284.00
Less: Sales Discounts . . . . $ 196.90		
Sales Returns and Allowances 1,835.10	2,032.00	
Net Sales . . . . $	21,252.00	
Commission on Net Sales . . . . $	212.52	

Extra form

COMMISSIONS RECORD

EMPLOYEE NO. _____   EMPLOYEE NAME _____

COMMISSION RATE _____   MONTH _____   YEAR _____

DEPT. _____   REGULAR BIWEEKLY SALARY _____

Sales

Sales on Account	$ _____	
Cash and Credit Card Sales	_____	
Total Sales	$ _____	
Less: Sales Discounts . . . . $ _____		
Sales Returns and Allowances . . . . _____	_____	
Net Sales . . . . $ _____		
Commission on Net Sales . . . . $ _____		

Name ______________________ Date ____________ Class ____________

3-2 WORK TOGETHER

(Note: The payroll register for this problem begins on page 54.)

Extra forms

PAYROLL REGISTER

DATE OF PAYMENT

	10	11	12	13	14	15	16	17	18	19	20	
	DEPARTMENT		ADMIN. SALARIES	DEDUCTIONS						PAID		
	HARDWARE	PAINT		FEDERAL INCOME TAX	STATE INCOME TAX	SOC. SEC. TAX	MEDICARE TAX	OTHER	TOTAL	NET PAY	CHECK NO.	
1												1
2												2
3												3
4												4
5												5
6												6
7												7
8												8
9												9
10												10
11												11
12												12
13												13
14												14
15												15

PAYROLL REGISTER

DATE OF PAYMENT

	10	11	12	13	14	15	16	17	18	19	20	
	DEPARTMENT		ADMIN. SALARIES	DEDUCTIONS						PAID		
	HARDWARE	PAINT		FEDERAL INCOME TAX	STATE INCOME TAX	SOC. SEC. TAX	MEDICARE TAX	OTHER	TOTAL	NET PAY	CHECK NO.	
1												1
2												2
3												3
4												4
5												5
6												6
7												7
8												8
9												9
10												10
11												11
12												12
13												13
14												14
15												15

3-2 WORK TOGETHER, p. 77

Completing payroll records

[5, 6]

PAY PERIOD ENDED 7/3/20--   **PAYROLL REGISTER**

	EMPL. NO.	EMPLOYEE NAME	MARITAL STATUS	NO. OF ALLOW-ANCES	TOTAL HOURS	EARNINGS REGULAR	OVERTIME	COMMISSION	TOTAL	
1	2	Balderas, John	M	2	—	1200 00		312 00	1512 00	1
2										2
3										3
4	4	Fulton, Susan	S	1	88	800 00	120 00		920 00	4
5										5
6										6
7										7
8										8
9										9
10										10
11										11
12										12
13										13
14										14
15							1418 0 00	776 40	582 00	1553 8 40	15

[7]

EARNINGS RECORD FOR QUARTER ENDED Sept. 30, 20--

EMPLOYEE NO. 4   NAME Fulton, Susan   SOCIAL SECURITY NO. 555-72-5782

MARITAL STATUS S   WITHHOLDING ALLOWANCES 1   HOURLY RATE $10.00   SALARY

DEPARTMENT Hardware   POSITION Salesclerk

PAY PERIOD NO.	ENDED	TOTAL EARNINGS	DEDUCTIONS FEDERAL INCOME TAX	STATE INCOME TAX	SOC. SEC. TAX	MEDICARE TAX	OTHER	TOTAL	NET PAY	ACCUMULATED EARNINGS
										1190 0 00
1	7/3	920 00	109 00	46 00	59 80	13 80 H	28 00	256 60	663 40	1282 0 00
2										
3										
4										
5										
6										
7										
8										
9										
10										

3-2 WORK TOGETHER (concluded)

[5, 6]

DATE OF PAYMENT 7/10/20--

PAYROLL REGISTER

	10	11	12	13	14	15	16	17	18	19	20
	DEPARTMENT		ADMIN. SALARIES	DEDUCTIONS						PAID	
	HARDWARE	PAINT		FEDERAL INCOME TAX	STATE INCOME TAX	SOC. SEC. TAX	MEDICARE TAX	OTHER	TOTAL	NET PAY	CHECK NO.
1			1512 00	159 00	75 60	98 28	22 68	H 56 00 / L 25 60	437 16	1074 84	
2											
3											
4	920 00			109 00	46 00	59 80	13 80	H 28 00	256 60	663 40	
5											
6											
7											
8											
9											
10											1
11											1
12											1
13											1
14											1
15	7605 80	5070 60	2862 00	1305 00	776 92	1010 00	233 08	H 588 00 / L 102 40	4015 40	11523 00	1

Extra form

EARNINGS RECORD FOR QUARTER ENDED _____

EMPLOYEE NO. _____ NAME _____ SOCIAL SECURITY NO. _____

MARITAL STATUS _____ WITHHOLDING ALLOWANCES _____ HOURLY RATE _____ SALARY _____

DEPARTMENT _____ POSITION _____

	1	2	3	4	5	6	7	8	9	10	11
	PAY PERIOD		TOTAL EARNINGS	DEDUCTIONS						NET PAY	ACCUMULATED EARNINGS
	NO.	ENDED		FEDERAL INCOME TAX	STATE INCOME TAX	SOC. SEC. TAX	MEDICARE TAX	OTHER	TOTAL		
1											
2											
3											
4											
5											
6											
7											
8											
9											
10											

3-2 WORK TOGETHER

Extra forms

PAY PERIOD ENDED					**PAYROLL REGISTER**				
						EARNINGS			
EMPL. NO.	EMPLOYEE NAME	MARI-TAL STATUS	NO. OF ALLOW-ANCES	TOTAL HOURS	REGULAR	OVERTIME	COMMISSION	TOTAL	
1									1
2									2
3									3
4									4
5									5
6									6
7									7
8									8
9									9
10									10
11									11
12									12
13									13
14									14
15									15

PAY PERIOD ENDED					**PAYROLL REGISTER**				
						EARNINGS			
EMPL. NO.	EMPLOYEE NAME	MARI-TAL STATUS	NO. OF ALLOW-ANCES	TOTAL HOURS	REGULAR	OVERTIME	COMMISSION	TOTAL	
1									1
2									2
3									3
4									4
5									5
6									6
7									7
8									8
9									9
10									10
11									11
12									12
13									13
14									14
15									15

3-2 ON YOUR OWN

(Note: The payroll register for this problem begins on page 58.)

Extra forms

PAYROLL REGISTER

DATE OF PAYMENT

	10	11	12	13	14	15	16	17	18	19	20	
	DEPARTMENT		ADMIN. SALARIES	DEDUCTIONS						PAID		
	HARDWARE	PAINT		FEDERAL INCOME TAX	STATE INCOME TAX	SOC. SEC. TAX	MEDICARE TAX	OTHER	TOTAL	NET PAY	CHECK NO.	
1												1
2												2
3												3
4												4
5												5
6												6
7												7
8												8
9												9
10												10
11												11
12												12
13												13
14												14
15												15

PAYROLL REGISTER

DATE OF PAYMENT

	10	11	12	13	14	15	16	17	18	19	20	
	DEPARTMENT		ADMIN. SALARIES	DEDUCTIONS						PAID		
	HARDWARE	PAINT		FEDERAL INCOME TAX	STATE INCOME TAX	SOC. SEC. TAX	MEDICARE TAX	OTHER	TOTAL	NET PAY	CHECK NO.	
1												1
2												2
3												3
4												4
5												5
6												6
7												7
8												8
9												9
10												10
11												11
12												12
13												13
14												14
15												15

3-2 ON YOUR OWN, p. 78

Completing payroll records   [8, 9]

PAY PERIOD ENDED 10/2/20--					PAYROLL REGISTER				
	1	2	3	4	5	6	7	8	9
	EMPL. NO.	EMPLOYEE NAME	MARI-TAL STATUS	NO. OF ALLOW-ANCES	TOTAL HOURS	EARNINGS			
						REGULAR	OVERTIME	COMMISSION	TOTAL
1										1
2										2
3										3
4										4
5										5
6										6
7										7
8										8
9										9
10										10
11	5	Paden, Anna	M	1	—	1100 00		305 00	1405 00	11
12	12	Parker, Keith	S	1	90	760 00	142 50		902 50	12
13										13
14										14
15						1490 00	815 00	611 00	1632 600	15

[10]

EARNINGS RECORD FOR QUARTER ENDED				Dec. 31, 20--						
EMPLOYEE NO. 12 NAME Parker, Keith							SOCIAL SECURITY NO. 555-75-1782			
MARITAL STATUS S WITHHOLDING ALLOWANCES 1						HOURLY RATE $9.50		SALARY		
DEPARTMENT Paint						POSITION Salesclerk				
1	2	3	4	5	6	7	8	9	10	11
PAY PERIOD		TOTAL EARNINGS	DEDUCTIONS						NET PAY	ACCUMULATED EARNINGS
NO.	ENDED		FEDERAL INCOME TAX	STATE INCOME TAX	SOC. SEC. TAX	MEDICARE TAX	OTHER	TOTAL		1900 000
1	10/2	902 50	106 00	45 13	58 66	13 54 H	28 00	251 33	651 17	1990 250
2										
3										
4										
5										
6										
7										
8										
9										
10										

3-2 ON YOUR OWN (concluded)

[8, 9]

DATE OF PAYMENT 10/9/20-- PAYROLL REGISTER

	10	11	12	13	14	15	16	17	18	19	20	
	DEPARTMENT		ADMIN. SALARIES	DEDUCTIONS						PAID		
	HARDWARE	PAINT		FEDERAL INCOME TAX	STATE INCOME TAX	SOC. SEC. TAX	MEDICARE TAX	OTHER	TOTAL	NET PAY	CHECK NO.	
1												1
2												2
3												3
4												4
5												5
6												6
7												7
8												8
9												9
10												10
11			1405 00	159 00	70 25	91 33	21 08	H 28 00 / L 25 60	395 26	1009 74		11
12		902 50		106 00	45 13	58 66	13 54	H 28 00	251 33	651 17		12
13												13
14												14
15	7266 00	5945 00	3115 00	1388 00	816 30	1061 19	244 89	H 588 00 / L 102 40	4200 78	12125 22		15

Extra form

EARNINGS RECORD FOR QUARTER ENDED _____

EMPLOYEE NO. _____ NAME _____ SOCIAL SECURITY NO. _____

MARITAL STATUS _____ WITHHOLDING ALLOWANCES _____ HOURLY RATE _____ SALARY _____

DEPARTMENT _____ POSITION _____

	1	2	3	4	5	6	7	8	9	10	11
	PAY PERIOD		TOTAL EARNINGS	DEDUCTIONS						NET PAY	ACCUMULATED EARNINGS
	NO.	ENDED		FEDERAL INCOME TAX	STATE INCOME TAX	SOC. SEC. TAX	MEDICARE TAX	OTHER	TOTAL		
1											
2											
3											
4											
5											
6											
7											
8											
9											
10											

3-2 ON YOUR OWN

Extra forms

PAYROLL REGISTER

PAY PERIOD ENDED

	EMPL. NO.	EMPLOYEE NAME	MARI-TAL STATUS	NO. OF ALLOW-ANCES	TOTAL HOURS	EARNINGS			
						REGULAR	OVERTIME	COMMISSION	TOTAL
1									
2									
3									
4									
5									
6									
7									
8									
9									
10									
11									
12									
13									
14									
15									

PAYROLL REGISTER

PAY PERIOD ENDED

	EMPL. NO.	EMPLOYEE NAME	MARI-TAL STATUS	NO. OF ALLOW-ANCES	TOTAL HOURS	EARNINGS			
						REGULAR	OVERTIME	COMMISSION	TOTAL
1									
2									
3									
4									
5									
6									
7									
8									
9									
10									
11									
12									
13									
14									
15									

Name _____ Date _____ Class _____

3-3 WORK TOGETHER, p. 84

Journalizing and paying payroll and payroll taxes

[3]

CASH PAYMENTS JOURNAL

PAGE 15

	DATE	ACCOUNT TITLE	CK. NO.	POST. REF.	GENERAL DEBIT	GENERAL CREDIT	ACCOUNTS PAYABLE DEBIT	PURCH. DISCOUNT CR.	CASH CREDIT	
1	July 10	Salary Exp.—Hardware	260		7605 80				11523 00	1
2		Salary Exp.—Paint			5070 60					2
3		Salary Exp.—Admin.			2862 00					3
4		Emp. Inc. Tax Pay.—Fed.				1305 00				4
5		Emp. Inc. Tax Pay.—State				776 92				5
6		Soc. Sec. Tax Payable				1010 00				6
7		Medicare Tax Payable				233 08				7
8		Health Ins. Prem. Pay.				588 00				8
9		Life Ins. Prem. Pay.				102 40				9
10	15	Emp. Inc. Tax Pay.—Fed.	265		1305 00				3791 16	10
11		Soc. Sec. Tax Payable			2020 00					11
12		Medicare Tax Payable			466 16					12
13	29	Unemploy. Tax Pay.—Fed	270		745 84				5780 28	13
14		Unemploy. Tax Pay.—State			5034 44					14
15										15
16										16
17										17
18										18
19										19
20										20
21										21
22										22
23										23
24										24
25										25

3-3 WORK TOGETHER (concluded)

[3]

GENERAL JOURNAL   PAGE 7

	DATE		ACCOUNT TITLE	DOC. NO.	POST. REF.	DEBIT	CREDIT	
1	July	10	Payroll Taxes Expense	M33		2 2 0 6 46		1
2			Social Security Tax Payable				1 0 1 0 00	2
3			Medicare Tax Payable				2 3 3 08	3
4			Unemploy. Tax Payable—Fed.				1 2 4 31	4
5			Unemploy. Tax Payable—State				8 3 9 07	5
6								6
7								7
8								8
9								9
10								10
11								11
12								12
13								13
14								14
15								15
16								16
17								17
18								18
19								19
20								20
21								21
22								22
23								23
24								24
25								25
26								26
27								27
28								28
29								29
30								30
31								31

Journalizing and paying payroll and payroll taxes [4]

CASH PAYMENTS JOURNAL   PAGE 18

	DATE	ACCOUNT TITLE	CK. NO.	POST. REF.	GENERAL DEBIT	GENERAL CREDIT	ACCOUNTS PAYABLE DEBIT	PURCH. DISCOUNT CR.	CASH CREDIT	
1	Oct. 9	Salary Exp.—Hardware	335		726600				1212522	1
2		Salary Exp.—Paint			594500					2
3		Salary Exp.—Admin.			311500					3
4		Emp. Inc. Tax Pay.—Fed.				138800				4
5		Emp. Inc. Tax Pay.—State				81630				5
6		Soc. Sec. Tax Payable				106119				6
7		Medicare Tax Payable				24489				7
8		Health Ins. Prem. Pay.				58800				8
9		Life Ins. Prem. Pay.				10240				9
10	14	Emp. Inc. Tax Pay.—Fed.	339		138800				400016	10
11		Soc. Sec. Tax Payable			212238					11
12		Medicare Tax Payable			48978					12
13	28	Unemploy. Tax Pay.—Fed.	344		78365				607327	13
14		Unemploy. Tax Pay.—State			528962					14
15										15
16										16
17										17
18										18
19										19
20										20
21										21
22										22
23										23
24										24
25										25

Name _____ Date _____ Class _____

GENERAL JOURNAL   PAGE 10

	DATE		ACCOUNT TITLE	DOC. NO.	POST. REF.	DEBIT	CREDIT	
1	20— Oct.	9	*Payroll Taxes Expense*			2 3 1 8 29		1
2			*Social Security Tax Payable*				1 0 6 1 19	2
3			*Medicare Tax Payable*				2 4 4 89	3
4			*Unemploy. Tax Payable—Fed.*				1 3 0 61	4
5			*Unemploy. Tax Payable—State*				8 8 1 60	5
6								6
7								7
8								8
9								9
10								10
11								11
12								12
13								13
14								14
15								15
16								16
17								17
18								18
19								19
20								20
21								21
22								22
23								23
24								24
25								25
26								26
27								27
28								28
29								29
30								30
31								31

Name _____ Date _____ Class _____

3-1 APPLICATION PROBLEM, p. 86

Preparing a benefits record

BENEFITS RECORD

EMPLOYEE NO. _9_ EMPLOYEE NAME _Monica Chaffee_ DEPARTMENT _Sports. Equip._

DATE OF INITIAL EMPLOYMENT _Apr. 1, 19--_ YEAR _20--_

		1	2	3	4	5	6	7	8	9	10	11	12
	PAY PERIOD ENDED	VACATION TIME				SICK LEAVE TIME				PERSONAL LEAVE TIME			
		BEGIN. HOURS AVAIL.	HOURS EARNED	HOURS USED	ACC. HOURS AVAIL.	BEGIN. HOURS AVAIL.	HOURS EARNED	HOURS USED	ACC. HOURS AVAIL.	BEGIN. HOURS AVAIL.	HOURS EARNED	HOURS USED	ACC. HOURS AVAIL.
1	1/2	92	4	16	80	100	2	2	100	20	1	2	19
2	1/16	80	4	0	84	100	2	4	98	19	1	4	16
3	1/30	84	4	0	88	98	2	8	92	16	1	0	17
4	2/13	88	4	16	76	92	2	0	94	17	1	4	14
5													
6													
7													
8													
9													
10													
11													
12													
13													
14													
15													

Extra form

BENEFITS RECORD

EMPLOYEE NO. _____ EMPLOYEE NAME _____ DEPARTMENT _____

DATE OF INITIAL EMPLOYMENT _____ YEAR _____

		1	2	3	4	5	6	7	8	9	10	11	12
	PAY PERIOD ENDED	VACATION TIME				SICK LEAVE TIME				PERSONAL LEAVE TIME			
		BEGIN. HOURS AVAIL.	HOURS EARNED	HOURS USED	ACC. HOURS AVAIL.	BEGIN. HOURS AVAIL.	HOURS EARNED	HOURS USED	ACC. HOURS AVAIL.	BEGIN. HOURS AVAIL.	HOURS EARNED	HOURS USED	ACC. HOURS AVAIL.
1													
2													
3													
4													
5													
6													
7													
8													
9													
10													
11													
12													
13													
14													
15													
16													

3-1 APPLICATION PROBLEM

Extra forms

BENEFITS RECORD

EMPLOYEE NO. _____   EMPLOYEE NAME _____   DEPARTMENT _____

DATE OF INITIAL EMPLOYMENT _____   YEAR _____

	1	2	3	4	5	6	7	8	9	10	11	12
PAY PERIOD ENDED	VACATION TIME				SICK LEAVE TIME				PERSONAL LEAVE TIME			
	BEGIN. HOURS AVAIL.	HOURS EARNED	HOURS USED	ACC. HOURS AVAIL.	BEGIN. HOURS AVAIL.	HOURS EARNED	HOURS USED	ACC. HOURS AVAIL.	BEGIN. HOURS AVAIL.	HOURS EARNED	HOURS USED	ACC. HOURS AVAIL.
1												
2												
3												
4												
5												
6												
7												
8												
9												
10												
11												
12												
13												
14												
15												
16												

BENEFITS RECORD

EMPLOYEE NO. _____   EMPLOYEE NAME _____   DEPARTMENT _____

DATE OF INITIAL EMPLOYMENT _____   YEAR _____

	1	2	3	4	5	6	7	8	9	10	11	12
PAY PERIOD ENDED	VACATION TIME				SICK LEAVE TIME				PERSONAL LEAVE TIME			
	BEGIN. HOURS AVAIL.	HOURS EARNED	HOURS USED	ACC. HOURS AVAIL.	BEGIN. HOURS AVAIL.	HOURS EARNED	HOURS USED	ACC. HOURS AVAIL.	BEGIN. HOURS AVAIL.	HOURS EARNED	HOURS USED	ACC. HOURS AVAIL.
1												
2												
3												
4												
5												
6												
7												
8												
9												
10												
11												
12												
13												
14												
15												
16												

3-2 APPLICATION PROBLEM, p. 86

Recording employee benefits and calculating earnings on time cards

BENEFITS AUTHORIZATION

EMPLOYEE NO. 3   EMPLOYEE Janet T. Aguilar

PAY PERIOD ENDED 3/12/--   DEPARTMENT Carpet

	HOURS AVAIL.	M	T	W	T	F	S	M	T	W	T	F	S	HOURS USED
VACATION	64			4					4					8
SICK LEAVE	46					4								4
PERSONAL LEAVE	12											2		2

_____   Eileen S. Johnson   3/12/--
MANAGER (only if needed)   DEPARTMENT SUPERVISOR   DATE

BENEFITS AUTHORIZATION

EMPLOYEE NO. 8   EMPLOYEE Bernard C. Parker

PAY PERIOD ENDED 3/12/--   DEPARTMENT Administrative

	HOURS AVAIL.	M	T	W	T	F	S	M	T	W	T	F	S	HOURS USED
VACATION	52	8												8
SICK LEAVE	30							8	4					12
PERSONAL LEAVE	17			2								1		3

Belinda F. Pullen   _____   3/12/--
MANAGER (only if needed)   DEPARTMENT SUPERVISOR   DATE

BENEFITS AUTHORIZATION

EMPLOYEE NO. 13   EMPLOYEE Natalie R. Sabo

PAY PERIOD ENDED 3/12/--   DEPARTMENT Drapery

	HOURS AVAIL.	M	T	W	T	F	S	M	T	W	T	F	S	HOURS USED
VACATION	68				8	8	8							24
SICK LEAVE	47												4	4
PERSONAL LEAVE	20										4			4

_____   Paul T. Burke   3/12/--
MANAGER (only if needed)   DEPARTMENT SUPERVISOR   DATE

3-2 APPLICATION PROBLEM (continued)

[1]

BENEFITS RECORD

EMPLOYEE NO. 3   EMPLOYEE NAME Janet T. Aquilar   DEPARTMENT Carpet

DATE OF INITIAL EMPLOYMENT February 8, 19--   YEAR 20--

		1	2	3	4	5	6	7	8	9	10	11	12
	PAY PERIOD ENDED	VACATION TIME				SICK LEAVE TIME				PERSONAL LEAVE TIME			
		BEGIN. HOURS AVAIL.	HOURS EARNED	HOURS USED	ACC. HOURS AVAIL.	BEGIN. HOURS AVAIL.	HOURS EARNED	HOURS USED	ACC. HOURS AVAIL.	BEGIN. HOURS AVAIL.	HOURS EARNED	HOURS USED	ACC. HOURS AVAIL.
6	3/12	64	4	8	60	46	2	4	44	12	1	2	11
7													
8													
9													
10													
11													

BENEFITS RECORD

EMPLOYEE NO. 8   EMPLOYEE NAME Bernard C. Parker   DEPARTMENT Administrative

DATE OF INITIAL EMPLOYMENT July 16, 19--   YEAR 20--

		1	2	3	4	5	6	7	8	9	10	11	12
	PAY PERIOD ENDED	VACATION TIME				SICK LEAVE TIME				PERSONAL LEAVE TIME			
		BEGIN. HOURS AVAIL.	HOURS EARNED	HOURS USED	ACC. HOURS AVAIL.	BEGIN. HOURS AVAIL.	HOURS EARNED	HOURS USED	ACC. HOURS AVAIL.	BEGIN. HOURS AVAIL.	HOURS EARNED	HOURS USED	ACC. HOURS AVAIL.
6	3/12	52	4	8	48	30	2	12	20	17	1	3	15
7													
8													
9													
10													
11													

BENEFITS RECORD

EMPLOYEE NO. 13   EMPLOYEE NAME Natalie R. Sabo   DEPARTMENT Drapery

DATE OF INITIAL EMPLOYMENT March 11, 19--   YEAR 20--

		1	2	3	4	5	6	7	8	9	10	11	12
	PAY PERIOD ENDED	VACATION TIME				SICK LEAVE TIME				PERSONAL LEAVE TIME			
		BEGIN. HOURS AVAIL.	HOURS EARNED	HOURS USED	ACC. HOURS AVAIL.	BEGIN. HOURS AVAIL.	HOURS EARNED	HOURS USED	ACC. HOURS AVAIL.	BEGIN. HOURS AVAIL.	HOURS EARNED	HOURS USED	ACC. HOURS AVAIL.
6	3/12	68	4	24	48	47	2	4	45	20	1	4	17
7													
8													
9													
10													
11													

3-2 APPLICATION PROBLEM (continued)

The time cards prepared in this problem are needed to complete Application Problem 3-4.   **[2–4]**

NAME Janet T. Aguilar

DEPARTMENT Carpet

EMPLOYEE NO. 3

PAY PERIOD ENDED 3/12/20--

MORNING		AFTERNOON		OVERTIME		HOURS	
IN	OUT	IN	OUT	IN	OUT	REG	OT
≥ 9:01	≥ 11:59	≥ 1:00	≥ 6:03			8	
⊢ 9:00	⊢ 12:01	⊢ 1:00	⊢ 6:00	⊢ 7:00	⊢ 9:00	8	2
≥ 8:58	≥ 12:00	≥ 1:01	≥ 2:03			4V4	
⊢ 9:02	⊢ 12:01	⊢ 1:00	⊢ 6:00	⊢ 7:30	⊢ 9:00	8	1½
		⊢ 2:00	⊢ 6:01			4S4	
≥ 9:01	≥ 12:00	≥ 1:00	≥ 6:01			8	
⊢ 9:00	⊢ 12:01	⊢ 1:01	⊢ 2:01			4V4	
≥ 9:00	≥ 12:00	≥ 1:00	≥ 6:01	≥ 7:30	≥ 8:30	8	1
⊢ 9:01	⊢ 12:00	⊢ 1:01	⊢ 6:00			8	
⊢ 9:00	⊢ 12:00	⊢ 1:02	⊢ 4:00			6P2	

	HOURS	RATE	AMOUNT
REGULAR	80	7.00	560.00
OVERTIME	4 ½	10.50	47.25
TOTAL HOURS	84 ½	TOTAL EARNINGS	607.25

NAME Bernard C. Parker

DEPARTMENT Administrative

EMPLOYEE NO. 8

PAY PERIOD ENDED 3/12/20--

MORNING		AFTERNOON		OVERTIME		HOURS	
IN	OUT	IN	OUT	IN	OUT	REG	OT
						V8	
⊢ 9:00	⊢ 12:01	⊢ 1:00	⊢ 6:00	⊢ 7:00	⊢ 8:30	8	1½
≥ 8:59	≥ 12:00	≥ 12:58	≥ 4:00			6P2	
≥ 9:01	⊢ 12:00	⊢ 1:02	⊢ 6:03	⊢ 7:30	⊢ 9:00	8	1½
⊢ 9:00	⊢ 12:02	⊢ 1:01	⊢ 6:00			8	
						S8	
		⊢ 2:00	⊢ 6:02			4S4	
≥ 8:58	≥ 12:01	≥ 1:01	≥ 6:00			8	
⊢ 9:01	⊢ 12:00	⊢ 1:00	⊢ 6:00	⊢ 7:00	⊢ 8:00	8	1
⊢ 9:00	12:02	⊢ 1:00	⊢ 5:00			7P1	

	HOURS	RATE	AMOUNT
REGULAR	80	6.50	520.00
OVERTIME	4	9.75	39.00
TOTAL HOURS	84	TOTAL EARNINGS	559.00

3-2 APPLICATION PROBLEM (concluded)

The time cards prepared in this problem are
needed to complete Application Problem 3-4.

Extra form

NAME __Natalie R. Sabo__

DEPARTMENT __Drapery__

EMPLOYEE NO. __13__

PAY PERIOD ENDED __3/12/20--__

MORNING		AFTERNOON		OVERTIME		HOURS	
IN	OUT	IN	OUT	IN	OUT	REG	OT
T 9:00	T 12:59	T 2:00	T 6:02	T 7:00	T 8:00	8	1
W 9:01	W 1:00	W 2:00	W 6:01			8	
						V8	
						V8	
						V8	
T 9:00	T 1:03	T 2:00	T 6:00	T 7:00	T 9:30	8	2½
W 8:58	W 1:00	W 2:01	W 6:01			8	
T 9:00	T 1:03					4P4	
F 9:00	F 1:00	F 2:02	F 6:03	F 7:00	F 8:00	8	1
S 9:03	S 1:00					4S4	

	HOURS	RATE	AMOUNT
REGULAR	80	6.50	520.00
OVERTIME	4½	9.75	43.88
TOTAL HOURS	84½	TOTAL EARNINGS	563.88

Extra form

NAME _____

DEPARTMENT _____

EMPLOYEE NO. _____

PAY PERIOD ENDED _____

MORNING		AFTERNOON		OVERTIME		HOURS	
IN	OUT	IN	OUT	IN	OUT	REG	OT
S	S	S	S				
M	M	M	M				
T	T	T	T				
W	W	W	W				
T	T	T	T				
F	F	F	F				
S	S	S	S				
S	S	S	S				
M	M	M	M				
T	T	T	T				
W	W	W	W				
T	T	T	T				
F	F	F	F				
S	S	S	S				

	HOURS	RATE	AMOUNT
REGULAR			
OVERTIME			
TOTAL HOURS		TOTAL EARNINGS	

3-3 APPLICATION PROBLEM, p. 86

Preparing departmental commissions records

The commissions records prepared in this problem are needed to complete Application Problem 3-4.

COMMISSIONS RECORD

EMPLOYEE NO. _9_   EMPLOYEE NAME _Heidi Gowens_

COMMISSION RATE _1.0%_   MONTH _February_   YEAR _20--_

DEPT. _Carpet_   REGULAR BIWEEKLY SALARY _$540.00_

Sales

Sales on Account.............................		$ 8,623.40
Cash and Credit Card Sales...................		12,936.20
Total Sales.................................		$ 21,559.60
Less: Sales Discounts.................	$ 148.90	
Sales Returns and Allowances..............	1,699.30	1,848.20
Net Sales....................................		$ 19,711.40
Commission on Net Sales......................		$ 197.11

COMMISSIONS RECORD

EMPLOYEE NO. _14_   EMPLOYEE NAME _Dale Mantle_

COMMISSION RATE _1.0%_   MONTH _February_   YEAR _20--_

DEPT. _Drapery_   REGULAR BIWEEKLY SALARY _$520.00_

Sales

Sales on Account.............................		$ 7,223.89
Cash and Credit Card Sales...................		13,987.11
Total Sales.................................		$ 21,211.00
Less: Sales Discounts.................	$ 337.17	
Sales Returns and Allowances..............	654.33	991.50
Net Sales....................................		$ 20,219.50
Commission on Net Sales......................		$ 202.20

Name _____ Date _____ Class _____

3-3 APPLICATION PROBLEM

Extra forms

COMMISSIONS RECORD

EMPLOYEE NO. _____   EMPLOYEE NAME _____

COMMISSION RATE _____   MONTH _____   YEAR _____

DEPT. _____   REGULAR BIWEEKLY SALARY _____

Sales

    Sales on Account . . . . $_____

    Cash and Credit Card Sales . . . . _____

    Total Sales . . . . $_____

    Less: Sales Discounts. . . . . $_____

        Sales Returns
        and Allowances . . . . _____   _____

    Net Sales. . . . . $_____

    Commission on Net Sales. . . . . $_____

COMMISSIONS RECORD

EMPLOYEE NO. _____   EMPLOYEE NAME _____

COMMISSION RATE _____   MONTH _____   YEAR _____

DEPT. _____   REGULAR BIWEEKLY SALARY _____

Sales

    Sales on Account . . . . $_____

    Cash and Credit Card Sales . . . . _____

    Total Sales . . . . $_____

    Less: Sales Discounts. . . . . $_____

        Sales Returns
        and Allowances . . . . _____   _____

    Net Sales. . . . . $_____

    Commission on Net Sales. . . . . $_____

3-5 APPLICATION PROBLEM, p. 87

Completing an employee earnings record

The payroll register prepared in Application Problem 3-4 is needed to complete this problem.

The working papers for Application Problem 3-4 are located on pages 74 and 75.

EARNINGS RECORD FOR QUARTER ENDED March 31, 20--

EMPLOYEE NO. 3 NAME Janet T. Aquilar SOCIAL SECURITY NO. 013-62-1432

MARITAL STATUS M WITHHOLDING ALLOWANCES 3 HOURLY RATE $7.00 SALARY

DEPARTMENT Carpet POSITION Salesclerk

PAY PERIOD		TOTAL EARNINGS	DEDUCTIONS						NET PAY	ACCUMULATED EARNINGS
NO.	ENDED		FEDERAL INCOME TAX	STATE INCOME TAX	SOC. SEC. TAX	MEDICARE TAX	OTHER	TOTAL		
5	2/27	560 00	2 00	28 00	36 40	8 40	D 9 40 / H 13 20	97 40	462 60	30 050 25
6	3/12	607 25	8 00	30 36	39 47	9 11	D 9 40 / H 13 20	109 54	497 71	36 575 50
QUARTERLY TOTALS										

EARNINGS RECORD FOR QUARTER ENDED March 31, 20--

EMPLOYEE NO. 8 NAME Bernard C. Parker SOCIAL SECURITY NO. 181-48-0482

MARITAL STATUS M WITHHOLDING ALLOWANCES 2 HOURLY RATE $6.50 SALARY

DEPARTMENT Administrative POSITION Clerk

PAY PERIOD		TOTAL EARNINGS	DEDUCTIONS						NET PAY	ACCUMULATED EARNINGS
NO.	ENDED		FEDERAL INCOME TAX	STATE INCOME TAX	SOC. SEC. TAX	MEDICARE TAX	OTHER	TOTAL		
5	2/27	520 00	12 00	26 00	33 80	7 80	D 9 40 / H 13 20	102 20	417 80	27 841 0
6	3/12	559 00	15 00	27 95	36 34	8 39	D 9 40 / H 13 20	110 28	448 72	33 431 0
QUARTERLY TOTALS										

3-4 APPLICATION PROBLEM, p. 87

Completing a payroll register

The time cards prepared in Application Problem 3-2 and the commissions records prepared in Application Problem 3-3 are needed to complete this problem. The payroll register prepared in Application Problem 3-4 is needed to complete Application Problems 3-5 and 3-6.

PAY PERIOD ENDED March 12, 20--   PAYROLL REGISTER

	EMPL. NO.	EMPLOYEE NAME	MARITAL STATUS	NO. OF ALLOW-ANCES	TOTAL HOURS	EARNINGS				
						REGULAR	OVERTIME	COMMISSION	TOTAL	
1	3	Aguilar, Janet T.	M	3	84 1/2	560 00	47 25		607 25	1
2	9	Gowens, Heidi	S	1	—	540 00		197 11	737 11	2
3	14	Mantle, Dale	M	2	—	520 00		202 20	722 20	3
4	8	Parker, Bernard C.	M	2	84	520 00	39 00		559 00	4
5	13	Sabo, Natalie R.	S	2	84 1/2	520 00	43 88		563 88	5
6		Totals				2660 00	130 13	399 31	3189 44	6
7										7
8										8
9										9

3-5 APPLICATION PROBLEM (continued)

EARNINGS RECORD FOR QUARTER ENDED   March 31, 20--

EMPLOYEE NO. 9   NAME Heidi Gowens   SOCIAL SECURITY NO. 311-32-1620

MARITAL STATUS S   WITHHOLDING ALLOWANCES 1   HOURLY RATE _____   SALARY $540.00

DEPARTMENT Carpet   POSITION Supervisor

PAY PERIOD		TOTAL EARNINGS	DEDUCTIONS						NET PAY	ACCUMULATED EARNINGS
NO.	ENDED		FEDERAL INCOME TAX	STATE INCOME TAX	SOC. SEC. TAX	MEDICARE TAX	OTHER	TOTAL		
5	2/27	540 00	52 00	27 00	35 10	8 10	DH 9 40 13 20	144 80	395 20	3165 20
6	3/12	737 11	79 00	36 86	47 91	11 06	DH 9 40 13 20	197 43	539 68	3902 31
	QUARTERLY TOTALS									

3-4 APPLICATION PROBLEM (concluded)

DATE OF PAYMENT March 19, 20-- **PAYROLL REGISTER**

	10	11	12	13	14	15	16	17		18	19	20	
	DEPARTMENT		ADMIN. SALARIES	DEDUCTIONS							PAID		
	CARPET	DRAPERY		FEDERAL INCOME TAX	STATE INCOME TAX	SOC. SEC. TAX	MEDICARE TAX	OTHER		TOTAL	NET PAY	CHECK NO.	
1	607 25			8 00	30 36	39 47	9 11	D 9 40 / H 13 20		109 54	497 71		1
2	737 11			79 00	36 86	47 91	11 06	D 9 40 / H 13 20		197 43	539 68		2
3		722 20		42 00	36 11	46 94	10 83	D 9 40 / H 13 20		158 48	563 72		3
4			559 00	15 00	27 95	36 34	8 39	D 9 40 / H 13 20		110 28	448 72		4
5		563 88		40 00	28 19	36 65	8 46	D 9 40 / H 13 20		135 90	427 98		5
6	1344 36	1286 08	559 00	184 00	159 47	207 31	47 85	D 47 00 / H 66 00		711 63	2477 81		6
7													7
8													8
9													9

3-5 APPLICATION PROBLEM (continued)

EARNINGS RECORD FOR QUARTER ENDED   March 31, 20-- _____

EMPLOYEE NO. ___13___   NAME Natalie R. Sabo _____   SOCIAL SECURITY NO. 214-36-1832 ___

MARITAL STATUS ___S___   WITHHOLDING ALLOWANCES ___2___   HOURLY RATE ___$6.50___   SALARY _____

DEPARTMENT Drapery _____   POSITION Salesclerk _____

	1	2	3	4	5	6	7	8	9	10	11
	PAY PERIOD		TOTAL EARNINGS	DEDUCTIONS						NET PAY	ACCUMULATED EARNINGS
	NO.	ENDED		FEDERAL INCOME TAX	STATE INCOME TAX	SOC. SEC. TAX	MEDICARE TAX	OTHER	TOTAL		
	5	2/27	520 00	34 00	26 00	33 80	7 80	D 9 40 / H 13 20	124 20	395 80	2676 90
	6	3/12	563 88	40 00	28 19	36 65	8 46	D 9 40 / H 13 20	135 90	427 98	3240 78
	QUARTERLY TOTALS										

Name _____ Date _____ Class _____

EARNINGS RECORD FOR QUARTER ENDED   March 31, 20--

EMPLOYEE NO. __14__   NAME __Dale Mantle_____   SOCIAL SECURITY NO. __192-40-2162__

MARITAL STATUS __M__   WITHHOLDING ALLOWANCES __2__   HOURLY RATE _____   SALARY __$520.00__

DEPARTMENT __Drapery_____   POSITION __Supervisor__

| PAY PERIOD | | TOTAL EARNINGS | DEDUCTIONS | | | | | | NET PAY | ACCUMULATED EARNINGS |
NO.	ENDED		FEDERAL INCOME TAX	STATE INCOME TAX	SOC. SEC. TAX	MEDICARE TAX	OTHER	TOTAL		
5	2/27	520 00	12 00	26 00	33 80	7 80	DH 9 40 13 20	102 20	417 80	3094 30
6	3/12	722 20	42 00	36 11	46 94	10 83	DH 9 40 13 20	158 48	563 72	3816 50
QUARTERLY TOTALS										

Extra forms

EARNINGS RECORD FOR QUARTER ENDED   _____

EMPLOYEE NO. _____   NAME _____   SOCIAL SECURITY NO. _____

MARITAL STATUS _____   WITHHOLDING ALLOWANCES _____   HOURLY RATE _____   SALARY _____

DEPARTMENT _____   POSITION _____

| PAY PERIOD | | TOTAL EARNINGS | DEDUCTIONS | | | | | | NET PAY | ACCUMULATED EARNINGS |
NO.	ENDED		FEDERAL INCOME TAX	STATE INCOME TAX	SOC. SEC. TAX	MEDICARE TAX	OTHER	TOTAL		
5										
6										
QUARTERLY TOTALS										

EARNINGS RECORD FOR QUARTER ENDED   _____

EMPLOYEE NO. _____   NAME _____   SOCIAL SECURITY NO. _____

MARITAL STATUS _____   WITHHOLDING ALLOWANCES _____   HOURLY RATE _____   SALARY _____

DEPARTMENT _____   POSITION _____

| PAY PERIOD | | TOTAL EARNINGS | DEDUCTIONS | | | | | | NET PAY | ACCUMULATED EARNINGS |
NO.	ENDED		FEDERAL INCOME TAX	STATE INCOME TAX	SOC. SEC. TAX	MEDICARE TAX	OTHER	TOTAL		
5										
6										
QUARTERLY TOTALS										

3-6 APPLICATION PROBLEM, p. 88

Journalizing payment of a departmental payroll

The payroll register prepared in Application Problem 3-4 is needed to complete this problem.

[1]

CASH PAYMENTS JOURNAL   PAGE 6

	DATE	ACCOUNT TITLE	CK. NO.	POST. REF.	GENERAL DEBIT	GENERAL CREDIT	ACCOUNTS PAYABLE DEBIT	PURCH. DISCOUNT CR. CARPET	PURCH. DISCOUNT CR. DRAPERY	CASH CREDIT	
1	Mar. 19	Salary Expense—Carpet	463		134436					247781	1
2		Salary Expense—Drapery			128608						2
3		Salary Expense—Administrative			55900						3
4		Employ. Income Tax Payable—Federal				18400					4
5		Employ. Income Tax Payable—State				15947					5
6		Social Security Tax Payable				20731					6
7		Medicare Tax Payable				4785					7
8		Dental Insurance Payable				4700					8
9		Health Insurance Payable				6600					9
10											10
11											11

[2]

GENERAL JOURNAL   PAGE 6

	DATE	ACCOUNT TITLE	DOC. NO.	POST. REF.	DEBIT	CREDIT	
1	Mar. 19	Payroll Taxes Expense	M41		45290		1
2		Social Security Tax Payable				20731	2
3		Medicare Tax Payable				4784	*3
4		Unemploy. Tax Payable—Federal				2552	4
5		Unemploy. Tax Payable—State				17223	5
6							6
7							7
8							8
9							9

*Differs from employees' tax from rounding difference.

Name _____ Date _____ Class _____

3-6 APPLICATION PROBLEM

Extra forms

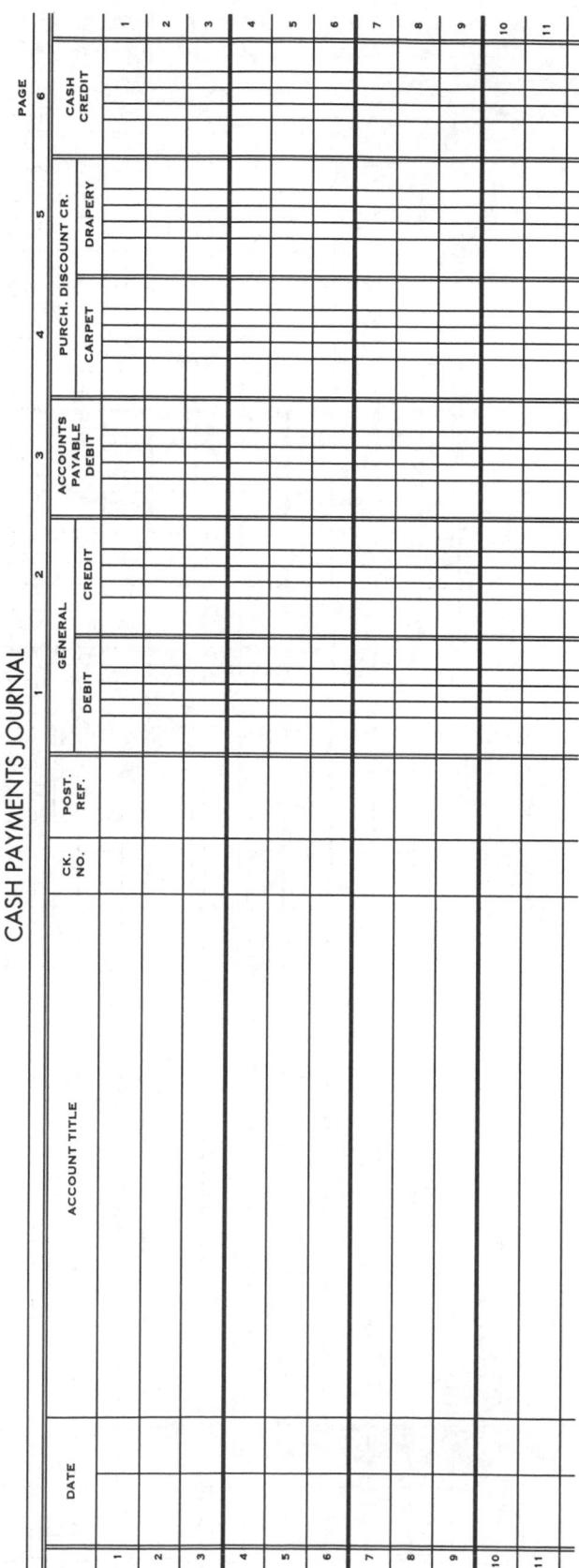

CASH PAYMENTS JOURNAL

GENERAL JOURNAL

Name _____ Date _____ Class _____

3-7 APPLICATION PROBLEM, p. 88

Calculating and journalizing payment of payroll tax liabilities

[1]

CASH PAYMENTS JOURNAL   PAGE 7

DATE		ACCOUNT TITLE	CK. NO.	POST. REF.	GENERAL DEBIT	GENERAL CREDIT	ACCOUNTS PAYABLE DEBIT	PURCH. DISCOUNT CR.	CASH CREDIT	
20-- Apr.	3	Employ. Income Tax Payable—Federal	492		91100				214952	1
		Social Security Tax Payable			100626					2
		Medicare Tax Payable			23226					3
										4
										5
										6
										7
										8
										9
										10
										11

[2, 3]

CASH PAYMENTS JOURNAL   PAGE 8

DATE		ACCOUNT TITLE	CK. NO.	POST. REF.	GENERAL DEBIT	GENERAL CREDIT	ACCOUNTS PAYABLE DEBIT	PURCH. DISCOUNT CR.	CASH CREDIT	
20-- Apr.	30	Unemploy. Tax Payable—Federal	515		37162				37162	1
	30	Unemploy. Tax Payable—State	516		250841				250841	2
										3
										4
										5
										6
										7
										8
										9
										10
										11

3-7 APPLICATION PROBLEM

Extra forms

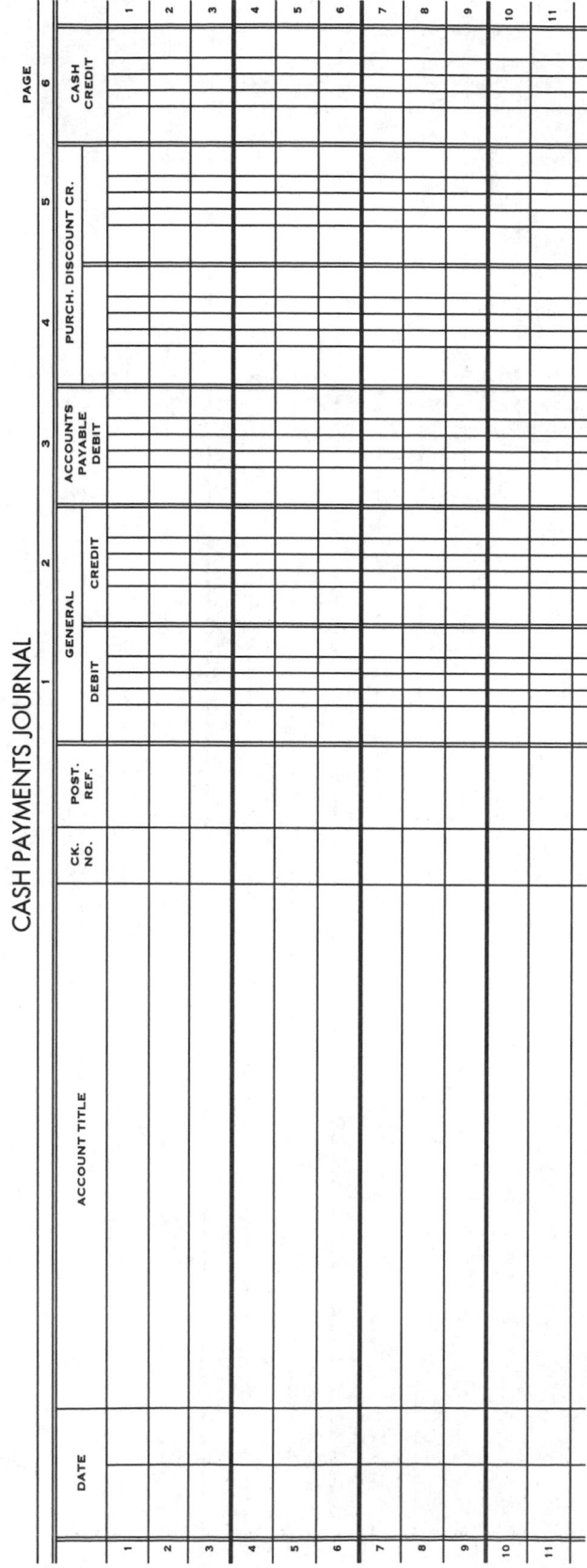

CASH PAYMENTS JOURNAL

GENERAL JOURNAL

Name _____ Date _____ Class _____

3-8 MASTERY PROBLEM, p. 88

Completing payroll records, journalizing payment of a payroll, and journalizing payroll taxes

BENEFITS AUTHORIZATION

EMPLOYEE NO. __1__ EMPLOYEE __Shanna L. Kim__

PAY PERIOD ENDED __2/13/--__ DEPARTMENT __Fabrics__

	HOURS AVAIL.	M	T	W	T	F	S	M	T	W	T	F	S	HOURS USED
VACATION	62				4									4
SICK LEAVE	42									1		5		6
PERSONAL LEAVE	20		4											4

_____ __Paula D. Brown__ __2/13/--__
MANAGER (only if needed) DEPARTMENT SUPERVISOR DATE

BENEFITS AUTHORIZATION

EMPLOYEE NO. __2__ EMPLOYEE __Paula D. Brown__

PAY PERIOD ENDED __2/13/--__ DEPARTMENT __Fabrics__

	HOURS AVAIL.	M	T	W	T	F	S	M	T	W	T	F	S	HOURS USED
VACATION	81										4			4
SICK LEAVE	72				8									8
PERSONAL LEAVE	22													0

__Maria C. Lucio__ _____ __2/13/--__
MANAGER (only if needed) DEPARTMENT SUPERVISOR DATE

BENEFITS AUTHORIZATION

EMPLOYEE NO. __3__ EMPLOYEE __Gary M. Evans__

PAY PERIOD ENDED __2/13/--__ DEPARTMENT __Supplies__

	HOURS AVAIL.	M	T	W	T	F	S	M	T	W	T	F	S	HOURS USED
VACATION	78	8												8
SICK LEAVE	52				5									5
PERSONAL LEAVE	20								3					3

_____ __Marcel P. Ostenbauer__ __2/13/--__
MANAGER (only if needed) DEPARTMENT SUPERVISOR DATE

3-8 MASTERY PROBLEM (continued)

BENEFITS AUTHORIZATION

EMPLOYEE NO. _____4_____   EMPLOYEE _Marcel P. Ostenbauer_____

PAY PERIOD ENDED ____2/13/--____   DEPARTMENT _Supplies_____

	HOURS AVAIL.	M	T	W	T	F	S	M	T	W	T	F	S	HOURS USED
VACATION	80				8	8		8						24
SICK LEAVE	52											4		4
PERSONAL LEAVE	16										3			3

_____Maria C. Lucio_____   2/13/--
MANAGER (only if needed)   DEPARTMENT SUPERVISOR   DATE

BENEFITS AUTHORIZATION

EMPLOYEE NO. _____5_____   EMPLOYEE _Jean R. Quigley_____

PAY PERIOD ENDED ____2/13/--____   DEPARTMENT _Fabrics_____

	HOURS AVAIL.	M	T	W	T	F	S	M	T	W	T	F	S	HOURS USED
VACATION	38											8	8	16
SICK LEAVE	70			4										4
PERSONAL LEAVE	18										2			2

                                  Paula D. Brown   2/13/--
MANAGER (only if needed)   DEPARTMENT SUPERVISOR   DATE

BENEFITS AUTHORIZATION

EMPLOYEE NO. _____6_____   EMPLOYEE _Robert J. Trumpley_____

PAY PERIOD ENDED ____2/13/--____   DEPARTMENT _Administrative_____

	HOURS AVAIL.	M	T	W	T	F	S	M	T	W	T	F	S	HOURS USED
VACATION	50	8												8
SICK LEAVE	52										4			4
PERSONAL LEAVE	22					3								3

_____Maria C. Lucio_____   2/13/--
MANAGER (only if needed)   DEPARTMENT SUPERVISOR   DATE

3-8 MASTERY PROBLEM (continued)

[1]

BENEFITS RECORD

EMPLOYEE NO. 1   EMPLOYEE NAME Shanna L. Kim   DEPARTMENT Fabrics

DATE OF INITIAL EMPLOYMENT April 16, 19--   YEAR 20--

	PAY PERIOD ENDED	VACATION TIME				SICK LEAVE TIME				PERSONAL LEAVE TIME			
		BEGIN. HOURS AVAIL.	HOURS EARNED	HOURS USED	ACC. HOURS AVAIL.	BEGIN. HOURS AVAIL.	HOURS EARNED	HOURS USED	ACC. HOURS AVAIL.	BEGIN. HOURS AVAIL.	HOURS EARNED	HOURS USED	ACC. HOURS AVAIL.
4	2/13	62	4	4	62	42	2	6	38	20	1	4	17
5													
6													
7													
8													
9													

BENEFITS RECORD

EMPLOYEE NO. 2   EMPLOYEE NAME Paula D. Brown   DEPARTMENT Fabrics

DATE OF INITIAL EMPLOYMENT February 19, 19--   YEAR 20--

	PAY PERIOD ENDED	VACATION TIME				SICK LEAVE TIME				PERSONAL LEAVE TIME			
		BEGIN. HOURS AVAIL.	HOURS EARNED	HOURS USED	ACC. HOURS AVAIL.	BEGIN. HOURS AVAIL.	HOURS EARNED	HOURS USED	ACC. HOURS AVAIL.	BEGIN. HOURS AVAIL.	HOURS EARNED	HOURS USED	ACC. HOURS AVAIL.
4	2/13	81	4	4	81	72	2	8	66	22	1	0	23
5													
6													
7													
8													
9													

BENEFITS RECORD

EMPLOYEE NO. 3   EMPLOYEE NAME Gary M. Evans   DEPARTMENT Supplies

DATE OF INITIAL EMPLOYMENT November 7, 19--   YEAR 20--

	PAY PERIOD ENDED	VACATION TIME				SICK LEAVE TIME				PERSONAL LEAVE TIME			
		BEGIN. HOURS AVAIL.	HOURS EARNED	HOURS USED	ACC. HOURS AVAIL.	BEGIN. HOURS AVAIL.	HOURS EARNED	HOURS USED	ACC. HOURS AVAIL.	BEGIN. HOURS AVAIL.	HOURS EARNED	HOURS USED	ACC. HOURS AVAIL.
4	2/13	78	4	8	74	52	2	5	49	20	1	3	18
5													
6													
7													
8													
9													

3-8 MASTERY PROBLEM (continued)

[1]

BENEFITS RECORD

EMPLOYEE NO. 4   EMPLOYEE NAME Marcel P. Ostenbauer   DEPARTMENT Supplies

DATE OF INITIAL EMPLOYMENT   June 3, 19--   YEAR 20--

	PAY PERIOD ENDED	VACATION TIME				SICK LEAVE TIME				PERSONAL LEAVE TIME			
		BEGIN. HOURS AVAIL.	HOURS EARNED	HOURS USED	ACC. HOURS AVAIL.	BEGIN. HOURS AVAIL.	HOURS EARNED	HOURS USED	ACC. HOURS AVAIL.	BEGIN. HOURS AVAIL.	HOURS EARNED	HOURS USED	ACC. HOURS AVAIL.
4	2/13	80	4	24	60	52	2	4	50	16	1	3	14
5													
6													
7													
8													
9													

BENEFITS RECORD

EMPLOYEE NO. 5   EMPLOYEE NAME Jean R. Quigley   DEPARTMENT Fabrics

DATE OF INITIAL EMPLOYMENT   July 9, 19--   YEAR 20--

	PAY PERIOD ENDED	VACATION TIME				SICK LEAVE TIME				PERSONAL LEAVE TIME			
		BEGIN. HOURS AVAIL.	HOURS EARNED	HOURS USED	ACC. HOURS AVAIL.	BEGIN. HOURS AVAIL.	HOURS EARNED	HOURS USED	ACC. HOURS AVAIL.	BEGIN. HOURS AVAIL.	HOURS EARNED	HOURS USED	ACC. HOURS AVAIL.
4	2/13	38	4	16	26	70	2	4	68	18	1	2	17
5													
6													
7													
8													
9													

BENEFITS RECORD

EMPLOYEE NO. 6   EMPLOYEE NAME Robert J. Trumpley   DEPARTMENT Administrative

DATE OF INITIAL EMPLOYMENT   August 3, 19--   YEAR 20--

	PAY PERIOD ENDED	VACATION TIME				SICK LEAVE TIME				PERSONAL LEAVE TIME			
		BEGIN. HOURS AVAIL.	HOURS EARNED	HOURS USED	ACC. HOURS AVAIL.	BEGIN. HOURS AVAIL.	HOURS EARNED	HOURS USED	ACC. HOURS AVAIL.	BEGIN. HOURS AVAIL.	HOURS EARNED	HOURS USED	ACC. HOURS AVAIL.
4	2/13	50	4	8	46	52	2	4	50	22	1	3	20
5													
6													
7													
8													
9													

3-8 MASTERY PROBLEM (continued)

[1–3]

Shanna L. Kim

NAME **Shanna L. Kim**

DEPARTMENT **Fabrics**

EMPLOYEE NO. **1**

PAY PERIOD ENDED **2/13/20--**

MORNING		AFTERNOON		OVERTIME		HOURS	
IN	OUT	IN	OUT	IN	OUT	REG	OT
M 8:58	M 11:58	M 1:00	M 6:00	M 7:00	M 8:30	8	1$\frac{1}{2}$
T 9:00	T 12:01	T 1:00	T 2:01			4P4	
W 8:59	W 12:00	W 12:58	W 6:00			8	
T 9:01	T 12:00	T 1:02	T 6:03			8	
		F 2:01	F 6:00			4V4	
M 8:58	M 12:01	M 1:00	M 6:01			8	
T 9:00	T 12:00	T 1:00	T 6:02			8	
W 8:58	W 12:01	W 1:01	W 5:00			7S1	
T 9:01	T 12:00	T 1:00	T 6:00	T 7:00	T 8:30	8	1$\frac{1}{2}$
F 9:00	F 12:02					3S5	

	HOURS	RATE	AMOUNT
REGULAR	80	7.50	600.00
OVERTIME	3	11.25	33.75
TOTAL HOURS	83	TOTAL EARNINGS	633.75

Gary M. Evans

NAME **Gary M. Evans**

DEPARTMENT **Supplies**

EMPLOYEE NO. **3**

PAY PERIOD ENDED **2/13/20--**

MORNING		AFTERNOON		OVERTIME		HOURS	
IN	OUT	IN	OUT	IN	OUT	REG	OT
						V8	
T 9:00	T 12:01	T 1:00	T 6:00	T 7:00	T 8:30	8	1$\frac{1}{2}$
W 8:58	W 12:00	W 1:01	W 6:03			8	
T 9:02	T 12:01					3S5	
F 9:00	F 12:00	F 1:00	F 6:01			8	
		M 1:00	M 6:01			5P3	
T 9:00	T 12:03	T 1:01	T 6:00			8	
W 9:00	W 12:00	W 1:00	W 6:01	W 7:00	W 8:00	8	1
T 9:01	T 12:00	T 1:01	T 6:00			8	
F 9:00	F 12:00	F 1:02	F 6:00			8	

	HOURS	RATE	AMOUNT
REGULAR	80	7.50	600.00
OVERTIME	2$\frac{1}{2}$	11.25	28.13
TOTAL HOURS	82$\frac{1}{2}$	TOTAL EARNINGS	628.13

3-8 MASTERY PROBLEM (continued)

[1-3]

NAME Jean R. Quigley
DEPARTMENT Fabrics
EMPLOYEE NO. 5
PAY PERIOD ENDED 2/13/20--

MORNING		AFTERNOON		OVERTIME		HOURS	
IN	OUT	IN	OUT	IN	OUT	REG	OT
						8	1½
⊢ 9:00	⊢ 12:59	⊢ 2:00	⊢ 6:02	⊢ 7:00	⊢ 8:30	4S4	
		≥ 2:00	≥ 6:01			8	
⊢ 8:58	⊢ 1:00	⊢ 2:01	⊢ 6:00			8	
⊢ 9:01	⊢ 1:02	⊢ 2:00	⊢ 6:03			8	
⊢ 9:00	⊢ 1:00	⊢ 2:01	⊢ 6:00				
⊢ 9:00	⊢ 1:03	⊢ 2:00	⊢ 6:00	⊢ 7:30	⊢ 9:30	8	2
≥ 8:58	≥ 1:00	≥ 2:01	≥ 6:01			8	
⊢ 9:00	⊢ 1:03	⊢ 2:00	⊢ 4:00			6P2	
						V8	
						V8	

	HOURS	RATE	AMOUNT
REGULAR	80	6.50	520.00
OVERTIME	3½	9.75	34.13
TOTAL HOURS	83½	**TOTAL EARNINGS**	554.13

NAME Robert J. Trumpley
DEPARTMENT Administrative
EMPLOYEE NO. 6
PAY PERIOD ENDED 2/13/20--

MORNING		AFTERNOON		OVERTIME		HOURS	
IN	OUT	IN	OUT	IN	OUT	REG	OT
						V8	
⊢ 9:00	⊢ 12:01	⊢ 1:00	⊢ 6:00	⊢ 7:00	⊢ 8:30	8	1½
≥ 8:58	≥ 12:00	≥ 1:01	≥ 6:03			8	
⊢ 9:02	⊢ 12:01	⊢ 1:00	⊢ 6:00	⊢ 7:30	⊢ 8:30	8	1
⊢ 9:00	⊢ 12:00	⊢ 1:00	⊢ 3:01			5P3	
≥ 9:01	≥ 12:00	≥ 1:00	≥ 6:01			8	
⊢ 9:00	⊢ 12:03	⊢ 1:01	⊢ 6:00	⊢ 7:00	⊢ 9:00	8	2
≥ 9:00	≥ 12:00	≥ 1:00	≥ 6:01	≥ 7:30	≥ 9:00	8	1½
⊢ 9:01	⊢ 12:00	⊢ 1:01	⊢ 2:00			4S4	
⊢ 9:00	⊢ 12:00	⊢ 1:02	⊢ 6:00			8	

	HOURS	RATE	AMOUNT
REGULAR	80	6.50	520.00
OVERTIME	6	9.75	58.50
TOTAL HOURS	86	**TOTAL EARNINGS**	578.50

3-8 **MASTERY PROBLEM (continued)**

[4]

COMMISSIONS RECORD

EMPLOYEE NO. 2   EMPLOYEE NAME Paula D. Brown

COMMISSION RATE 1.0%   MONTH January   YEAR 20--

DEPT. Fabrics   REGULAR BIWEEKLY SALARY $600.00

Sales

Sales on Account	$	5,443.89
Cash and Credit Card Sales		8,017.02
Total Sales	$	13,460.91
Less: Sales Discounts. . . . . $ 85.86		
Sales Returns and Allowances 296.66	382.52	
Net Sales.	$	13,078.39
Commission on Net Sales.	$	130.78

COMMISSIONS RECORD

EMPLOYEE NO. 4   EMPLOYEE NAME Marcel P. Ostenbauer

COMMISSION RATE 1.0%   MONTH January   YEAR 20--

DEPT. Supplies   REGULAR BIWEEKLY SALARY $600.00

Sales

Sales on Account	$	5,209.33
Cash and Credit Card Sales		9,903.55
Total Sales	$	15,112.88
Less: Sales Discounts. . . . . $ 156.67		
Sales Returns and Allowances 1,302.31	1,458.98	
Net Sales.	$	13,653.90
Commission on Net Sales.	$	136.54

3-8 MASTERY PROBLEM (continued)

[5]

	EMPL. NO.	EMPLOYEE NAME	MARI-TAL STATUS	NO. OF ALLOW-ANCES	TOTAL HOURS	EARNINGS			
						REGULAR	OVERTIME	COMMISSION	TOTAL
1	2	Brown, Paula D.	M	3	—	600 00		130 78	730 78
2	3	Evans, Gary M.	S	2	82½	600 00	28 13		628 13
3	1	Kim, Shanna L.	S	1	83	600 00	33 75		633 75
4	4	Ostenbauer, Marcel P.	M	2	—	600 00		136 54	736 54
5	5	Quigley, Jean R.	M	2	83½	520 00	34 13		554 13
6	6	Trumpley, Robert J.	S	1	86	520 00	58 50		578 50
7		Totals				3440 00	154 51	267 32	3861 83

PAY PERIOD ENDED February 13, 20--   PAYROLL REGISTER

[6]

EARNINGS RECORD FOR QUARTER ENDED   March 31, 20--

EMPLOYEE NO. 1   NAME Shanna L. Kim   SOCIAL SECURITY NO. 213-30-9403

MARITAL STATUS S   WITHHOLDING ALLOWANCES 1   HOURLY RATE $7.50   SALARY _____

DEPARTMENT Fabrics   POSITION Salesclerk

PAY PERIOD		TOTAL EARNINGS	DEDUCTIONS						NET PAY	ACCUMULATED EARNINGS
NO.	ENDED		FEDERAL INCOME TAX	STATE INCOME TAX	SOC. SEC. TAX	MEDICARE TAX	OTHER	TOTAL		
3	1/30	600 00	61 00	30 00	39 00	9 00	H 14 80 L 8 20	162 00	438 00	1833 75
4	2/13	633 75	64 00	31 69	41 19	9 51	H 14 80 L 8 20	169 39	464 36	2467 50
QUARTERLY TOTALS										

3-8 MASTERY PROBLEM (continued)

[5]

PAYROLL REGISTER

DATE OF PAYMENT Feb. 20, 20--

	DEPARTMENT		ADMIN. SALARIES	DEDUCTIONS						PAID	
	FABRIC	SUPPLIES		FEDERAL INCOME TAX	STATE INCOME TAX	SOC. SEC. TAX	MEDICARE TAX	OTHER	TOTAL	NET PAY	CHECK NO.
	10	11	12	13	14	15	16	17	18	19	20
1	730.78			26.00	36.54	47.50	10.96	H 14.80 / L 8.20	144.00	586.78	
2		628.13		49.00	31.41	40.83	9.42	H 14.80 / L 8.20	153.66	474.47	
3	633.75			64.00	31.69	41.19	9.51	H 14.80 / L 8.20	169.39	464.36	
4		736.54		42.00	36.83	47.88	11.05	H 14.80 / L 8.20	160.76	575.78	
5	554.13			15.00	27.71	36.02	8.31	H 14.80 / L 8.20	110.04	444.09	
6			578.50	55.00	28.93	37.60	8.68	H 14.80 / L 8.20	153.21	425.29	
7	1,918.66	1,364.67	578.50	251.00	193.11	251.02	57.93	H 88.80 / L 49.20	891.06	2,970.77	
8											
9											
10											
11											
12											

[6]

EARNINGS RECORD FOR QUARTER ENDED March 31, 20--

EMPLOYEE NO. 2 NAME Paula D. Brown SOCIAL SECURITY NO. 212-60-3120

MARITAL STATUS M WITHHOLDING ALLOWANCES 3 HOURLY RATE _____ SALARY $600.00

DEPARTMENT Fabrics POSITION Supervisor

PAY PERIOD		TOTAL EARNINGS	DEDUCTIONS						NET PAY	ACCUMULATED EARNINGS
NO.	ENDED		FEDERAL INCOME TAX	STATE INCOME TAX	SOC. SEC. TAX	MEDICARE TAX	OTHER	TOTAL		
1	2	3	4	5	6	7	8	9	10	11
3	1/30	600.00	8.00	30.00	39.00	9.00	H 14.80 / L 8.20	109.00	491.00	1,938.40
4	2/13	730.78	26.00	36.54	47.50	10.96	H 14.80 / L 8.20	144.00	586.78	2,669.18
QUARTERLY TOTALS										

3-8 MASTERY PROBLEM (continued)

[6]

EARNINGS RECORD FOR QUARTER ENDED   March 31, 20--

EMPLOYEE NO. 3   NAME Gary M. Evans   SOCIAL SECURITY NO. 162-04-1612

MARITAL STATUS S   WITHHOLDING ALLOWANCES 2   HOURLY RATE $7.50   SALARY ____

DEPARTMENT Supplies   POSITION Salesclerk

1	2	3	4	5	6	7	8		9	10	11
PAY PERIOD		TOTAL EARNINGS	DEDUCTIONS							NET PAY	ACCUMULATED EARNINGS
NO.	ENDED		FEDERAL INCOME TAX	STATE INCOME TAX	SOC. SEC. TAX	MEDICARE TAX	OTHER		TOTAL		
3	1/30	560 00	40 00	28 00	36 40	8 40	HL	14 80 / 8 20	135 80	424 20	1 722 00
4	2/13	628 13	49 00	31 41	40 83	9 42	HL	14 80 / 8 20	153 66	474 47	2 350 13
QUARTERLY TOTALS											

EARNINGS RECORD FOR QUARTER ENDED   March 31, 20--

EMPLOYEE NO. 4   NAME Marcel P. Ostenbauer   SOCIAL SECURITY NO. 265-14-3810

MARITAL STATUS M   WITHHOLDING ALLOWANCES 2   HOURLY RATE ____   SALARY $600.00

DEPARTMENT Supplies   POSITION Supervisor

1	2	3	4	5	6	7	8		9	10	11
PAY PERIOD		TOTAL EARNINGS	DEDUCTIONS							NET PAY	ACCUMULATED EARNINGS
NO.	ENDED		FEDERAL INCOME TAX	STATE INCOME TAX	SOC. SEC. TAX	MEDICARE TAX	OTHER		TOTAL		
3	1/30	600 00	24 00	30 00	39 00	9 00	HL	14 80 / 8 20	125 00	475 00	1 943 15
4	2/13	736 54	42 00	36 83	47 88	11 05	HL	14 80 / 8 20	160 76	575 78	2 679 69
QUARTERLY TOTALS											

3-8 MASTERY PROBLEM (continued)

[6]

EARNINGS RECORD FOR QUARTER ENDED — March 31, 20--

EMPLOYEE NO. 5   NAME Jean R. Quigley   SOCIAL SECURITY NO. 196-36-4402

MARITAL STATUS M   WITHHOLDING ALLOWANCES 2   HOURLY RATE $6.50   SALARY ____

DEPARTMENT Fabrics   POSITION Salesclerk

| PAY PERIOD | | TOTAL EARNINGS | DEDUCTIONS | | | | | | NET PAY | ACCUMULATED EARNINGS |
NO.	ENDED		FEDERAL INCOME TAX	STATE INCOME TAX	SOC. SEC. TAX	MEDICARE TAX	OTHER	TOTAL		
3	1/30	520 00	12 00	26 00	33 80	7 80	H 14 80 / L 8 20	102 60	417 40	1 599 00
4	2/13	554 13	15 00	27 71	36 02	8 31	H 14 80 / L 8 20	110 04	444 09	2 153 13
QUARTERLY TOTALS										

EARNINGS RECORD FOR QUARTER ENDED — March 31, 20--

EMPLOYEE NO. 6   NAME Robert J. Trumpley   SOCIAL SECURITY NO. 262-36-3136

MARITAL STATUS S   WITHHOLDING ALLOWANCES 1   HOURLY RATE $6.50   SALARY ____

DEPARTMENT Administrative   POSITION Clerk

| PAY PERIOD | | TOTAL EARNINGS | DEDUCTIONS | | | | | | NET PAY | ACCUMULATED EARNINGS |
NO.	ENDED		FEDERAL INCOME TAX	STATE INCOME TAX	SOC. SEC. TAX	MEDICARE TAX	OTHER	TOTAL		
3	1/30	520 00	49 00	26 00	33 80	7 80	H 14 80 / L 8 20	131 80	388 20	1 608 75
4	2/13	578 50	55 00	28 93	37 60	8 68	H 14 80 / L 8 20	153 21	425 29	2 187 25
QUARTERLY TOTALS										

3-8 MASTERY PROBLEM (concluded)

[7]

CASH PAYMENTS JOURNAL PAGE 4

	DATE	ACCOUNT TITLE	CK. NO.	POST. REF.	GENERAL DEBIT	GENERAL CREDIT	ACCOUNTS PAYABLE DEBIT	PURCH. DISCOUNT CR. FABRIC	PURCH. DISCOUNT CR. SUPPLIES	CASH CREDIT
1	20— Feb. 20	Salary Expense—Fabric	143		191866					297077
2		Salary Expense—Supplies			136467					
3		Salary Expense—Administrative			57850					
4		Employ. Income Tax Payable—Federal				25100				
5		Employ. Income Tax Payable—State				19311				
6		Social Security Tax Payable				25102				
7		Medicare Tax Payable				5793				
8		Health Insurance Premiums Payable				8880				
9		Life Insurance Premiums Payable				4920				
10										

[8]

GENERAL JOURNAL PAGE 4

	DATE	ACCOUNT TITLE	DOC. NO.	POST. REF.	DEBIT	CREDIT
1	20— Feb. 20	Payroll Taxes Expense	M14		54838	
2		Social Security Taxes Payable				25102
3		Medicare Taxes Payable				5793
4		Unemploy. Tax Payable—Federal				3089
5		Unemploy. Tax Payable—State				20854
6						
7						
8						

Name _____ Date _____ Class _____

3-9 CHALLENGE PROBLEM, p. 90

Preparing a benefits record

BENEFITS RECORD

EMPLOYEE NO. 7   EMPLOYEE NAME Arthur J. Delgado   DEPARTMENT Men's Shoes

DATE OF INITIAL EMPLOYMENT June 5, 1986   YEAR 20--

	PAY PERIOD ENDED	VACATION TIME				SICK LEAVE TIME				PERSONAL LEAVE TIME			
		1	2	3	4	5	6	7	8	9	10	11	12
		BEGIN. HOURS AVAIL.	HOURS EARNED	HOURS USED	ACC. HOURS AVAIL.	BEGIN. HOURS AVAIL.	HOURS EARNED	HOURS USED	ACC. HOURS AVAIL.	BEGIN. HOURS AVAIL.	HOURS EARNED	HOURS USED	ACC. HOURS AVAIL.
1	1/15	$32^1/_3$	$3^1/_3$	0	$35^2/_3$	$25^2/_3$	$1^2/_3$	4	$23^1/_3$	15	1	2	14
2	1/31	$35^2/_3$	$3^1/_3$	4	35	$23^1/_3$	$1^2/_3$	0	25	14	1	3	12
3	2/15	35	$3^1/_3$	8	$30^1/_3$	25	$1^2/_3$	8	$18^2/_3$	12	1	0	13
4	2/29	$30^1/_3$	$3^1/_3$	0	$33^2/_3$	$18^2/_3$	$1^2/_3$	0	$20^1/_3$	13	1	2	12
5													
6													
7													
8													
9													
10													
11													
12													
13													

Extra form

BENEFITS RECORD

EMPLOYEE NO. _____   EMPLOYEE NAME _____   DEPARTMENT _____

DATE OF INITIAL EMPLOYMENT _____   YEAR _____

	PAY PERIOD ENDED	VACATION TIME				SICK LEAVE TIME				PERSONAL LEAVE TIME			
		1	2	3	4	5	6	7	8	9	10	11	12
		BEGIN. HOURS AVAIL.	HOURS EARNED	HOURS USED	ACC. HOURS AVAIL.	BEGIN. HOURS AVAIL.	HOURS EARNED	HOURS USED	ACC. HOURS AVAIL.	BEGIN. HOURS AVAIL.	HOURS EARNED	HOURS USED	ACC. HOURS AVAIL.
1													
2													
3													
4													
5													
6													
7													
8													
9													
10													
11													
12													
13													
14													
15													
16													

Name _____ Date _____ Class _____

Extra forms

BENEFITS RECORD

EMPLOYEE NO. _____ EMPLOYEE NAME _____ DEPARTMENT _____

DATE OF INITIAL EMPLOYMENT _____ YEAR _____

	1	2	3	4	5	6	7	8	9	10	11	12
PAY PERIOD ENDED	VACATION TIME				SICK LEAVE TIME				PERSONAL LEAVE TIME			
	BEGIN. HOURS AVAIL.	HOURS EARNED	HOURS USED	ACC. HOURS AVAIL.	BEGIN. HOURS AVAIL.	HOURS EARNED	HOURS USED	ACC. HOURS AVAIL.	BEGIN. HOURS AVAIL.	HOURS EARNED	HOURS USED	ACC. HOURS AVAIL.
1												
2												
3												
4												
5												
6												
7												
8												
9												
10												
11												
12												
13												
14												
15												
16												

BENEFITS RECORD

EMPLOYEE NO. _____ EMPLOYEE NAME _____ DEPARTMENT _____

DATE OF INITIAL EMPLOYMENT _____ YEAR _____

	1	2	3	4	5	6	7	8	9	10	11	12
PAY PERIOD ENDED	VACATION TIME				SICK LEAVE TIME				PERSONAL LEAVE TIME			
	BEGIN. HOURS AVAIL.	HOURS EARNED	HOURS USED	ACC. HOURS AVAIL.	BEGIN. HOURS AVAIL.	HOURS EARNED	HOURS USED	ACC. HOURS AVAIL.	BEGIN. HOURS AVAIL.	HOURS EARNED	HOURS USED	ACC. HOURS AVAIL.
1												
2												
3												
4												
5												
6												
7												
8												
9												
10												
11												
12												
13												
14												
15												
16												

4-1 WORK TOGETHER, p. 100

Preparing an interim departmental statement of gross profit   [4]

ESTIMATED MERCHANDISE INVENTORY SHEET
Gross Profit Method

DEPARTMENT _Kitchen_   DATE _5/31/--_

1	Beginning inventory, January 1 . . . . $	110,000.00
2	Net purchases to date . . . . (42,500 + 8,300)	50,800.00
3	Merchandise available for sale . . . . $	160,800.00
4	Net sales to date . . . . $ 98,800.00 (78,600 + 20,200)	
5	Less estimated gross profit 47,424.00	
	(Net sales × Estimated gross profit _48.0_%)	
6	Estimated cost of merchandise sold	51,376.00
7	Estimated ending inventory . . . . $	109,424.00

ESTIMATED MERCHANDISE INVENTORY SHEET
Gross Profit Method

DEPARTMENT _Bath_   DATE _5/31/--_

1	Beginning inventory, January 1 . . . . $	84,000.00
2	Net purchases to date . . . . (30,100 + 5,400)	35,500.00
3	Merchandise available for sale . . . . $	119,500.00
4	Net sales to date . . . . $ 60,700.00 (52,300 + 8,400)	
5	Less estimated gross profit 29,136.00	
	(Net sales × Estimated gross profit _48.0_%)	
6	Estimated cost of merchandise sold	31,564.00
7	Estimated ending inventory . . . . $	87,936.00

4-1 WORK TOGETHER (concluded)

[5]

Willow Glen Interior Design

Interim Departmental Statement of Gross Profit

For Month Ended May 31, 20--

	KITCHEN	% OF NET SALES	BATH	% OF NET SALES	TOTAL	% OF NET SALES
Operating Revenue:						
Net Sales	20,200.00	100.0	8,400.00	100.0	28,600.00	100.0
Cost of Merchandise Sold:						
Est. Mdse. Inventory, May 1	111,426.00		87,072.00		198,498.00	
Net Purchases	8,300.00		5,400.00		13,700.00	
Mdse. Available for Sale	119,726.00		92,472.00		212,198.00	
Less Est. End. Inv., May 31	109,424.00		87,936.00		197,360.00	
Cost of Merchandise Sold	10,302.00	51.0	4,536.00	54.0	14,838.00	51.9
Gross Profit on Operations	9,898.00	49.0	3,864.00	46.0	13,762.00	48.1

4-1 ON YOUR OWN, p. 100

Preparing an interim departmental statement of gross profit [6]

ESTIMATED MERCHANDISE INVENTORY SHEET
Gross Profit Method

DEPARTMENT _Commercial_   DATE _4/30/--_

1	Beginning inventory, January 1. . . . . $	280,000.00
2	Net purchases to date . . . . (120,500 + 66,200)	186,700.00
3	Merchandise available for sale. . . . . $	466,700.00
4	Net sales to date. . . . . $ _267,700.00_ (196,600 + 71,100)	
5	Less estimated gross profit . . . . _112,434.00_	
	(Net sales × Estimated gross profit _42.0_ %)	
6	Estimated cost of merchandise sold	155,266.00
7	Estimated ending inventory. . . . . $	311,434.00

ESTIMATED MERCHANDISE INVENTORY SHEET
Gross Profit Method

DEPARTMENT _Residential_   DATE _4/30/--_

1	Beginning inventory, January 1. . . . . $	108,000.00
2	Net purchases to date . . . . (62,300 + 13,400)	75,700.00
3	Merchandise available for sale. . . . . $	183,700.00
4	Net sales to date. . . . . $ _102,800.00_ (88,400 + 14,400)	
5	Less estimated gross profit . . . . _43,176.00_	
	(Net sales × Estimated gross profit _42.0_ %)	
6	Estimated cost of merchandise sold	59,624.00
7	Estimated ending inventory. . . . . $	124,076.00

4-1 ON YOUR OWN (concluded)

Lassen Heating and Air Conditioning, Inc.

Interim Departmental Statement of Gross Profit

For Month Ended April 30, 20--

	COMMERCIAL	% OF NET SALES	RESIDENTIAL	% OF NET SALES	TOTAL	% OF NET SALES
Operating Revenue:						
Net Sales	71,100.00	100.0	14,400.00	100.0	85,500.00	100.0
Cost of Merchandise Sold:						
Est. Mdse. Inv., April 1	287,894.00		118,884.00		406,778.00	
Net Purchases	66,200.00		13,400.00		79,600.00	
Mdse. Available for Sale	354,094.00		132,284.00		486,378.00	
Less Est. End. Inv., April 30	311,434.00		124,076.00		435,510.00	
Cost of Merchandise Sold	42,660.00	60.0	8,208.00	57.0	50,868.00	59.5
Gross Profit on Operations	28,440.00	40.0	6,192.00	43.0	34,632.00	40.5

Name _____ Date _____ Class _____

4-2 WORK TOGETHER, p. 111

Analyzing adjusting entries   **[4]**

Allowance for Uncollectible Accounts	
	Bal. 450.00
	Adj. (d) **3,500.00**

Federal Income Tax Payable	
	Adj. (c) **1,110.00**

Merchandise Inventory—Stereos	
Bal. 56,120.00	*Adj. (a)* **6,690.00**

Income Summary—Stereos	
Adj. (a) **6,690.00**	

Merchandise Inventory—Accessories	
Bal. 9,590.00	*Adj. (b)* **4,960.00**

Income Summary—Accessories	
Adj. (b) **4,960.00**	

Federal Income Tax Expense	
Bal. 12,000.00	
Adj. (c) **1,110.00**	

Uncollectible Accounts Expense	
Adj. (d) **3,500.00**	

4-2 WORK TOGETHER

Extra form

4-2 ON YOUR OWN, p. 111

Analyzing adjusting entries   [5]

Allowance for Uncollectible Accounts	
	Bal. 370.00
	Adj. (d) 1,523.00

Income Summary—Washers	
Adj. (a) 3,760.00	

Merchandise Inventory—Washers	
Bal. 83,670.00	
Adj. (a) 3,760.00	

Income Summary—Dryers	
Adj. (b) 4,340.00	

Merchandise Inventory—Dryers	
Bal. 68,560.00	Adj. (b) 4,340.00

Depreciation Expense—Equipment	
Adj. (c) 920.00	

Accumulated Depreciation—Equipment	
	Bal. 2,300.00
	Adj. (c) 920.00

Uncollectible Accounts Expense	
Adj. (d) 1,523.00	

4-2 ON YOUR OWN

Extra form

4-3 WORK TOGETHER, p. 118

Preparing an income statement with component percentages

(Note: The partial work sheet is also needed to complete Work Together 4-4.)

Video Scene
Partial Work Sheet
For Year Ended December 31, 20--

	ACCOUNT TITLE	INCOME STATEMENT DEBIT	INCOME STATEMENT CREDIT
31	Income Summary—CDs	9 4 6 0 00	
32	Income Summary—Videos		26 0 9 0 00
33	Income Summary—General		
34	Sales—CDs		113 6 4 0 00
35	Sales—Videos		144 7 3 0 00
36	Sales Ret. and Allow.—CDs	3 2 1 0 00	
37	Sales Ret. and Allow.—Videos	4 1 2 0 00	
38	Purchases—CDs	45 0 8 2 00	
39	Purchases—Videos	80 5 7 0 00	
40	Purchases Discounts—CDs		1 6 4 0 00
41	Purchases Discounts—Videos		2 1 5 0 00
42	Purchases Ret. and Allow.—CDs		1 0 0 0 00
43	Purchases Ret. and Allow.—Videos		2 0 0 0 00
44	Advertising Expense	12 6 5 0 00	
45	Depr. Expense—Store Equip.	6 0 4 0 00	
46	Supplies Expense—Store	5 8 2 3 00	
47	Insurance Expense	8 4 0 0 00	
48	Rent Expense	44 0 0 0 00	
49	Uncollectible Accounts Expense	2 9 9 0 00	
50	Federal Income Tax Expense	12 2 2 6 00	
51		234 5 7 1 00	291 2 5 0 00
52	Net Income after Fed. Inc. Tax	56 6 7 9 00	
53		291 2 5 0 00	291 2 5 0 00
54			

4-3 WORK TOGETHER (continued)

Video Scene

Departmental Statement of Gross Profit

For Year Ended December 31, 20--

	CDs	% OF NET SALES	VIDEOS	% OF NET SALES	TOTAL	% OF NET SALES
Operating Revenue:						
Net Sales	$110,430.00	100.0	$140,610.00	100.0	$251,040.00	100.0
Cost of Merchandise Sold:						
Est. Mdse. Inv., Jan. 1	$ 38,910.00		$ 42,100.00		$ 81,010.00	
Net Purchases	42,442.00		76,420.00		118,862.00	
Mdse. Available for Sale	$ 81,352.00		$118,520.00		$199,872.00	
Less Est. End. Inv., December 31	29,450.00		68,190.00		97,640.00	
Cost of Merchandise Sold	51,902.00	47.0	50,330.00	35.8	102,232.00	40.7
Gross Profit on Operations	$ 58,528.00	53.0	$ 90,280.00	64.2	$148,808.00	59.3

4-3 WORK TOGETHER (concluded)

[4]

Video Scene

Income Statement

For Year Ended December 31, 20--

					% OF NET SALES
Operating Revenue:					
Sales			258 3 7 0 00		
Less: Sales Returns and Allow.			7 3 3 0 00		
Net Sales				251 0 4 0 00	100.0
Cost of Merchandise Sold:					
Merchandise Inv., Jan. 1, 20--			81 0 1 0 00		
Purchases		125 6 5 2 00			
Less: Purchases Discount	3 7 9 0 00				
Purchases Ret. & Allow.	3 0 0 0 00	6 7 9 0 00			
Net Purchases			118 8 6 2 00		
Total Cost of Mdse. Avail. for Sale			199 8 7 2 00		
Less Mdse. Inv., Dec. 31, 20--			97 6 4 0 00		
Cost of Merchandise Sold				102 2 3 2 00	40.7
Gross Profit on Operations				148 8 0 8 00	59.3
Operating Expenses:					
Selling Expenses:					
Advertising Expense		12 6 5 0 00			
Depr. Expense--Store Equip.		6 0 4 0 00			
Supplies Expense--Store		5 8 2 3 00			
Total Selling Expenses			24 5 1 3 00		
Administrative Expenses:					
Insurance Expense		8 4 0 0 00			
Rent Expense		44 0 0 0 00			
Uncollectible Accts. Expense		2 9 9 0 00			
Total Administrative Expenses			55 3 9 0 00		
Total Operating Expenses				79 9 0 3 00	31.8
Net Income before Fed. Inc. Tax				68 9 0 5 00	27.4
Less Federal Inc. Tax Expense				12 2 2 6 00	4.9
Net Income after Fed. Inc. Tax				56 6 7 9 00	22.6

4-3 WORK TOGETHER

Extra form

														% OF NET SALES

4-3 ON YOUR OWN, p. 118

Preparing an income statement with component percentages

(Note: The partial work sheet is also needed to complete On Your Own 4-4.)

Fremont Sign

Partial Work Sheet

For Year Ended December 31, 20--

	ACCOUNT TITLE	INCOME STATEMENT	
		DEBIT	CREDIT
31	Income Summary—Commercial		4 2 3 0 00
32	Income Summary—Residential		24 9 1 5 00
33	Income Summary—General		
34	Sales—Commercial		162 7 0 0 00
35	Sales—Residential		81 9 0 0 00
36	Sales Discounts—Commercial	8 5 0 0 00	
37	Sales Discounts—Residential	3 1 0 0 00	
38	Purchases—Commercial	74 5 3 0 00	
39	Purchases—Residential	55 5 5 5 00	
40	Purchases Discounts—Commercial		1 8 7 0 00
41	Purchases Discounts—Residential		7 1 5 00
42	Purchases Ret. and Allow.—Commercial		6 3 0 00
43	Purchases Ret. and Allow.—Residential		8 4 0 00
44	Depr. Expense—Shop Equipment	21 3 0 0 00	
45	Salary Expense—Commercial	36 7 2 0 00	
46	Salary Expense—Residential	30 1 0 0 00	
47	Payroll Taxes Expense	9 8 7 0 00	
48	Rent Expense	8 2 0 0 00	
49	Salary Expense—Admin.	29 0 0 0 00	
50	Federal Inc. Tax Expense	1 3 9 00	
51		277 0 1 4 00	277 8 0 0 00
52	Net Income after Fed. Inc. Tax	7 8 6 00	
53		277 8 0 0 00	277 8 0 0 00
54			

4-3 ON YOUR OWN (continued)

Fremont Sign

Departmental Statement of Gross Profit

For Year Ended December 31, 20--

	COMMERCIAL	% OF NET SALES	RESIDENTIAL	% OF NET SALES	TOTAL	% OF NET SALES
Operating Revenue:						
Net Sales	$154,200.00	100.0	$ 78,800.00	100.0	$233,000.00	100.0
Cost of Merchandise Sold:						
Est. Mdse. Inv., Jan. 1	$ 18,710.00		$ 12,715.00		$ 31,425.00	
Net Purchases	72,030.00		54,000.00		126,030.00	
Mdse. Available for Sale	$ 90,740.00		$ 66,715.00		$157,455.00	
Less Est. End. Inv., Dec. 31	22,940.00		37,630.00		60,570.00	
Cost of Merchandise Sold	67,800.00	44.0	29,085.00	36.9	96,885.00	41.6
Gross Profit on Operations	$ 86,400.00	56.0	$ 49,715.00	63.1	$136,115.00	58.4

Name _____ Date _____ Class _____

4-3 ON YOUR OWN (concluded)

[5]

Fremont Sign

Income Statement

For Year Ended December 31, 20--

					% OF NET SALES
Operating Revenue:					
Sales			244 6 0 0 00		
Less: Sales Discount			11 6 0 0 00		
Net Sales				233 0 0 0 00	100.0
Cost of Merchandise Sold:					
Merchandise Inv., Jan. 1, 20--			31 4 2 5 00		
Purchases		130 0 8 5 00			
Less: Purchases Discount	2 5 8 5 00				
Purchases Ret. & Allow.	1 4 7 0 00	4 0 5 5 00			
Net Purchases			126 0 3 0 00		
Total Cost of Mdse. Avail. for Sale			157 4 5 5 00		
Less Mdse. Inv., Dec. 31, 20--			60 5 7 0 00		
Cost of Merchandise Sold				96 8 8 5 00	41.6
Gross Profit on Operations				136 1 1 5 00	58.4
Operating Expenses:					
Selling Expenses:					
Depreciation Expense--Shop Eq.		21 3 0 0 00			
Salary Expense--Commercial		36 7 2 0 00			
Salary Expense--Residential		30 1 0 0 00			
Total Selling Expenses			88 1 2 0 00		
Administrative Expenses:					
Payroll Taxes Expense		9 8 7 0 00			
Rent Expense		8 2 0 0 00			
Salary Expense--Admin.		29 0 0 0 00			
Total Administrative Expense			47 0 7 0 00		
Total Operating Expenses				135 1 9 0 00	58.0
Net Income before Fed. Inc. Tax				9 2 5 00	0.4
Less Federal Inc. Tax Expense				1 3 9 00	0.1
Net Income after Fed. Inc. Tax				7 8 6 00	0.3

4-3 ON YOUR OWN

Extra form

		% OF NET SALES

4-4 WORK TOGETHER, p. 124

Journalizing closing entries

[5]

Use the income statement columns of Video Scene's work sheet on page 103.

GENERAL JOURNAL   PAGE 4

	DATE		ACCOUNT TITLE	DOC. NO.	POST. REF.	DEBIT	CREDIT	
1			*Closing Entries*					1
2	20— Dec.	31	Income Summary—Videos			26 090 00		2
3			Sales—CDs			113 640 00		3
4			Sales—Videos			144 730 00		4
5			Purchases Discounts—CDs			1 640 00		5
6			Purchases Discounts—Videos			2 150 00		6
7			Purchases Ret. and Allow.—CDs			1 000 00		7
8			Purchases Ret. and Allow.—Videos			2 000 00		8
9			Income Summary—General				291 250 00	9
10		31	Income Summary—General			234 571 00		10
11			Income Summary—CDs				9 460 00	11
12			Sales Ret. and Allow.—CDs				3 210 00	12
13			Sales Ret. and Allow.—Videos				4 120 00	13
14			Purchases—CDs				45 082 00	14
15			Purchases—Videos				80 570 00	15
16			Advertising Expense				12 650 00	16
17			Depr. Exp.—Store Equip.				6 040 00	17
18			Supplies Expense—Store				5 823 00	18
19			Insurance Expense				8 400 00	19
20			Rent Expense				44 000 00	20
21			Uncollectible Accts. Exp.				2 990 00	21
22			Federal Income Tax Exp.				12 226 00	22
23		31	Income Summary—General			56 679 00		23
24			Retained Earnings				56 679 00	24
25		31	Retained Earnings			8 000 00		25
26			Dividends				8 000 00	26
27								27
28								28
29								29
30								30

4-4 WORK TOGETHER

Extra form

GENERAL JOURNAL

PAGE _____

	DATE	ACCOUNT TITLE	DOC. NO.	POST. REF.	DEBIT	CREDIT	
1							1
2							2
3							3
4							4
5							5
6							6
7							7
8							8
9							9
10							10
11							11
12							12
13							13
14							14
15							15
16							16
17							17
18							18
19							19
20							20
21							21
22							22
23							23
24							24
25							25
26							26
27							27
28							28
29							29
30							30
31							31

4-4 ON YOUR OWN, p. 124

Journalizing closing entries

[6]

Use the income statement columns of Fremont Sign's work sheet on page 107.

GENERAL JOURNAL   PAGE 6

	DATE	ACCOUNT TITLE	DOC. NO.	POST. REF.	DEBIT	CREDIT	
1		*Closing Entries*					1
2	20— Dec. 31	Income Summary—Commercial			4 2 3 0 00		2
3		Income Summary—Residential			2 4 9 1 5 00		3
4		Sales—Commercial			162 7 0 0 00		4
5		Sales—Residential			81 9 0 0 00		5
6		Purchases Discounts—Commercial			1 8 7 0 00		6
7		Purchases Discounts—Residential			7 1 5 00		7
8		Purchases Returns and Allowances—Commercial			6 3 0 00		8
9		Purchases Returns and Allowances—Residential			8 4 0 00		9
10		Income Summary—General				277 8 0 0 00	10
11	31	Income Summary—General			277 0 1 4 00		11
12		Sales Discounts—Commercial				8 5 0 0 00	12
13		Sales Discounts—Residential				3 1 0 0 00	13
14		Purchases—Commercial				74 5 3 0 00	14
15		Purchases—Residential				55 5 5 5 00	15
16		Depr. Exp.—Shop Equip.				21 3 0 0 00	16
17		Salary Expense—Commercial				36 7 2 0 00	17
18		Salary Expense—Residential				30 1 0 0 00	18
19		Payroll Taxes Expense				9 8 7 0 00	19
20		Rent Expense				8 2 0 0 00	20
21		Salary Expense—Administrative				29 0 0 0 00	21
22		Federal Income Tax Expense				1 3 9 00	22
23	31	Income Summary—General			7 8 6 00		23
24		Retained Earnings				7 8 6 00	24
25	31	Retained Earnings			10 0 0 0 00		25
26		Dividends				10 0 0 0 00	26
27							27
28							28
29							29
30							30

Name _____ Date _____ Class _____

4-4 ON YOUR OWN

Extra form

GENERAL JOURNAL   PAGE _____

	DATE		ACCOUNT TITLE	DOC. NO.	POST. REF.	DEBIT	CREDIT	
1								1
2								2
3								3
4								4
5								5
6								6
7								7
8								8
9								9
10								10
11								11
12								12
13								13
14								14
15								15
16								16
17								17
18								18
19								19
20								20
21								21
22								22
23								23
24								24
25								25
26								26
27								27
28								28
29								29
30								30
31								31

4-1 APPLICATION PROBLEM, p. 126

Estimating ending merchandise inventory

ESTIMATED MERCHANDISE INVENTORY SHEET
Gross Profit Method

DEPARTMENT *Equipment*   DATE *1/31/--*

1	Beginning inventory, January 1.		$ 145,000.00
2	Net purchases to date		14,300.00
3	Merchandise available for sale.		$ 159,300.00
4	Net sales to date.	$ 49,200.00	
5	Less estimated gross profit	21,156.00	
	(Net sales × Estimated gross profit _43.0_%)		
6	Estimated cost of merchandise sold		28,044.00
7	Estimated ending inventory.		$ 131,256.00

ESTIMATED MERCHANDISE INVENTORY SHEET
Gross Profit Method

DEPARTMENT *Accessories*   DATE *1/31/--*

1	Beginning inventory, January 1.		$ 153,000.00
2	Net purchases to date		14,100.00
3	Merchandise available for sale.		$ 167,100.00
4	Net sales to date.	$ 53,400.00	
5	Less estimated gross profit	22,962.00	
	(Net sales × Estimated gross profit _43.0_%)		
6	Estimated cost of merchandise sold		30,438.00
7	Estimated ending inventory.		$ 136,662.00

Name _____ Date _____ Class _____

4-1 APPLICATION PROBLEM

Extra forms

ESTIMATED MERCHANDISE INVENTORY SHEET
Gross Profit Method

DEPARTMENT _____ DATE _____

1	Beginning inventory, January 1	$_____
2	Net purchases to date	_____
3	Merchandise available for sale	$_____
4	Net sales to date . . . . $_____	
5	Less estimated gross profit . . . . _____	
	(Net sales × Estimated gross profit _____%)	
6	Estimated cost of merchandise sold . . . . _____	
7	Estimated ending inventory . . . . $_____	

ESTIMATED MERCHANDISE INVENTORY SHEET
Gross Profit Method

DEPARTMENT _____ DATE _____

1	Beginning inventory, January 1	$_____
2	Net purchases to date	_____
3	Merchandise available for sale	$_____
4	Net sales to date . . . . $_____	
5	Less estimated gross profit . . . . _____	
	(Net sales × Estimated gross profit _____%)	
6	Estimated cost of merchandise sold . . . . _____	
7	Estimated ending inventory . . . . $_____	

116 • Working Papers

COPYRIGHT © SOUTH-WESTERN EDUCATIONAL PUBLISHING

Name _____ Date _____ Class _____

4-2 APPLICATION PROBLEM, p. 126

Preparing an interim departmental statement of gross profit, calculating component percentages

[1]

ESTIMATED MERCHANDISE INVENTORY SHEET
Gross Profit Method

DEPARTMENT _Office_   DATE _3/31/--_

1	Beginning inventory, January 1		$ 154,640.00
2	Net purchases to date		36,857.20
3	Merchandise available for sale		$ 191,497.20
4	Net sales to date	$ 106,960.00	
5	Less estimated gross profit	42,784.00	
	(Net sales × Estimated gross profit _40.0_%)		
6	Estimated cost of merchandise sold		64,176.00
7	Estimated ending inventory		$ 127,321.20

ESTIMATED MERCHANDISE INVENTORY SHEET
Gross Profit Method

DEPARTMENT _Residential_   DATE _3/31/--_

1	Beginning inventory, January 1		$ 166,500.00
2	Net purchases to date		34,818.40
3	Merchandise available for sale		$ 201,318.40
4	Net sales to date	$ 126,400.00	
5	Less estimated gross profit	50,560.00	
	(Net sales × Estimated gross profit _40.0_%)		
6	Estimated cost of merchandise sold		75,840.00
7	Estimated ending inventory		$ 125,478.40

4-2 APPLICATION PROBLEM (concluded)

[2]

Allied Lighting
Interim Departmental Statement of Gross Profit
For Month Ended March 31, 20--

	OFFICE	% OF NET SALES	RESIDENTIAL	% OF NET SALES	TOTAL	% OF NET SALES
Operating Revenue:						
Net Sales	29,200.00	100.0	33,600.00	100.0	62,800.00	100.0
Cost of Merchandise Sold:						
Est. Mdse. Inv., March 1	131,344.00		135,660.00		267,004.00	
Net Purchases	13,497.20		9,978.40		23,475.60	
Mdse. Available for Sale	144,841.20		145,638.40		290,479.60	
Less Est. End. Inv., March 31	127,321.20		125,478.40		252,799.60	
Cost of Merchandise Sold	17,520.00	60.0	20,160.00	60.0	37,680.00	60.0
Gross Profit on Operations	11,680.00	40.0	13,440.00	40.0	25,120.00	40.0

4-3 APPLICATION PROBLEM, p. 126

Preparing subsidiary schedules

[1]

Gabriel's Gourmet Shop

Schedule of Accounts Payable

December 31, 20--

Barnett Co.		2	2	5	0	40
Gould Associates		1	5	2	0	30
Hills Supply			9	3	6	80
Kroy Enterprises		1	2	6	2	50
Swedberg, Inc.			8	2	6	10
Williamson Products		2	2	7	0	60
Total Accounts Payable		9	0	6	6	70

[2]

Gabriel's Gourmet Shop

Schedule of Accounts Receivable

December 31, 20--

Mary Anacker		1	3	1	0	20
Alice Conroy			8	2	0	70
Raymond Gaetz			8	2	6	10
John Klem		1	3	0	4	20
Irma Musgrove			6	1	9	60
Richard Wimer		2	0	2	6	40
Total Accounts Receivable		6	9	0	7	20

4-3 APPLICATION PROBLEM

Extra forms

Name _____ Date _____ Class _____

4-4 APPLICATION PROBLEM, p. 127

Calculating and analyzing component percentage for total operating expenses   [1, 2]

1 Business	2 Net Sales	3 Total Operating Expenses	4 Performance Standard— Not more than	5 Component Percentage	6 Performance Level
1	$148,000.00	$43,500.00	32.0%	29.4%	A
2	$175,500.00	$51,750.00	30.0%	*29.5%*	A
3	$130,300.00	$36,500.00	26.0%	*28.0%*	U
4	$145,600.00	$35,930.00	25.0%	*24.7%*	A
5	$185,300.00	$58,250.00	30.0%	*31.4%*	U
6	$163,900.00	$44,980.00	28.0%	*27.4%*	A

Extra form

1 Business	2 Net Sales	3 Total Operating Expenses	4 Performance Standard— Not more than	5 Component Percentage	6 Performance Level

4-4 APPLICATION PROBLEM

Extra forms

1 Business	2 Net Sales	3 Total Operating Expenses	4 Performance Standard— Not more than	5 Component Percentage	6 Performance Level

1 Business	2 Net Sales	3 Total Operating Expenses	4 Performance Standard— Not more than	5 Component Percentage	6 Performance Level

4-5 APPLICATION PROBLEM

(Note: Work sheet for Application Problem 4-5 begins on page 124.)

Extra form

ACCOUNT TITLE	TRIAL BALANCE		ADJUSTMENTS		INCOME STATEMENT		BALANCE SHEET	
	1 DEBIT	2 CREDIT	3 DEBIT	4 CREDIT	5 DEBIT	6 CREDIT	7 DEBIT	8 CREDIT
1								
2								
3								
4								
5								
6								
7								
8								
9								
10								
11								
12								
13								
14								
15								
16								
17								
18								
19								
20								
21								
22								
23								
24								
25								
26								
27								
28								
29								
30								

4-5 APPLICATION PROBLEM, p. 128

Completing a work sheet for a departmentalized business

Note: This work sheet is needed to complete Application Problems 4-6 and 4-7.

Regis Bookstore
Work Sheet
For Year Ended December 31, 20--

#	ACCOUNT TITLE	TRIAL BALANCE DEBIT	TRIAL BALANCE CREDIT	ADJUSTMENTS DEBIT	ADJUSTMENTS CREDIT	INCOME STATEMENT DEBIT	INCOME STATEMENT CREDIT	BALANCE SHEET DEBIT	BALANCE SHEET CREDIT
1	Cash	3760068						3760068	
2	Petty Cash	50000						50000	
3	Accounts Receivable	2094860						2094860	
4	Allowance for Uncollectible Accounts		32080		(a) 125910				157990
5	Mdse. Inventory—Teens	17896030			(b) 1014020			16882010	
6	Mdse. Inventory—Adults	16038040		(c) 1307040				17345080	
7	Supplies—Office	1094000			(d) 600940			493060	
8	Supplies—Store	962060			(e) 390020			572040	
9	Prepaid Insurance	880000			(f) 420000			460000	
10	Office Equipment	1890000						1890000	
11	Accum. Depr.—Office Equipment		884000		(g) 128000				1012000
12	Store Equipment	2160000						2160000	
13	Accum. Depr.—Store Equipment		1031000		(h) 280000				1311000
14	Accounts Payable		2998030						2998030
15	Employee Income Tax Pay.—Federal		132040						132040
16	Employee Income Tax Pay.—State		86010						86010
17	Federal Income Tax Payable				(i) 134788				134788
18	Social Security Tax Payable		170950						170950
19	Medicare Tax Payable		39450						39450
20	Sales Tax Payable		683040						683040
21	Unemploy. Tax Pay.—Federal		1930						1930
22	Unemploy. Tax Pay.—State		13028						13028
23	Health Ins. Prem. Payable		299000						299000
24	Dividends Payable								
25	Capital Stock		20000000						20000000
26	Dividends	3000000						3000000	
27	Retained Earnings		15567500						15567500
28	Income Summary—Teens			(b) 1014020		1014020			
29	Income Summary—Adults				(c) 1307040		1307040		
30	Income Summary—General								

4-5 APPLICATION PROBLEM (concluded)

| | TRIAL BALANCE | | ADJUSTMENTS | | INCOME STATEMENT | | BALANCE SHEET | |
ACCOUNT TITLE	DEBIT	CREDIT	DEBIT	CREDIT	DEBIT	CREDIT	DEBIT	CREDIT
31 Sales—Teens		38716980				38716980		
32 Sales—Adults		33789470				33789470		
33 Sales Discount—Teens	361080				361080			
34 Sales Discount—Adults	379010				379010			
35 Sales Ret. & Allow.—Teens	231080				231080			
36 Sales Ret. & Allow.—Adults	294060				294060			
37 Purchases—Teens	20221190				20221190			
38 Purchases—Adults	19694150				19694150			
39 Purchases Discount—Teens		513080				513080		
40 Purchases Discount—Adults		473020				473020		
41 Purch. Ret. & Allow.—Teens		396030				396030		
42 Purch. Ret. & Allow.—Adults		428070				428070		
43 Advertising Expense	548000				548000			
44 Credit Card Fee Expense	476080				476080			
45 Depr. Exp.—Store Equipment			(h) 280000		280000			
46 Salary Expense—Teens	7280000				7280000			
47 Salary Expense—Adults	7630000				7630000			
48 Supplies Expense—Store			(e) 390020		390020			
49 Depr. Exp.—Office Equipment			(g) 128000		128000			
50 Insurance Expense			(f) 420000		420000			
51 Miscellaneous Expense	463000				463000			
52 Payroll Taxes Expense	1834000				1834000			
53 Rent Expense	1800000				1800000			
54 Salary Expense—Administrative	3986000				3986000			
55 Supplies Expense—Office			(d) 600940		600940			
56 Uncollectible Accounts Expense			(a) 125910		125910			
57 Federal Income Tax Expense	1232000		(i) 134788		1366788			
58	116254708	116254708	4400718	4400718	69523328	75623690	48707118	42606756
59 Net Income after Federal Income Tax					6100362			6100362
60					75623690	75623690	48707118	48707118
61								

Name _____ Date _____ Class _____

4-5 APPLICATION PROBLEM

Extra form

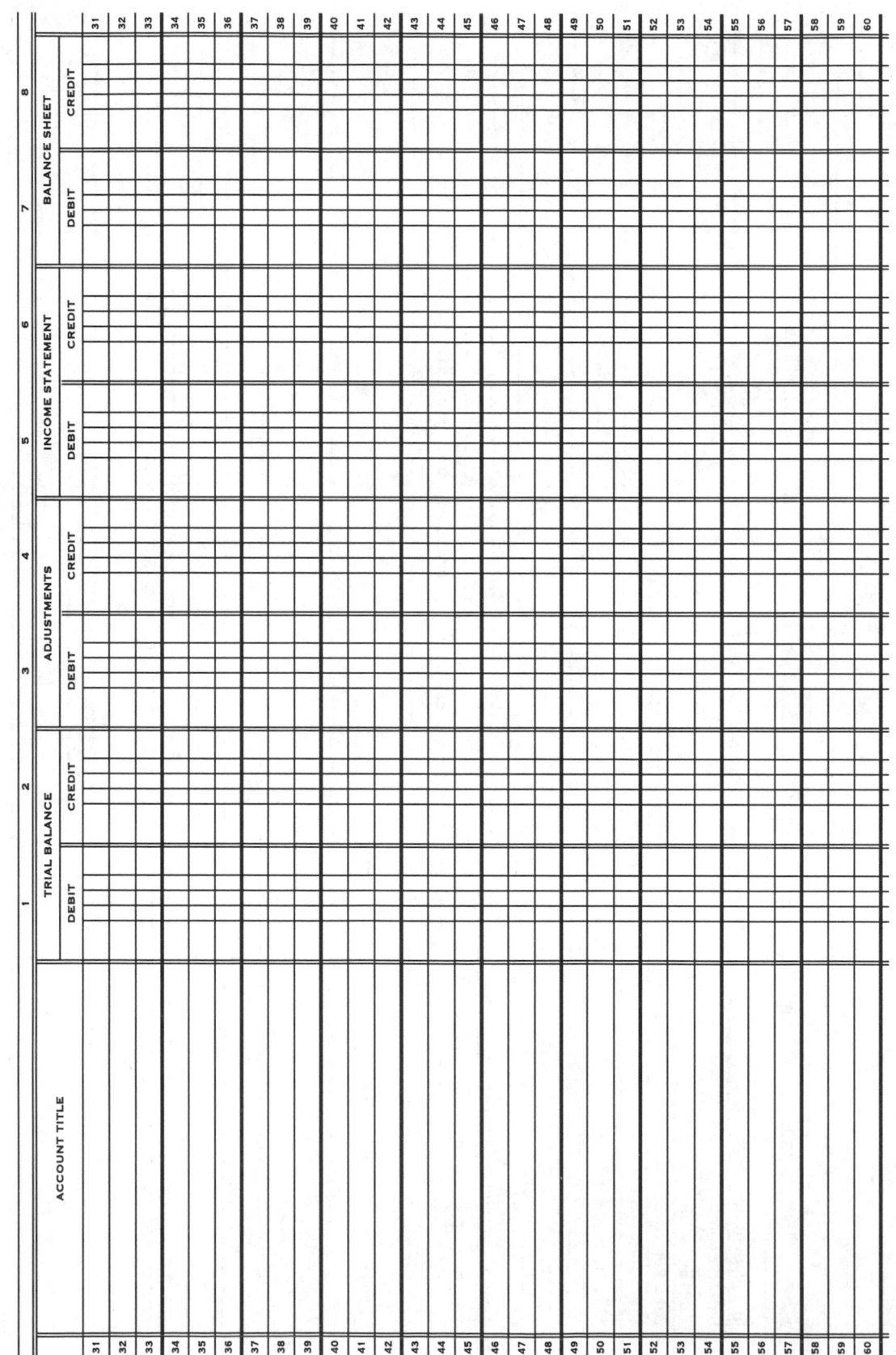

4-6 APPLICATION PROBLEM, p. 128

Preparing financial statements for a departmentalized business [1]

Note: The work sheet from Application Problem 4-5 is needed to complete this problem.

Regis Bookstore

Departmental Statement of Gross Profit

For Year Ended December 31, 20--

	TEENS	% OF NET SALES	ADULTS	% OF NET SALES	TOTAL	% OF NET SALES
Operating Revenue:						
Net Sales	381,248.20	100.0	331,164.00	100.0	712,412.20	100.0
Cost of Merchandise Sold:						
Mdse. Inv., Jan. 1	178,960.30		160,380.40		339,340.70	
Net Purchases	193,120.80		187,930.60		381,051.40	
Mdse. Available for Sale	372,081.10		348,311.00		720,392.10	
Less End. Inv., Dec. 31	168,820.10		173,450.80		342,270.90	
Cost of Merchandise Sold	203,261.00	53.3	174,860.20	52.8	378,121.20	53.1
Gross Profit on Operations	177,987.20	46.7	156,303.80	47.2	334,291.00	46.9

4-6 APPLICATION PROBLEM (continued)

[2]

Regis Bookstore

Income Statement

For Year Ended December 31, 20--

					% OF NET SALES
Operating Revenue:					
Sales:			725 0 6 4 50		
Less: Sales Discount		7 4 0 0 90			
Sales Returns & Allow.		5 2 5 1 40	12 6 5 2 30		
Net Sales				712 4 1 2 20	100.0
Cost of Merchandise Sold:					
Mdse. Inv., Jan. 1, 20--			339 3 4 0 70		
Purchases		399 1 5 3 40			
Less: Purchases Discount	9 8 6 1 00				
Purch. Returns & Allow.	8 2 4 1 00	18 1 0 2 00			
Net Purchases			381 0 5 1 40		
Total Cost of Mdse. Avail. for Sale			720 3 9 2 10		
Less Mdse. Inv., Dec. 31, 20--			342 2 7 0 90		
Cost of Merchandise Sold				378 1 2 1 20	53.1
Gross Profit on Operations				334 2 9 1 00	46.9
Operating Expenses:					
Selling Expenses:					
Advertising Expense		5 4 8 0 00			
Credit Card Fee Expense		4 7 6 0 80			
Depr. Exp.—Store Equipment		2 8 0 0 00			
Salary Expense—Teens		72 8 0 0 00			
Salary Expense—Adults		76 3 0 0 00			
Supplies Expense—Store		3 9 0 0 20			
Total Selling Expenses			166 0 4 1 00		
Administrative Expenses:					
Depr. Exp.—Office Equipment		1 2 8 0 00			
Insurance Expense		4 2 0 0 00			
Miscellaneous Expense		4 6 3 0 00			
Payroll Taxes Expense		18 3 4 0 00			
Rent Expense		18 0 0 0 00			
Salary Expense—Administrative		39 8 6 0 00			

4-6 APPLICATION PROBLEM (continued)

[2]

Regis Bookstore

Income Statement (continued)

For Year Ended December 31, 20--

				% OF NET SALES
Supplies Expense—Office		6 0 0 9 40		
Uncollectible Accounts Expense		1 2 5 9 10		
Total Administrative Expenses		93 5 7 8 50		
Total Operating Expenses			259 6 1 9 50	36.4
Net Income before Fed. Inc. Tax			74 6 7 1 50	10.5
Less Federal Income Tax Expense			13 6 6 7 88	
Net Income after Fed. Inc. Tax			61 0 0 3 62	8.6

4-6 APPLICATION PROBLEM (continued)

Regis Bookstore

Statement of Stockholders' Equity

For Year Ended December 31, 20--

Capital Stock:				
$100.00 Per Share				
January 1, 20--, 2,000 Shares Issued		200 0 0 0 00		
Issued during Current Year, None		- 0 -		
Balance, December 31, 20--, 2,000 Shares Issued			200 0 0 0 00	
Retained Earnings:				
Balance, January 1, 20--		155 6 7 5 00		
Net Income after Federal Income Tax for 20--	61 0 0 3 62			
Less Dividends Declared during 20--	30 0 0 0 00			
Net Increase during 20--		31 0 0 3 62		
Balance, December 31, 20--			186 6 7 8 62	
Total Stockholders' Equity, December 31, 20--			386 6 7 8 62	

4-6 APPLICATION PROBLEM (continued)

[4]

Regis Bookstore

Balance Sheet

December 31, 20--

Assets																	
Current Assets:																	
Cash							37	6	0	0	68						
Petty Cash								5	0	0	00						
Accounts Receivable	20	9	4	8	60												
Less Allowance for Uncollectible Accounts	1	5	7	9	90		19	3	6	8	70						
Merchandise Inventory—Teens							168	8	2	0	10						
Merchandise Inventory—Adults							173	4	5	0	80						
Supplies—Office							4	9	3	0	60						
Supplies—Store							5	7	2	0	40						
Prepaid Insurance							4	6	0	0	00						
Total Current Assets													414	9	9	1	28
Plant Assets:																	
Office Equipment	18	9	0	0	00												
Less Accumulated Depr.—Office Equipment	10	1	2	0	00		8	7	8	0	00						
Store Equipment	21	6	0	0	00												
Less Accumulated Depr.—Store Equipment	13	1	1	0	00		8	4	9	0	00						
Total Plant Assets													17	2	7	0	00
Total Assets													432	2	6	1	28
Liabilities																	
Current Liabilities:																	
Accounts Payable							29	9	8	0	30						
Employee Income Tax Payable—Federal							1	3	2	0	40						
Employee Income Tax Payable—State								8	6	0	10						
Federal Income Tax Payable							1	3	4	7	88						
Social Security Tax Payable							1	7	0	9	50						
Medicare Tax Payable								3	9	4	50						
Sales Tax Payable							6	8	3	0	40						
Unemployment Tax Payable—Federal									1	9	30						
Unemployment Tax Payable—State								1	3	0	28						
Health Insurance Premiums Payable							2	9	9	0	00						
Total Liabilities													45	5	8	2	66

4-6 APPLICATION PROBLEM (concluded)

[4]

Regis Bookstore															
Balance Sheet (continued)															
December 31, 20--															
Stockholders' Equity															
Capital Stock						200	0	0	0	00					
Retained Earnings						186	6	7	8	62					
Total Stockholders' Equity											386	6	7	8	62
Total Liabilities & Stockholders' Equity											432	2	6	1	28

4-7 APPLICATION PROBLEM, p. 129

Journalizing adjusting and closing entries for a departmentalized business [1, 2]

Note: The work sheet from Application Problem 4-5 is needed to complete this problem.

GENERAL JOURNAL PAGE 15

	DATE		ACCOUNT TITLE	DOC. NO.	POST. REF.	DEBIT	CREDIT	
1			*Adjusting Entries*					1
2	20-- Dec.	31	Uncollectible Accounts Expense			1 2 5 9 10		2
3			Allowance for Uncollectible Accounts				1 2 5 9 10	3
4		31	Income Summary—Teens			10 1 4 0 20		4
5			Merchandise Inventory—Teens				10 1 4 0 20	5
6		31	Merchandise Inventory—Adults			13 0 7 0 40		6
7			Income Summary—Adults				13 0 7 0 40	7
8		31	Supplies Expense—Office			6 0 0 9 40		8
9			Supplies—Office				6 0 0 9 40	9
10		31	Supplies Expense—Store			3 9 0 0 20		10
11			Supplies—Store				3 9 0 0 20	11
12		31	Insurance Expense			4 2 0 0 00		12
13			Prepaid Insurance				4 2 0 0 00	13
14		31	Depreciation Expense—Office Equipment			1 2 8 0 00		14
15			Accum. Depreciation—Office Equip.				1 2 8 0 00	15
16		31	Depreciation Expense—Store Equipment			2 8 0 0 00		16
17			Accum. Depreciation—Store Equip.				2 8 0 0 00	17
18		31	Federal Income Tax Expense			1 3 4 7 88		18
19			Federal Income Tax Payable				1 3 4 7 88	19
20			*Closing Entries*					20
21		31	Income Summary—Adults			13 0 7 0 40		21
22			Sales—Teens			387 1 6 9 80		22
23			Sales—Adults			337 8 9 4 70		23
24			Purchases Discount—Teens			5 1 3 0 80		24
25			Purchases Discount—Adults			4 7 3 0 20		25
26			Purchases Ret. & Allow.—Teens			3 9 6 0 30		26
27			Purchases Ret. & Allow.—Adults			4 2 8 0 70		27
28			Income Summary—General				756 2 3 6 90	28
29								29
30								30

4-7 **APPLICATION PROBLEM (continued)**

[2]

GENERAL JOURNAL   PAGE 16

	DATE		ACCOUNT TITLE	DOC. NO.	POST. REF.	DEBIT	CREDIT	
1	20— Dec.	31	Income Summary—General			695 23 3 28		1
2			Income Summary—Teens				10 1 4 0 20	2
3			Sales Discount—Teens				3 6 1 0 80	3
4			Sales Discount—Adults				3 7 9 0 10	4
5			Sales Returns and Allow.—Teens				2 3 1 0 80	5
6			Sales Returns and Allow.—Adults				2 9 4 0 60	6
7			Purchases—Teens				202 2 1 1 90	7
8			Purchases—Adults				196 9 4 1 50	8
9			Advertising Expense				5 4 8 0 00	9
10			Credit Card Fee Expense				4 7 6 0 80	10
11			Depr. Expense—Store Equipment				2 8 0 0 00	11
12			Salary Expense—Teens				72 8 0 0 00	12
13			Salary Expense—Adults				76 3 0 0 00	13
14			Supplies Expense—Store				3 9 0 0 20	14
15			Depr. Expense—Office Equipment				1 2 8 0 00	15
16			Insurance Expense				4 2 0 0 00	16
17			Miscellaneous Expense				4 6 3 0 00	17
18			Payroll Taxes Expense				18 3 4 0 00	18
19			Rent Expense				18 0 0 0 00	19
20			Salary Expense—Administrative				39 8 6 0 00	20
21			Supplies Expense—Office				6 0 0 9 40	21
22			Uncollectible Accounts Expense				1 2 5 9 10	22
23			Federal Income Tax Expense				13 6 6 7 88	23
24		31	Income Summary—General			61 0 0 3 62		24
25			Retained Earnings				61 0 0 3 62	25
26		31	Retained Earnings			30 0 0 0 00		26
27			Dividends				30 0 0 0 00	27
28								28
29								29
30								30
31								31

4-8 MASTERY PROBLEM, p. 129

(Note: The work sheet for this problem begins on page 136.)

Preparing end-of-fiscal-period work for a departmentalized business [2]

Home Plate Sporting Goods

Departmental Statement of Gross Profit

For Year Ended December 31, 20--

	SOFTBALL		% OF NET SALES	BASEBALL		% OF NET SALES	TOTAL		% OF NET SALES
Operating Revenue:									
Net Sales		381,430.00	100.0		361,160.00	100.0		742,590.00	100.0
Cost of Merchandise Sold:									
Mdse. Inv., Jan. 1	220,180.00			247,240.00			467,420.00		
Net Purchases	193,486.00			180,508.00			373,994.00		
Mdse. Available for Sale	413,666.00			427,748.00			841,414.00		
Less End. Inv., Dec. 31	205,380.20			236,520.80			441,901.00		
Cost of Merchandise Sold		208,285.80	54.6		191,227.20	52.9		399,513.00	53.8
Gross Profit on Operations		173,144.20	45.4		169,932.80	47.1		343,077.00	46.2

Home Plate Sporting Goods
Work Sheet
For Year Ended December 31, 20--

#	ACCOUNT TITLE	TRIAL BALANCE DEBIT	TRIAL BALANCE CREDIT	ADJUSTMENTS DEBIT	ADJUSTMENTS CREDIT	INCOME STATEMENT DEBIT	INCOME STATEMENT CREDIT	BALANCE SHEET DEBIT	BALANCE SHEET CREDIT
1	Cash	38 560 40						38 560 40	
2	Petty Cash	6 000 00						6 000 00	
3	Accounts Receivable	26 364 20						26 364 20	
4	Allowance for Uncollectible Accounts		460 80		(a) 1 970 40				2 431 20
5	Mdse. Inventory—Softball	220 180 00			(b) 14 799 80			205 380 20	
6	Mdse. Inventory—Baseball	247 240 00			(c) 10 719 20			236 520 80	
7	Supplies—Office	14 440 00			(d) 8 429 70			6 010 30	
8	Supplies—Store	9 483 60			(e) 5 263 10			4 220 50	
9	Prepaid Insurance	8 550 00			(f) 5 750 00			2 800 00	
10	Office Equipment	17 940 00						17 940 00	
11	Accum. Depr.—Office Equipment		9 360 00		(g) 1 200 00				10 560 00
12	Store Equipment	22 860 00						22 860 00	
13	Accum. Depr.—Store Equipment		11 430 00		(h) 2 600 00				14 030 00
14	Accounts Payable		32 740 00						32 740 00
15	Employee Income Tax Pay.—Federal		1 340 90						1 340 90
16	Employee Income Tax Pay.—State		930 60						930 60
17	Federal Income Tax Payable				(i) 1 302 45				1 302 45
18	Social Security Tax Payable		1 917 50						1 917 50
19	Medicare Tax Payable		442 50						442 50
20	Sales Tax Payable		7 240 30						7 240 30
21	Unemploy. Tax Pay.—Federal		22 40						22 40
22	Unemploy. Tax Pay.—State		151 20						151 20
23	Health Ins. Prem. Payable		3 540 00						3 540 00
24	Dividends Payable								
25	Capital Stock		300 000 00						300 000 00
26	Dividends	30 000 00						30 000 00	
27	Retained Earnings		155 000 00						155 000 00
28	Income Summary—Softball			(b) 14 799 80		14 799 80			
29	Income Summary—Baseball			(c) 10 719 20		10 719 20			
30	Income Summary—General								

4-8 MASTERY PROBLEM (continued)

[1]

	ACCOUNT TITLE	TRIAL BALANCE DEBIT	TRIAL BALANCE CREDIT	ADJUSTMENTS DEBIT	ADJUSTMENTS CREDIT	INCOME STATEMENT DEBIT	INCOME STATEMENT CREDIT	BALANCE SHEET DEBIT	BALANCE SHEET CREDIT	
31	Sales—Softball		38693030				38693030			31
32	Sales—Baseball		36680080				36680080			32
33	Sales Discount—Softball	286000				286000				33
34	Sales Discount—Baseball	243080				243080				34
35	Sales Ret. & Allow.—Softball	264030				264030				35
36	Sales Ret. & Allow.—Baseball	321000				321000				36
37	Purchases—Softball	20108690				20108690				37
38	Purchases—Baseball	18809800				18809800				38
39	Purchases Discount—Softball		339010				339010			39
40	Purchases Discount—Baseball		363000				363000			40
41	Purch. Ret. & Allow.—Softball		421080				421080			41
42	Purch. Ret. & Allow.—Baseball		396000				396000			42
43	Advertising Expense	573000				573000				43
44	Credit Card Fee Expense	516000				516000				44
45	Depr. Exp.—Store Equipment			(h) 260000		260000				45
46	Salary Expense—Softball	6830000				6830000				46
47	Salary Expense—Baseball	7250000				7250000				47
48	Supplies Expense—Store			(e) 526310		526310				48
49	Depr. Exp.—Office Equipment			(g) 120000		120000				49
50	Insurance Expense			(f) 575000		575000				50
51	Miscellaneous Expense	486000				486000				51
52	Payroll Taxes Expense	2560400				2560400				52
53	Rent Expense	2160000				2160000				53
54	Salary Expense—Administrative	4130000				4130000				54
55	Supplies Expense—Office			(d) 842970		842970				55
56	Uncollectible Accounts Expense			(a) 197040		197040				56
57	Federal Income Tax Expense	1190000		(i) 130245		1320245				57
58		129349820	129349820	5203465	5203465	70931465	76892200	59125640	53164905	58
59	Net Income after Federal Income Tax					5960735			5960735	59
60						76892200	76892200	59125640	59125640	60

4-8 **MASTERY PROBLEM (continued)**

Home Plate Sporting Goods

Income Statement

For Year Ended December 31, 20--

					% OF NET SALES
Operating Revenue:					
Sales:			753 7 3 1 10		
Less: Sales Discount		5 2 9 0 80			
Sales Returns & Allow.		5 8 5 0 30	11 1 4 1 10		
Net Sales				742 5 9 0 00	100.0
Cost of Merchandise Sold:					
Mdse. Inv., Jan. 1, 20--			467 4 2 0 00		
Purchases		389 1 8 4 90			
Less: Purchases Discount	7 0 2 0 10				
Purch. Returns & Allow.	8 1 7 0 80	15 1 9 0 90			
Net Purchases			373 9 9 4 00		
Total Cost of Mdse. Available			841 4 1 4 00		
Less Mdse. Inv., Dec. 31, 20--			441 9 0 1 00		
Cost of Merchandise Sold				399 5 1 3 00	53.8
Gross Profit on Operations				343 0 7 7 00	46.2
Operating Expenses:					
Selling Expenses:					
Advertising Expense		5 7 3 0 00			
Credit Card Fee Expense		5 1 6 0 00			
Depr. Exp.—Store Equipment		2 6 0 0 00			
Salary Expense—Softball		68 3 0 0 00			
Salary Expense—Baseball		72 5 0 0 00			
Supplies Expense—Store		5 2 6 3 10			
Total Selling Expenses			159 5 5 3 10		
Administrative Expenses:					
Depr. Exp.—Office Equipment		1 2 0 0 00			
Insurance Expense		5 7 5 0 00			
Miscellaneous Expense		4 8 6 0 00			
Payroll Taxes Expense		25 6 0 4 00			
Rent Expense		21 6 0 0 00			
Salary Expense—Administrative		41 3 0 0 00			

4-8 MASTERY PROBLEM (continued)

[3]

Home Plate Sporting Goods

Income Statement (continued)

For Year Ended December 31, 20--

							% OF NET SALES
Supplies Expense—Office			8 4 2 9 70				
Uncollectible Accounts Expense			1 9 7 0 40				
Total Administrative Expenses				110 7 1 4 10			
Total Operating Expenses						270 2 6 7 20	36.4
Net Income before Fed. Inc. Tax						72 8 0 9 80	9.8
Less Federal Income Tax Expense						13 2 0 2 45	
Net Income after Fed. Inc. Tax						59 6 0 7 35	8.0

[4]

Home Plate Sporting Goods

Statement of Stockholders' Equity

For Year Ended December 31, 20--

Capital Stock:			
$200.00 Per Share			
January 1, 20--, 1,500 Shares Issued		300 0 0 0 00	
Issued during Current Year, None		-0-	
Balance, December 31, 20--, 1,500 Shares Issued			300 0 0 0 00
Retained Earnings:			
Balance, January 1, 20--		155 0 0 0 00	
Net Income after Federal Income Tax for 20--	59 6 0 7 35		
Less Dividends Declared during 20--	30 0 0 0 00		
Net Increase during 20--		29 6 0 7 35	
Balance, December 31, 20--			184 6 0 7 35
Total Stockholders' Equity, December 31, 20--			484 6 0 7 35

4-8 MASTERY PROBLEM (continued)

Home Plate Sporting Goods

Balance Sheet

December 31, 20--

Assets															
Current Assets:															
Cash						38	5	6	0	40					
Petty Cash							6	0	0	00					
Accounts Receivable	26	3	6	4	20										
Less Allowance for Uncollectible Accounts	2	4	3	1	20	23	9	3	3	00					
Merchandise Inventory—Softball						205	3	8	0	20					
Merchandise Inventory—Baseball						236	5	2	0	80					
Supplies—Office						6	0	1	0	30					
Supplies—Store						4	2	2	0	50					
Prepaid Insurance						2	8	0	0	00					
Total Current Assets											518	0	2	5	20
Plant Assets:															
Office Equipment	17	9	4	0	00										
Less Accumulated Depr.—Office Equipment	10	5	6	0	00	7	3	8	0	00					
Store Equipment	22	8	6	0	00										
Less Accumulated Depr.—Store Equipment	14	0	3	0	00	8	8	3	0	00					
Total Plant Assets											16	2	1	0	00
Total Assets											534	2	3	5	20
Liabilities															
Current Liabilities:															
Accounts Payable						32	7	4	0	00					
Employee Income Tax Payable—Federal						1	3	4	0	90					
Employee Income Tax Payable—State							9	3	0	60					
Federal Income Tax Payable						1	3	0	2	45					
Social Security Tax Payable						1	9	1	7	50					
Medicare Tax Payable							4	4	2	50					
Sales Tax Payable						7	2	4	0	30					
Unemployment Tax Payable—Federal								2	2	40					
Unemployment Tax Payable—State							1	5	1	20					
Health Insurance Premiums Payable						3	5	4	0	00					
Total Liabilities											49	6	2	7	85

4-8 **MASTERY PROBLEM (continued)**

[5]

Home Plate Sporting Goods

Balance Sheet (continued)

December 31, 20--

Stockholders' Equity			
Capital Stock	300 0 0 0 00		
Retained Earnings	184 6 0 7 35		
Total Stockholders' Equity		484 6 0 7 35	
Total Liabilities & Stockholders' Equity		534 2 3 5 20	

Name _____ Date _____ Class _____

[6, 7]

GENERAL JOURNAL   PAGE 18

	DATE		ACCOUNT TITLE	DOC. NO.	POST. REF.	DEBIT	CREDIT	
1			*Adjusting Entries*					1
2	20— Dec.	31	Uncollectible Accounts Expense			1 9 7 0 40		2
3			Allowance for Uncollectible Accounts				1 9 7 0 40	3
4		31	Income Summary—Softball			14 7 9 9 80		4
5			Merchandise Inventory—Softball				14 7 9 9 80	5
6		31	Income Summary—Baseball			10 7 1 9 20		6
7			Merchandise Inventory—Baseball				10 7 1 9 20	7
8		31	Supplies Expense—Office			8 4 2 9 70		8
9			Supplies—Office				8 4 2 9 70	9
10		31	Supplies Expense—Store			5 2 6 3 10		10
11			Supplies—Store				5 2 6 3 10	11
12		31	Insurance Expense			5 7 5 0 00		12
13			Prepaid Insurance				5 7 5 0 00	13
14		31	Depreciation Expense—Office Equipment			1 2 0 0 00		14
15			Accum. Depreciation—Office Equipment				1 2 0 0 00	15
16		31	Depreciation Expense—Store Equipment			2 6 0 0 00		16
17			Accum. Depreciation—Store Equipment				2 6 0 0 00	17
18		31	Federal Income Tax Expense			1 3 0 2 45		18
19			Federal Income Tax Payable				1 3 0 2 45	19
20			*Closing Entries*					20
21		31	Sales—Softball			386 9 3 0 30		21
22			Sales—Baseball			366 8 0 0 80		22
23			Purchases Discount—Softball			3 3 9 0 10		23
24			Purchases Discount—Baseball			3 6 3 0 00		24
25			Purchases Returns and Allow.—Softball			4 2 1 0 80		25
26			Purchases Returns and Allow.—Baseball			3 9 6 0 00		26
27			Income Summary—General				768 9 2 2 00	27
28								28
29								29
30								30
31								31

4-8 MASTERY PROBLEM (concluded)

[7]

GENERAL JOURNAL   PAGE 19

	DATE		ACCOUNT TITLE	DOC. NO.	POST. REF.	DEBIT	CREDIT	
1	20— Dec.	31	Income Summary—General			709 31 4 65		1
2			Income Summary—Softball				14 79 9 80	2
3			Income Summary—Baseball				10 7 1 9 20	3
4			Sales Discount—Softball				2 8 6 0 00	4
5			Sales Discount—Baseball				2 4 3 0 80	5
6			Sales Returns and Allow.—Softball				2 6 4 0 30	6
7			Sales Returns and Allow.—Baseball				3 2 1 0 00	7
8			Purchases—Softball				201 0 8 6 90	8
9			Purchases—Baseball				188 0 9 8 00	9
10			Advertising Expense				5 7 3 0 00	10
11			Credit Card Fee Expense				5 1 6 0 00	11
12			Depreciation Expense—Store Equipment				2 6 0 0 00	12
13			Salary Expense—Softball				68 3 0 0 00	13
14			Salary Expense—Baseball				72 5 0 0 00	14
15			Supplies Expense—Store				5 2 6 3 10	15
16			Depreciation Expense—Office Equipment				1 2 0 0 00	16
17			Insurance Expense				5 7 5 0 00	17
18			Miscellaneous Expense				4 8 6 0 00	18
19			Payroll Taxes Expense				25 6 0 4 00	19
20			Rent Expense				21 6 0 0 00	20
21			Salary Expense—Administrative				41 3 0 0 00	21
22			Supplies Expense—Office				8 4 2 9 70	22
23			Uncollectible Accounts Expense				1 9 7 0 40	23
24			Federal Income Tax Expense				13 2 0 2 45	24
25		31	Income Summary—General			59 6 0 7 35		25
26			Retained Earnings				59 6 0 7 35	26
27		31	Retained Earnings			30 0 0 0 00		27
28			Dividends				30 0 0 0 00	28
29								29
30								30
31								31

4-8 MASTERY PROBLEM

Extra form

GENERAL JOURNAL

PAGE _____

	DATE		ACCOUNT TITLE	DOC. NO.	POST. REF.	DEBIT	CREDIT	
1								1
2								2
3								3
4								4
5								5
6								6
7								7
8								8
9								9
10								10
11								11
12								12
13								13
14								14
15								15
16								16
17								17
18								18
19								19
20								20
21								21
22								22
23								23
24								24
25								25
26								26
27								27
28								28
29								29
30								30
31								31

4-9 CHALLENGE PROBLEM, p. 130

Preparing a 10-column work sheet for a departmentalized business   [2]

(Note: The work sheet for this problem begins on page 146.)

Student answers may vary. The primary advantage of the 10-column work sheet is that only one step is performed in each set of columns. The Adjusted Trial Balance columns extend the amounts from the Trial Balance and Adjustments columns. From the Adjusted Trial Balance columns, amounts are extended to the proper statement columns (Income Statement or Balance Sheet).

The primary disadvantages are that additional errors may be made and two additional columns of numbers must be written and totaled.

4-9 CHALLENGE PROBLEM (continued)

White Cliff

Work

For Year Ended

	ACCOUNT TITLE	TRIAL BALANCE DEBIT (1)	TRIAL BALANCE CREDIT (2)	ADJUSTMENTS DEBIT (3)	ADJUSTMENTS CREDIT (4)	
1	Cash	26 30 0 71				1
2	Accounts Receivable	13 58 9 20				2
3	Allowance for Uncollectible Accts.		2 5 0 00		(a) 3 5 0 00	3
4	Mdse. Inventory—Skiing	111 78 6 00		(b) 3 6 4 4 00		4
5	Mdse. Inventory—Snowboarding	102 86 9 11			(c) 5 1 8 9 11	5
6	Supplies	3 5 7 0 00			(d) 1 1 9 3 00	6
7	Prepaid Insurance	1 2 0 0 00			(e) 7 0 0 00	7
8	Accounts Payable		57 98 6 00			8
9	Federal Income Tax Payable				(f) 3 9 5 18	9
10	Capital Stock		120 00 0 00			10
11	Dividends	10 00 0 00				11
12	Retained Earnings		59 72 3 02			12
13	Income Summary—Skiing				(b) 3 6 4 4 00	13
14	Income Summary—Snowboarding			(c) 5 1 8 9 11		14
15	Income Summary—General					15
16	Sales—Skiing		153 54 0 00			16
17	Sales—Snowboarding		118 73 2 00			17
18	Sales Ret. & Allow.—Skiing	1 64 8 00				18
19	Sales Ret. & Allow.—Snowboarding	9 6 0 00				19
20	Purchases—Skiing	110 03 0 00				20
21	Purchases—Snowboarding	85 67 0 00				21
22	Purch. Ret. & Allow.—Skiing		2 3 0 5 00			22
23	Purch. Ret. & Allow.—Snowboarding		1 7 8 6 00			23
24	Salary Expense—Skiing	26 75 9 00				24
25	Salary Expense—Snowboarding	15 54 0 00				25
26	Supplies Expense			(d) 1 1 9 3 00		26
27	Insurance Expense			(e) 7 0 0 00		27
28	Uncollectible Accounts Expense			(a) 3 5 0 00		28
29	Federal Income Tax Expense	4 40 0 00		(f) 3 9 5 18		29
30		514 32 2 02	514 32 2 02	11 4 7 1 29	11 4 7 1 29	30
31	*Net Income after Federal Income Tax*					31
32						32

4-9 CHALLENGE PROBLEM (concluded)

[1]

Sport Clothing
Sheet
December 31, 20--

	5 ADJUSTED TRIAL BALANCE DEBIT	6 CREDIT	7 INCOME STATEMENT DEBIT	8 CREDIT	9 BALANCE SHEET DEBIT	10 CREDIT	
1	26 30 0 71				26 30 0 71		1
2	13 58 9 20				13 58 9 20		2
3		6 00 00				6 00 00	3
4	115 43 0 00				115 43 0 00		4
5	97 68 0 00				97 68 0 00		5
6	2 37 7 00				2 37 7 00		6
7	5 00 00				5 00 00		7
8		57 98 6 00				57 98 6 00	8
9		3 95 18				3 95 18	9
10		120 00 0 00				120 00 0 00	10
11	10 00 0 00				10 00 0 00		11
12		59 72 3 02				59 72 3 02	12
13		3 64 4 00		3 64 4 00			13
14	5 18 9 11		5 18 9 11				14
15							15
16		153 54 0 00		153 54 0 00			16
17		118 73 2 00		118 73 2 00			17
18	1 64 8 00		1 64 8 00				18
19	96 0 00		96 0 00				19
20	110 03 0 00		110 03 0 00				20
21	85 67 0 00		85 67 0 00				21
22		2 30 5 00		2 30 5 00			22
23		1 78 6 00		1 78 6 00			23
24	26 75 9 00		26 75 9 00				24
25	15 54 0 00		15 54 0 00				25
26	1 19 3 00		1 19 3 00				26
27	7 00 00		7 00 00				27
28	3 50 00		3 50 00				28
29	4 79 5 18		4 79 5 18				29
30	518 71 1 20	518 71 1 20	252 83 4 29	280 00 7 00	265 87 6 91	238 70 4 20	30
31			27 17 2 71			27 17 2 71	31
32			280 00 7 00	280 00 7 00	265 87 6 91	265 87 6 91	32

4-9 CHALLENGE PROBLEM

Extra form

1 REINFORCEMENT ACTIVITY, p. 135

[1]

ESTIMATED MERCHANDISE INVENTORY SHEET
Gross Profit Method

DEPARTMENT _Books_   DATE _11/30/--_

1	Beginning inventory, January 1	$	164,164.20
2	Net purchases to date		146,846.80
3	Merchandise available for sale	$	311,011.00
4	Net sales to date	$ 233,660.15	
5	Less estimated gross profit	105,147.07	
	(Net sales × Estimated gross profit _45.0_%)		
6	Estimated cost of merchandise sold		128,513.08
7	Estimated ending inventory	$	182,497.92

ESTIMATED MERCHANDISE INVENTORY SHEET
Gross Profit Method

DEPARTMENT _Supplies_   DATE _11/30/--_

1	Beginning inventory, January 1	$	147,840.30
2	Net purchases to date		144,611.78
3	Merchandise available for sale	$	292,452.08
4	Net sales to date	$ 240,410.70	
5	Less estimated gross profit	108,184.82	
	(Net sales × Estimated gross profit _45.0_%)		
6	Estimated cost of merchandise sold		132,225.88
7	Estimated ending inventory	$	160,226.20

1 REINFORCEMENT ACTIVITY (continued)

[2]

Campus Books, Inc.

Interim Departmental Statement of Gross Profit

For Month Ended November 30, 20--

	BOOKS	% OF NET SALES	SUPPLIES	% OF NET SALES	TOTAL	% OF NET SALES
Operating Revenue:						
Net Sales	19,480.60	100.0	20,240.30	100.0	39,720.90	100.0
Cost of Merchandise Sold:						
Est. Mdse. Inv., Nov. 1	180,205.05		157,195.78		337,400.83	
Net Purchases	13,007.20		14,162.58		27,169.78	
Mdse. Available for Sale	193,212.25		171,358.36		364,570.61	
Less Est. End. Inv., Nov. 30	182,497.92		160,226.20		342,724.12	
Cost of Merchandise Sold	10,714.33	55.0	11,132.16	55.0	21,846.49	55.0
Gross Profit on Operations	8,766.27	45.0	9,108.14	45.0	17,874.41	45.0

1 REINFORCEMENT ACTIVITY (continued)

[3, 5, 6]

SALES JOURNAL PAGE 12

	DATE	ACCOUNT DEBITED	SALE NO.	POST. REF.	ACCOUNTS RECEIVABLE DEBIT	SALES TAX PAYABLE CREDIT	SALES CREDIT BOOKS	SALES CREDIT SUPPLIES	
1	20-- Dec. 5	Matthew Barasso	97	120	924 00	44 00	880 00		1
2	13	Marcello Amco	98	110	472 50	22 50		450 00	2
3	22	Renville Public Schools	99	190	4750 00			4750 00	3
4	23	Brian Fadstad	100	140	1806 00	86 00	1720 00		4
5	23	Janelle Kamschorr	101	170	966 00	46 00		920 00	5
6	26	Donald Lindgren	102	180	567 00	27 00		540 00	6
7	28	Donald Lindgren	103	180	682 50	32 50	650 00		7
8	31	Gilmore Public Schools	104	150	6200 00		6200 00		8
9	31	Totals			16368 00	258 00	9450 00	6660 00	9
10					(1115)	(2130)	(4105-1)	(4105-2)	10

SALES RETURNS AND ALLOWANCES JOURNAL PAGE 12

	DATE	ACCOUNT CREDITED	CREDIT MEMO. NO.	POST. REF.	ACCOUNTS RECEIVABLE CREDIT	SALES TAX PAYABLE DEBIT	SALES RETURNS AND ALLOWANCES DEBIT BOOKS	SALES RETURNS AND ALLOWANCES DEBIT SUPPLIES	
1	20-- Dec. 2	Gilmore Public Schools	31	150	250 00			250 00	1
2	3	Belinda Judd	32	160	78 75	3 75	75 00		2
3	9	Matthew Barasso	33	120	105 00	5 00	100 00		3
4	31	Renville Public Schools	34	190	1500 00			1500 00	4
5	31	Totals			1933 75	8 75	175 00	1750 00	5
6					(1115)	(2130)	(4115-1)	(4115-2)	6

1 REINFORCEMENT ACTIVITY (continued)

[3, 7]

PURCHASES JOURNAL
PAGE 12

	DATE		ACCOUNT CREDITED	PURCH. NO.	POST. REF.	ACCOUNTS PAYABLE CREDIT (1)	PURCHASES DEBIT BOOKS (2)	PURCHASES DEBIT SUPPLIES (3)	
1	20-- Dec.	2	Oliver Books, Inc.	115	260	1 9 3 3 00	1 9 3 3 00		1
2		22	Strup Supplies	116	270	1 6 4 7 00		1 6 4 7 00	2
3		22	A-1 Supplies	117	210	1 2 7 8 50		1 2 7 8 50	3
4		24	CBG Distributors	118	220	1 5 0 0 00	1 5 0 0 00		4
5		27	Maryland Books & Supplies	119	250	2 4 4 0 50	2 4 4 0 50		5
6		27	Grandway Products	120	230	3 1 5 7 99		3 1 5 7 99	6
7		31	Totals			11 9 5 6 99	5 8 7 3 50	6 0 8 3 49	7
8						(2105)	(5105-1)	(5105-2)	8
9									9

PURCHASES RETURNS AND ALLOWANCES JOURNAL
PAGE 12

	DATE		ACCOUNT DEBITED	DEBIT MEMO. NO.	POST. REF.	ACCOUNTS PAYABLE DEBIT (1)	PURCHASES RETURNS AND ALLOWANCES CREDIT BOOKS (2)	PURCHASES RETURNS AND ALLOWANCES CREDIT SUPPLIES (3)	
1	20-- Dec.	5	H&B Books	58	240	1 4 3 5 00	1 4 3 5 00		1
2		7	Oliver Books, Inc.	59	260	3 0 0 00	3 0 0 00		2
3		26	A-1 Supplies	60	210	2 6 5 00		2 6 5 00	3
4		31	Totals			2 0 0 0 00	1 7 3 5 00	2 6 5 00	4
5						(2105)	(5115-1)	(5115-2)	5
6									6

[3]

GENERAL JOURNAL
PAGE 12

	DATE		ACCOUNT TITLE	DOC. NO.	POST. REF.	DEBIT	CREDIT	
1	20-- Dec.	1	Payroll Taxes Expense	M40	6220	9 6 4 38		1
2			Social Security Tax Payable		2125		7 4 5 09	2
3			Medicare Tax Payable		2128		1 7 1 94	3
4			Unemployment Tax Payable—Federal		2135		6 11	4
5			Unemployment Tax Payable—State		2140		4 1 24	5
6								6

[3, 5, 8, 10]

CASH RECEIPTS JOURNAL

PAGE 23

DATE	ACCOUNT TITLE	DOC. NO.	POST. REF.	GENERAL DEBIT	GENERAL CREDIT	ACCOUNTS RECEIVABLE CREDIT	SALES TAX PAYABLE DEBIT	SALES TAX PAYABLE CREDIT	SALES CREDIT BOOKS	SALES CREDIT SUPPLIES	SALES DISCOUNT DEBIT BOOKS	SALES DISCOUNT DEBIT SUPPLIES	CASH DEBIT
20-- Dec. 3	✓	T3						25333	247800	258850			531983
5	Tanya Dockman	R139	130			50400	48					960	49392
8	Gilmore Public Schools	R140	150			599020						11980	587040
8	Belinda Judd	R141	160			18375	18				350		18007
8	Renville Public Schools	R142	190			958150					19163		938987
10	✓	T10						42983	494650	365000			902633
15	Matthew Barasso	R143	120			81900	78				1560		80262
17	✓	T17						35306	382060	324050			741416
23	Marcello Amco	R144	110			47250	45					900	46305
24	✓	T24						37903	416010	342050			795963
31	✓	T31						30302	358040	248000			636342
31	Totals					1755095	189	171827	1898560	1537950	21073	13840	5328330
						(1115)	(2130)	(2130)	(4105-1)	(4105-2)	(4110-1)	(4110-2)	(1105)

1 REINFORCEMENT ACTIVITY (continued)

[3, 5, 8, 11]

CASH PAYMENTS JOURNAL

PAGE 23

	DATE	ACCOUNT TITLE	CK. NO.	POST. REF.	GENERAL DEBIT	GENERAL CREDIT	ACCOUNTS PAYABLE DEBIT	PURCH. DISCOUNT CR. BOOKS	PURCH. DISCOUNT CR. SUPPLIES	CASH CREDIT
1	Dec. 1	Salary Expense—Books	340	6120-1	4522220					785971
2		Salary Expense—Supplies		6120-2	431040					
3		Salary Expense—Administrative		6230	263025					
4		Employee Inc. Tax Pay.—Federal		2110		120451				
5		Employee Inc. Tax Pay.—State		2115		53760				
6		Social Security Tax Payable		2125		74509				
7		Medicare Tax Payable		2128		17194				
8		Health Insurance Prem. Payable		2145		94400				
9	1	Rent Expense	341	6225	120000					120000
10	2	Supplies—Office	342	1130	13500					13500
11	6	CBG Distributors	343	220			223010	4460		218550
12	7	H&B Books	344	240			399515	7990		391525
13	8	Maryland Books & Supplies	345	250			56540		1131	55409
14	9	Oliver Books, Inc.	346	260			492020	9840		482180
15	12	Oliver Books, Inc.	347	260			163300	3266		160034
16	15	Employee Inc. Tax Pay.—Federal	348	2110	124080					282370
17		Social Security Tax Payable		2125	128611					
18		Medicare Tax Payable		2128	29679					
19	15	Federal Income Tax Expense	349	7105	120000					120000
20	30	Miscellaneous Expense	M41	6215	1140					1140
21	30	Credit Card Fee Expense	M42	6110	35420					35420
22	31	Supplies—Store	350	1135	14500					41500
23		Advertising Expense		6105	16000					
24		Miscellaneous Expense		6215	11000					
25	31	Totals			1760215	360314	1334385	25556	1131	2707599
26					(✓)	(✓)	(2105)	(5110-1)	(5110-2)	(1105)

Name _____ Date _____ Class _____

GENERAL LEDGER

ACCOUNT Cash   ACCOUNT NO. 1105

DATE	ITEM	POST. REF.	DEBIT	CREDIT	BALANCE DEBIT	BALANCE CREDIT
20-- Dec. 1	Balance	✓			35 1 9 0 60	
31		CR23	53 2 8 3 30		88 4 7 3 90	
31		CP23		27 0 7 5 99	61 3 9 7 91	

ACCOUNT Petty Cash   ACCOUNT NO. 1110

DATE	ITEM	POST. REF.	DEBIT	CREDIT	BALANCE DEBIT	BALANCE CREDIT
20-- Dec. 1	Balance	✓			5 0 0 00	

ACCOUNT Accounts Receivable   ACCOUNT NO. 1115

DATE	ITEM	POST. REF.	DEBIT	CREDIT	BALANCE DEBIT	BALANCE CREDIT
20-- Dec. 1	Balance	✓			16 5 8 8 20	
31		S12	16 3 6 8 00		32 9 5 6 20	
31		SR12		1 9 3 3 75	31 0 2 2 45	
31		CR23		17 5 5 0 95	13 4 7 1 50	

ACCOUNT Allowance for Uncollectible Accounts   ACCOUNT NO. 1120

DATE	ITEM	POST. REF.	DEBIT	CREDIT	BALANCE DEBIT	BALANCE CREDIT
20-- Dec. 1	Balance	✓				3 4 0 20
31		G13		2 4 1 2 57		2 7 5 2 77

ACCOUNT Merchandise Inventory—Books   ACCOUNT NO. 1125-1

DATE	ITEM	POST. REF.	DEBIT	CREDIT	BALANCE DEBIT	BALANCE CREDIT
20-- Jan. 1	Balance	✓			164 1 6 4 20	
Dec. 31		G13	10 3 0 5 05		174 4 6 9 25	

ACCOUNT Merchandise Inventory—Supplies   ACCOUNT NO. 1125-2

DATE	ITEM	POST. REF.	DEBIT	CREDIT	BALANCE DEBIT	BALANCE CREDIT
20-- Jan. 1	Balance	✓			147 8 4 0 30	
Dec. 31		G13	3 5 9 9 55		151 4 3 9 85	

ACCOUNT Supplies—Office   ACCOUNT NO. 1130

DATE	ITEM	POST. REF.	DEBIT	CREDIT	BALANCE DEBIT	BALANCE CREDIT
20-- Dec. 1	Balance	✓			6 0 8 0 20	
2		CP23	1 3 5 00		6 2 1 5 20	
31		G13		1 5 8 0 20	4 6 3 5 00	

1 REINFORCEMENT ACTIVITY (continued)

[3, 5–7, 9–11, 19, 20]

GENERAL LEDGER

ACCOUNT Supplies—Store   **ACCOUNT NO.** 1135

DATE		ITEM	POST. REF.	DEBIT	CREDIT	BALANCE DEBIT	BALANCE CREDIT
20-- Dec.	1	Balance	✓			4 9 6 0 80	
	31		CP23	1 4 5 00		5 1 0 5 80	
	31		G13		1 1 4 5 80	3 9 6 0 00	

ACCOUNT Prepaid Insurance   **ACCOUNT NO.** 1140

DATE		ITEM	POST. REF.	DEBIT	CREDIT	BALANCE DEBIT	BALANCE CREDIT
20-- Dec.	1	Balance	✓			5 2 8 0 00	
	31		G13		8 8 0 00	4 4 0 0 00	

ACCOUNT Office Equipment   **ACCOUNT NO.** 1205

DATE		ITEM	POST. REF.	DEBIT	CREDIT	BALANCE DEBIT	BALANCE CREDIT
20-- Dec.	1	Balance	✓			19 2 1 0 00	

ACCOUNT Accumulated Depreciation—Office Equipment   **ACCOUNT NO.** 1210

DATE		ITEM	POST. REF.	DEBIT	CREDIT	BALANCE DEBIT	BALANCE CREDIT
20-- Dec.	1	Balance	✓				8 7 6 0 00
	31		G13		8 7 0 00		9 6 3 0 00

ACCOUNT Store Equipment   **ACCOUNT NO.** 1215

DATE		ITEM	POST. REF.	DEBIT	CREDIT	BALANCE DEBIT	BALANCE CREDIT
20-- Dec.	1	Balance	✓			21 1 8 0 00	

ACCOUNT Accumulated Depreciation—Store Equipment   **ACCOUNT NO.** 1220

DATE		ITEM	POST. REF.	DEBIT	CREDIT	BALANCE DEBIT	BALANCE CREDIT
20-- Dec.	1	Balance	✓				13 6 2 0 00
	31		G13		9 4 0 00		14 5 6 0 00

ACCOUNT Accounts Payable   **ACCOUNT NO.** 2105

DATE		ITEM	POST. REF.	DEBIT	CREDIT	BALANCE DEBIT	BALANCE CREDIT
20-- Dec.	1	Balance	✓				13 1 4 5 85
	31		P12		11 9 5 6 99		25 1 0 2 84
	31		PR12	2 0 0 0 00			23 1 0 2 84
	31		CP23	13 3 4 3 85			9 7 5 8 99

1 REINFORCEMENT ACTIVITY (continued)

[3, 5–7, 9–11, 19, 20]

GENERAL LEDGER

ACCOUNT Employee Income Tax Payable—Federal   ACCOUNT NO. 2110

DATE		ITEM	POST. REF.	DEBIT	CREDIT	BALANCE DEBIT	BALANCE CREDIT
20-- Dec.	1	Balance	✓				1 2 4 0 80
	1		CP23		1 2 0 4 51		2 4 4 5 31
	15		CP23	1 2 4 0 80			1 2 0 4 51

ACCOUNT Employee Income Tax Payable—State   ACCOUNT NO. 2115

DATE		ITEM	POST. REF.	DEBIT	CREDIT	BALANCE DEBIT	BALANCE CREDIT
20-- Dec.	1	Balance	✓				5 6 5 40
	1		CP23		5 3 7 60		1 1 0 3 00

ACCOUNT Federal Income Tax Payable   ACCOUNT NO. 2120

DATE		ITEM	POST. REF.	DEBIT	CREDIT	BALANCE DEBIT	BALANCE CREDIT
20-- Dec.	31		G13		2 1 3 75		2 1 3 75

ACCOUNT Social Security Tax Payable   ACCOUNT NO. 2125

DATE		ITEM	POST. REF.	DEBIT	CREDIT	BALANCE DEBIT	BALANCE CREDIT
20-- Dec.	1	Balance	✓				1 2 8 6 11
	1		G12		7 4 5 09		2 0 3 1 20
	1		CP23		7 4 5 09		2 7 7 6 29
	15		CP23	1 2 8 6 11			1 4 9 0 18

ACCOUNT Medicare Tax Payable   ACCOUNT NO. 2128

DATE		ITEM	POST. REF.	DEBIT	CREDIT	BALANCE DEBIT	BALANCE CREDIT
20-- Dec.	1	Balance	✓				2 9 6 79
	1		G12		1 7 1 94		4 6 8 73
	1		CP23		1 7 1 94		6 4 0 67
	15		CP23	2 9 6 79			3 4 3 88

ACCOUNT Sales Tax Payable   ACCOUNT NO. 2130

DATE		ITEM	POST. REF.	DEBIT	CREDIT	BALANCE DEBIT	BALANCE CREDIT
20-- Dec.	1	Balance	✓				2 5 7 0 30
	31		S12		2 5 8 00		2 8 2 8 30
	31		SR12	8 75			2 8 1 9 55
	31		CR23	1 89			2 8 1 7 66
	31		CR23		1 7 1 8 27		4 5 3 5 93

1 REINFORCEMENT ACTIVITY (continued)

[3, 5–7, 9–11, 19, 20]

GENERAL LEDGER

ACCOUNT Unemployment Tax Payable—Federal   ACCOUNT NO. 2135

DATE		ITEM	POST. REF.	DEBIT	CREDIT	BALANCE DEBIT	BALANCE CREDIT
20-- Dec.	1	Balance	✓				3 2 80
	1		G12		6 11		3 8 91

ACCOUNT Unemployment Tax Payable—State   ACCOUNT NO. 2140

DATE		ITEM	POST. REF.	DEBIT	CREDIT	BALANCE DEBIT	BALANCE CREDIT
20-- Dec.	1	Balance	✓				2 2 1 40
	1		G12		4 1 24		2 6 2 64

ACCOUNT Health Insurance Premiums Payable   ACCOUNT NO. 2145

DATE		ITEM	POST. REF.	DEBIT	CREDIT	BALANCE DEBIT	BALANCE CREDIT
20-- Dec.	1	Balance	✓				1 8 8 8 00
	1		CP23		9 4 4 00		2 8 3 2 00

ACCOUNT Dividends Payable   ACCOUNT NO. 2150

DATE		ITEM	POST. REF.	DEBIT	CREDIT	BALANCE DEBIT	BALANCE CREDIT

ACCOUNT Capital Stock   ACCOUNT NO. 3105

DATE		ITEM	POST. REF.	DEBIT	CREDIT	BALANCE DEBIT	BALANCE CREDIT
20-- Jan.	1	Balance	✓				300 0 0 0 00

ACCOUNT Retained Earnings   ACCOUNT NO. 3110

DATE		ITEM	POST. REF.	DEBIT	CREDIT	BALANCE DEBIT	BALANCE CREDIT
20-- Jan.	1	Balance	✓				97 5 2 5 70
Dec.	31		G14		28 4 1 1 25		125 9 3 6 95
	31		G14	20 0 0 0 00			105 9 3 6 95

ACCOUNT Dividends   ACCOUNT NO. 3115

DATE		ITEM	POST. REF.	DEBIT	CREDIT	BALANCE DEBIT	BALANCE CREDIT
20-- Dec.	1	Balance	✓			20 0 0 0 00	
	31		G14		20 0 0 0 00		

1 REINFORCEMENT ACTIVITY (continued)

[3, 5–7, 9–11, 19, 20]

GENERAL LEDGER

ACCOUNT Income Summary—Books   **ACCOUNT NO.** 3120-1

DATE	ITEM	POST. REF.	DEBIT	CREDIT	BALANCE DEBIT	BALANCE CREDIT
20-- Dec. 31		G13		10 3 0 5 05		10 3 0 5 05
31		G13	10 3 0 5 05		—	—

ACCOUNT Income Summary—Supplies   **ACCOUNT NO.** 3120-2

DATE	ITEM	POST. REF.	DEBIT	CREDIT	BALANCE DEBIT	BALANCE CREDIT
20-- Dec. 31		G13		3 5 9 9 55		3 5 9 9 55
31		G13	3 5 9 9 55		—	—

ACCOUNT Income Summary—General   **ACCOUNT NO.** 3125

DATE	ITEM	POST. REF.	DEBIT	CREDIT	BALANCE DEBIT	BALANCE CREDIT
20-- Dec. 31		G13		521 6 8 9 57		521 6 8 9 57
31		G14	493 2 7 8 32			28 4 1 1 25
31		G14	28 4 1 1 25		—	—

ACCOUNT Sales—Books   **ACCOUNT NO.** 4105-1

DATE	ITEM	POST. REF.	DEBIT	CREDIT	BALANCE DEBIT	BALANCE CREDIT
20-- Dec. 1	Balance	✓				216 9 2 0 30
31		S12		9 4 5 0 00		226 3 7 0 30
31		CR23		18 9 8 5 60		245 3 5 5 90
31		G13	245 3 5 5 90		—	—

ACCOUNT Sales—Supplies   **ACCOUNT NO.** 4105-2

DATE	ITEM	POST. REF.	DEBIT	CREDIT	BALANCE DEBIT	BALANCE CREDIT
20-- Dec. 1	Balance	✓				223 6 1 0 90
31		S12		6 6 6 0 00		230 2 7 0 90
31		CR23		15 3 7 9 50		245 6 5 0 40
31		G13	245 6 5 0 40		—	—

ACCOUNT Sales Discount—Books   **ACCOUNT NO.** 4110-1

DATE	ITEM	POST. REF.	DEBIT	CREDIT	BALANCE DEBIT	BALANCE CREDIT
20-- Dec. 1	Balance	✓			1 4 8 0 75	
31		CR23	2 1 0 73		1 6 9 1 48	
31		G14		1 6 9 1 48	—	—

1 REINFORCEMENT ACTIVITY (continued)

[3, 5–7, 9–11, 19, 20]

GENERAL LEDGER

ACCOUNT Sales Discount—Supplies   ACCOUNT NO. 4110-2

DATE		ITEM	POST. REF.	DEBIT	CREDIT	BALANCE DEBIT	BALANCE CREDIT
20-- Dec.	1	Balance	✓			1 8 1 0 30	
	31		CR23	1 3 8 40		1 9 4 8 70	
	31		G14		1 9 4 8 70	——	——

ACCOUNT Sales Returns and Allowances—Books   ACCOUNT NO. 4115-1

DATE		ITEM	POST. REF.	DEBIT	CREDIT	BALANCE DEBIT	BALANCE CREDIT
20-- Dec.	1	Balance	✓			1 7 6 0 00	
	31		SR12	1 7 5 00		1 9 3 5 00	
	31		G14		1 9 3 5 00	——	——

ACCOUNT Sales Returns and Allowances—Supplies   ACCOUNT NO. 4115-2

DATE		ITEM	POST. REF.	DEBIT	CREDIT	BALANCE DEBIT	BALANCE CREDIT
20-- Dec.	1	Balance	✓			2 1 3 0 20	
	31		SR12	1 7 5 0 00		3 8 8 0 20	
	31		G14		3 8 8 0 20	——	——

ACCOUNT Purchases—Books   ACCOUNT NO. 5105-1

DATE		ITEM	POST. REF.	DEBIT	CREDIT	BALANCE DEBIT	BALANCE CREDIT
20-- Dec.	1	Balance	✓			140 3 1 0 40	
	31		P12	5 8 7 3 50		146 1 8 3 90	
	31		G14		146 1 8 3 90	——	——

ACCOUNT Purchases—Supplies   ACCOUNT NO. 5105-2

DATE		ITEM	POST. REF.	DEBIT	CREDIT	BALANCE DEBIT	BALANCE CREDIT
20-- Dec.	1	Balance	✓			137 4 9 0 20	
	31		P12	6 0 8 3 49		143 5 7 3 69	
	31		G14		143 5 7 3 69	——	——

ACCOUNT Purchases Discount—Books   ACCOUNT NO. 5110-1

DATE		ITEM	POST. REF.	DEBIT	CREDIT	BALANCE DEBIT	BALANCE CREDIT
20-- Dec.	1	Balance	✓				3 1 6 0 80
	31		CP23		2 5 5 56		3 4 1 6 36
	31		G13	3 4 1 6 36		——	——

Name _____ Date _____ Class _____

1 REINFORCEMENT ACTIVITY (continued)

[3, 5–7, 9–11, 19, 20]

GENERAL LEDGER

ACCOUNT Purchases Discount—Supplies   ACCOUNT NO. 5110-2

DATE		ITEM	POST. REF.	DEBIT	CREDIT	BALANCE DEBIT	BALANCE CREDIT
20-- Dec.	1	Balance	✓				3 4 2 0 30
	31		CP23		1 1 31		3 4 3 1 61
	31		G13	3 4 3 1 61		—	—

ACCOUNT Purchases Returns and Allowances—Books   ACCOUNT NO. 5115-1

DATE		ITEM	POST. REF.	DEBIT	CREDIT	BALANCE DEBIT	BALANCE CREDIT
20-- Dec.	1	Balance	✓				3 8 1 0 00
	31		PR12		1 7 3 5 00		5 5 4 5 00
	31		G13	5 5 4 5 00		—	—

ACCOUNT Purchases Returns and Allowances—Supplies   ACCOUNT NO. 5115-2

DATE		ITEM	POST. REF.	DEBIT	CREDIT	BALANCE DEBIT	BALANCE CREDIT
20-- Dec.	1	Balance	✓				4 1 2 0 70
	31		PR12		2 6 5 00		4 3 8 5 70
	31		G13	4 3 8 5 70		—	—

ACCOUNT Advertising Expense   ACCOUNT NO. 6105

DATE		ITEM	POST. REF.	DEBIT	CREDIT	BALANCE DEBIT	BALANCE CREDIT
20-- Dec.	1	Balance	✓			4 9 7 0 20	
	31		CP23	1 6 0 00		5 1 3 0 20	
	31		G14		5 1 3 0 20	—	—

ACCOUNT Credit Card Fee Expense   ACCOUNT NO. 6110

DATE		ITEM	POST. REF.	DEBIT	CREDIT	BALANCE DEBIT	BALANCE CREDIT
20-- Dec.	1	Balance	✓			4 8 9 0 60	
	30		CP23	3 5 4 20		5 2 4 4 80	
	31		G14		5 2 4 4 80	—	—

ACCOUNT Depreciation Expense—Store Equipment   ACCOUNT NO. 6115

DATE		ITEM	POST. REF.	DEBIT	CREDIT	BALANCE DEBIT	BALANCE CREDIT
20-- Dec.	31		G13	9 4 0 00		9 4 0 00	
	31		G14		9 4 0 00	—	—

1 ▪ REINFORCEMENT ACTIVITY (continued)

[3, 5–7, 9–11, 19, 20]

GENERAL LEDGER

ACCOUNT Salary Expense—Books   **ACCOUNT NO.** 6120-1

DATE	ITEM	POST. REF.	DEBIT	CREDIT	BALANCE DEBIT	BALANCE CREDIT
20-- Dec. 1	Balance	✓			49 5 0 0 00	
1		CP23	4 5 2 2 20		54 0 2 2 20	
31		G14		54 0 2 2 20	—	—

ACCOUNT Salary Expense—Supplies   **ACCOUNT NO.** 6120-2

DATE	ITEM	POST. REF.	DEBIT	CREDIT	BALANCE DEBIT	BALANCE CREDIT
20-- Dec. 1	Balance	✓			46 2 0 0 00	
1		CP23	4 3 1 0 40		50 5 1 0 40	
31		G14		50 5 1 0 40	—	—

ACCOUNT Supplies Expense—Store   **ACCOUNT NO.** 6125

DATE	ITEM	POST. REF.	DEBIT	CREDIT	BALANCE DEBIT	BALANCE CREDIT
20-- Dec. 31		G13	1 1 4 5 80		1 1 4 5 80	
31		G14		1 1 4 5 80	—	—

ACCOUNT Depreciation Expense—Office Equipment   **ACCOUNT NO.** 6205

DATE	ITEM	POST. REF.	DEBIT	CREDIT	BALANCE DEBIT	BALANCE CREDIT
20-- Dec. 31		G13	8 7 0 00		8 7 0 00	
31		G14		8 7 0 00	—	—

ACCOUNT Insurance Expense   **ACCOUNT NO.** 6210

DATE	ITEM	POST. REF.	DEBIT	CREDIT	BALANCE DEBIT	BALANCE CREDIT
20-- Dec. 31		G13	8 8 0 00		8 8 0 00	
31		G14		8 8 0 00	—	—

ACCOUNT Miscellaneous Expense   **ACCOUNT NO.** 6215

DATE	ITEM	POST. REF.	DEBIT	CREDIT	BALANCE DEBIT	BALANCE CREDIT
20-- Dec. 1	Balance	✓			5 2 0 8 80	
30		CP23	1 1 40		5 2 2 0 20	
31		CP23	1 1 0 00		5 3 3 0 20	
31		G14		5 3 3 0 20	—	—

1 REINFORCEMENT ACTIVITY (continued)

[3, 5–7, 9–11, 19, 20]

GENERAL LEDGER

ACCOUNT Payroll Taxes Expense   ACCOUNT NO. 6220

DATE		ITEM	POST. REF.	DEBIT	CREDIT	BALANCE DEBIT	BALANCE CREDIT
20-- Dec.	1	Balance	✓			14 3 9 0 60	
	1		G12	9 6 4 38		15 3 5 4 98	
	31		G14		15 3 5 4 98	—	—

ACCOUNT Rent Expense   ACCOUNT NO. 6225

DATE		ITEM	POST. REF.	DEBIT	CREDIT	BALANCE DEBIT	BALANCE CREDIT
20-- Dec.	1	Balance	✓			13 2 0 0 00	
	1		CP23	1 2 0 0 00		14 4 0 0 00	
	31		G14		14 4 0 0 00	—	—

ACCOUNT Salary Expense—Administrative   ACCOUNT NO. 6230

DATE		ITEM	POST. REF.	DEBIT	CREDIT	BALANCE DEBIT	BALANCE CREDIT
20-- Dec.	1	Balance	✓			28 6 0 0 00	
	1		CP23	2 6 3 0 25		31 2 3 0 25	
	31		G14		31 2 3 0 25	—	—

ACCOUNT Supplies Expense—Office   ACCOUNT NO. 6235

DATE		ITEM	POST. REF.	DEBIT	CREDIT	BALANCE DEBIT	BALANCE CREDIT
20-- Dec.	31		G13	1 5 8 0 20		1 5 8 0 20	
	31		G14		1 5 8 0 20	—	—

ACCOUNT Uncollectible Accounts Expense   ACCOUNT NO. 6240

DATE		ITEM	POST. REF.	DEBIT	CREDIT	BALANCE DEBIT	BALANCE CREDIT
20-- Dec.	31		G13	2 4 1 2 57		2 4 1 2 57	
	31		G14		2 4 1 2 57	—	—

ACCOUNT Federal Income Tax Expense   ACCOUNT NO. 7105

DATE		ITEM	POST. REF.	DEBIT	CREDIT	BALANCE DEBIT	BALANCE CREDIT
20-- Dec.	1	Balance	✓			3 6 0 0 00	
	15		CP23	1 2 0 0 00		4 8 0 0 00	
	31		G13	2 1 3 75		5 0 1 3 75	
	31		G14		5 0 1 3 75	—	—

1 REINFORCEMENT ACTIVITY (continued)

[3, 5]

ACCOUNTS RECEIVABLE LEDGER

CUSTOMER Marcello Amco   CUSTOMER NO. 110

DATE		ITEM	POST. REF.	DEBIT	CREDIT	DEBIT BALANCE
20-- Dec.	13		S12	4 7 2 50		4 7 2 50
	23		CR23		4 7 2 50	—

CUSTOMER Matthew Barasso   CUSTOMER NO. 120

DATE		ITEM	POST. REF.	DEBIT	CREDIT	DEBIT BALANCE
20-- Dec.	5		S12	9 2 4 00		9 2 4 00
	9		SR12		1 0 5 00	8 1 9 00
	15		CR23		8 1 9 00	—

CUSTOMER Tanya Dockman   CUSTOMER NO. 130

DATE		ITEM	POST. REF.	DEBIT	CREDIT	DEBIT BALANCE
20-- Dec.	1	Balance	✓			5 0 4 00
	5		CR23		5 0 4 00	—

CUSTOMER Brian Fadstad   CUSTOMER NO. 140

DATE		ITEM	POST. REF.	DEBIT	CREDIT	DEBIT BALANCE
20-- Dec.	23		S12	1 8 0 6 00		1 8 0 6 00

CUSTOMER Gilmore Public Schools   CUSTOMER NO. 150

DATE		ITEM	POST. REF.	DEBIT	CREDIT	DEBIT BALANCE
20-- Dec.	1	Balance	✓			6 2 4 0 20
	2		SR12		2 5 0 00	5 9 9 0 20
	8		CR23		5 9 9 0 20	—
	31		S12	6 2 0 0 00		6 2 0 0 00

CUSTOMER Belinda Judd   CUSTOMER NO. 160

DATE		ITEM	POST. REF.	DEBIT	CREDIT	DEBIT BALANCE
20-- Dec.	1	Balance	✓			2 6 2 50
	3		SR12		7 8 75	1 8 3 75
	8		CR23		1 8 3 75	—

1 REINFORCEMENT ACTIVITY (continued)

[3, 5]

ACCOUNTS RECEIVABLE LEDGER

CUSTOMER Janelle Kamschorr   **CUSTOMER NO.** 170

DATE	ITEM	POST. REF.	DEBIT	CREDIT	DEBIT BALANCE
20-- Dec. 23		S12	9 6 6 00		9 6 6 00

CUSTOMER Donald Lindgren   **CUSTOMER NO.** 180

DATE	ITEM	POST. REF.	DEBIT	CREDIT	DEBIT BALANCE
20-- Dec. 26		S12	5 6 7 00		5 6 7 00
28		S12	6 8 2 50		1 2 4 9 50

CUSTOMER Renville Public Schools   **CUSTOMER NO.** 190

DATE	ITEM	POST. REF.	DEBIT	CREDIT	DEBIT BALANCE
20-- Dec. 1	Balance	✓			9 5 8 1 50
8		CR23		9 5 8 1 50	——
22		S12	4 7 5 0 00		4 7 5 0 00
31		SR12		1 5 0 0 00	3 2 5 0 00

[3, 5]

ACCOUNTS PAYABLE LEDGER

VENDOR A-1 Supplies   **VENDOR NO.** 210

DATE	ITEM	POST. REF.	DEBIT	CREDIT	CREDIT BALANCE
20-- Dec. 22		P12		1 2 7 8 50	1 2 7 8 50
26		PR12	2 6 5 00		1 0 1 3 50

VENDOR CBG Distributors   **VENDOR NO.** 220

DATE	ITEM	POST. REF.	DEBIT	CREDIT	CREDIT BALANCE
20-- Dec. 1	Balance	✓			2 2 3 0 10
6		CP23	2 2 3 0 10		——
24		P12		1 5 0 0 00	1 5 0 0 00

1 REINFORCEMENT ACTIVITY (continued)

[3, 5]

ACCOUNTS PAYABLE LEDGER

VENDOR Grandway Products   VENDOR NO. 230

DATE	ITEM	POST. REF.	DEBIT	CREDIT	CREDIT BALANCE
20-- Dec. 27		P12		3 1 5 7 99	3 1 5 7 99

VENDOR H & B Books   VENDOR NO. 240

DATE	ITEM	POST. REF.	DEBIT	CREDIT	CREDIT BALANCE
20-- Dec. 1	Balance	✓			5 4 3 0 15
5		PR12	1 4 3 5 00		3 9 9 5 15
7		CP23	3 9 9 5 15		—

VENDOR Maryland Books & Supplies   VENDOR NO. 250

DATE	ITEM	POST. REF.	DEBIT	CREDIT	CREDIT BALANCE
20-- Dec. 1	Balance	✓			5 6 5 40
8		CP23	5 6 5 40		—
27		P12		2 4 4 0 50	2 4 4 0 50

VENDOR Oliver Books, Inc.   VENDOR NO. 260

DATE	ITEM	POST. REF.	DEBIT	CREDIT	CREDIT BALANCE
20-- Dec. 1	Balance	✓			4 9 2 0 20
2		P12		1 9 3 3 00	6 8 5 3 20
7		PR12	3 0 0 00		6 5 5 3 20
9		CP23	4 9 2 0 20		1 6 3 3 00
12		CP23	1 6 3 3 00		—

VENDOR Strup Supplies   VENDOR NO. 270

DATE	ITEM	POST. REF.	DEBIT	CREDIT	CREDIT BALANCE
20-- Dec. 22		P12		1 6 4 7 00	1 6 4 7 00

1 REINFORCEMENT ACTIVITY (continued)

[4]

RECONCILIATION OF BANK STATEMENT   Date _12/29/--_

1. Enter CHECKBOOK BALANCE as shown on check stub.
2. Enter and add bank charges to obtain TOTAL BANK CHARGES.
3. Deduct TOTAL BANK CHARGES from CHECKBOOK BALANCE to obtain ADJUSTED CHECKBOOK BALANCE.
4. Enter BANK BALANCE as shown on bank statement.
5. Enter and add the amounts of any outstanding deposits recorded on the check stubs but not listed on the bank statement to obtain TOTAL OUTSTANDING DEPOSITS.
6. Add TOTAL OUTSTANDING DEPOSITS to BANK BALANCE to obtain TOTAL.
7. Sort all checks included in the statement numerically or by date issued.
   a. Check off on the check stubs of the checkbook each of the checks paid by the bank.
   b. Enter the check numbers and amounts of checks still outstanding.
   c. Add the outstanding checks to obtain TOTAL OUTSTANDING CHECKS.
8. Deduct TOTAL OUTSTANDING CHECKS from TOTAL to obtain ADJUSTED BANK BALANCE.
9. The ADJUSTED CHECKBOOK BALANCE and the ADJUSTED BANK BALANCE should agree, proving that both the checkbook balance and the bank balance are correct.

(1) CHECKBOOK BALANCE............ $ _52,665.09_   **(4) BANK BALANCE**........................ $ _48,363.56_

BANK CHARGES

Description	Amount	
Service Charge	11	40
Credit Card	354	20
Charge		

OUTSTANDING DEPOSITS

Date	Amount	
12/29	7,959	63

(5) ADD TOTAL OUTSTANDING DEPOSITS................................... $ _7,959.63_

(6) TOTAL...................................... $ _56,323.19_

OUTSTANDING CHECKS

CK. NO.	Amount	
348	2,823	70
349	1,200	00

(2) DEDUCT TOTAL BANK CHARGES.... $ _365.60_

(7) DEDUCT TOTAL OUTSTANDING CHECKS................................... $ _4,023.70_

(3) ADJUSTED CHECKBOOK BALANCE. $ _52,299.49_   **(8) ADJUSTED BANK BALANCE**.......... $ _52,299.49_

[9]

Prove Cash:

Cash on hand at the beginning of the month .... $ _35,190.60_

Plus total cash received during the month .... $ _53,283.30_

Equals total.. $ _88,473.90_

Less total cash paid during the month .... $ _27,075.99_

Equals total cash on hand at the end of the month........................... $ _61,397.91_

1 **REINFORCEMENT ACTIVITY (continued)**

Campus Books, Inc.

Schedule of Accounts Receivable

December 31, 20--

Brian Fadstad	1	8	0	6	00	
Gilmore Public Schools	6	2	0	0	00	
Janelle Kamschorr		9	6	6	00	
Donald Lindgren	1	2	4	9	50	
Renville Public Schools	3	2	5	0	00	
Total Accounts Receivable	13	4	7	1	50	

Campus Books, Inc.

Schedule of Accounts Payable

December 31, 20--

A-1 Supplies	1	0	1	3	50	
CBG Distributors	1	5	0	0	00	
Grandway Products	3	1	5	7	99	
Maryland Books & Supplies	2	4	4	0	50	
Strup Supplies	1	6	4	7	00	
Total Accounts Payable	9	7	5	8	99	

Campus Books, Inc.

Departmental Statement of Gross Profit

For Year Ended December 31, 20--

	BOOKS	% OF NET SALES	SUPPLIES	% OF NET SALES	TOTAL	% OF NET SALES
Operating Revenue:						
Net Sales	241,729.42	100.0	239,821.50	100.0	481,550.92	100.0
Cost of Merchandise Sold:						
Mdse. Inv., Jan. 1	164,164.20		147,840.30		312,004.50	
Net Purchases	137,222.54		135,756.38		272,978.92	
Mdse. Available for Sale	301,386.74		283,596.68		584,983.42	
Less End. Inv., Dec. 31	174,469.25		151,439.85		325,909.10	
Cost of Merchandise Sold	126,917.49	52.5	132,156.83	55.1	259,074.32	53.8
Gross Profit on Operations	114,811.93	47.5	107,664.67	44.9	222,476.60	46.2

1 REINFORCEMENT ACTIVITY (continued)

[13, 14]

Campus Books, Inc.
Work Sheet
For Year Ended December 31, 20--

#	ACCOUNT TITLE	TRIAL BALANCE DEBIT	TRIAL BALANCE CREDIT	ADJUSTMENTS DEBIT	ADJUSTMENTS CREDIT	INCOME STATEMENT DEBIT	INCOME STATEMENT CREDIT	BALANCE SHEET DEBIT	BALANCE SHEET CREDIT
1	Cash	6139791						6139791	
2	Petty Cash	50000						50000	
3	Accounts Receivable	13471150						13471150	
4	Allowance for Uncollectible Accounts		34020		(a)241257				275277
5	Mdse. Inv.—Books	16416420		(b)1030505				17446925	
6	Mdse. Inv.—Supplies	14784030		(c)359955				15143985	
7	Supplies—Office	6215520			(d)1580020			4635500	
8	Supplies—Store	5105580			(e)1114580			3991000	
9	Prepaid Insurance	528000			(f)88000			440000	
10	Office Equipment	1921000						1921000	
11	Accum. Depr.—Office Equipment		876000		(g)87000				963000
12	Store Equipment	2118000						2118000	
13	Accum. Depr.—Store Equipment		1362000		(h)94000				1456000
14	Accounts Payable		975899						975899
15	Employee Income Tax Pay.—Fed.		120451						120451
16	Employee Income Tax Pay.—State		110300						110300
17	Federal Income Tax Payable				(i)21375				21375
18	Social Security Tax Payable		149018						149018
19	Medicare Tax Payable		34388						34388
20	Sales Tax Payable		453593						453593
21	Unemployment Tax Pay.—Fed.		3891						3891
22	Unemployment Tax Pay.—State		26264						26264
23	Health Ins. Prem. Payable		283200						283200
24	Dividends Payable								
25	Capital Stock		30000000						30000000
26	Retained Earnings		9752570						9752570
27	Dividends	2000000						2000000	
28	Income Summary—Books				(b)1030505		1030505		
29	Income Summary—Supplies				(c)359955		359955		
30	Income Summary—General								

1 REINFORCEMENT ACTIVITY (continued)

[13, 14]

ACCOUNT TITLE	TRIAL BALANCE DEBIT	TRIAL BALANCE CREDIT	ADJUSTMENTS DEBIT	ADJUSTMENTS CREDIT	INCOME STATEMENT DEBIT	INCOME STATEMENT CREDIT	BALANCE SHEET DEBIT	BALANCE SHEET CREDIT
31 Sales—Books		2453535590				2453535590		
32 Sales—Supplies		24565040				24565040		
33 Sales Discount—Books	169148				169148			
34 Sales Discount—Supplies	194870				194870			
35 Sales Ret. & Allow.—Books	193500				193500			
36 Sales Ret. & Allow.—Supplies	388020				388020			
37 Purchases—Books	14618390				14618390			
38 Purchases—Supplies	14357369				14357369			
39 Purchases Discount—Books		341636				341636		
40 Purchases Discount—Supplies		343161				343161		
41 Pur. Ret. & Allow.—Books		554500				554500		
42 Pur. Ret. & Allow.—Supplies		438570				438570		
43 Advertising Expense	513020				513020			
44 Credit Card Fee Expense	524480				524480			
45 Depr. Exp.—Store Equip.			(h) 94000		94000			
46 Salary Expense—Books	54022220				54022220			
47 Salary Expense—Supplies	50510040				50510040			
48 Supplies Expense—Store			(e) 1114580		1114580			
49 Depr. Exp.—Office Equip.			(g) 87000		87000			
50 Insurance Expense			(f) 88000		88000			
51 Miscellaneous Expense	533020				533020			
52 Payroll Taxes Expense	1535498				1535498			
53 Rent Expense	1440000				1440000			
54 Salary Expense—Admin.	3123025				3123025			
55 Supplies Expense—Office			(d) 1580020		1580020			
56 Uncollectible Accounts Expense			(a) 241257		241257			
57 Federal Income Tax Expense	480000		(i) 21375		501375			
58	949600091	949600091	2194692	2194692	49327832	52168957	47466351	44625226
59					2841125			2841125
60					52168957	52168957	47466351	47466351
61								

1 REINFORCEMENT ACTIVITY (continued)

[16]

Campus Books, Inc.

Income Statement

For Year Ended December 31, 20--

						% OF NET SALES
Operating Revenue:						
Sales:			491 0 0 6 30			
Less: Sales Discount		3 6 4 0 18				
Sales Ret. & Allow.		5 8 1 5 20	9 4 5 5 38			
Net Sales				481 5 5 0 92		100.0
Cost of Merchandise Sold:						
Mdse. Inv., Jan. 1, 20--			312 0 0 4 50			
Purchases		289 7 5 7 59				
Less: Purchases Discount	6 8 4 7 97					
Pur. Returns & Allow.	9 9 3 0 70	16 7 7 8 67				
Net Purchases			272 9 7 8 92			
Total Cost of Mdse. Available			584 9 8 3 42			
Less Mdse. Inv., Dec. 31, 20--			325 9 0 9 10			
Cost of Merchandise Sold				259 0 7 4 32		53.8
Gross Profit on Operations				222 4 7 6 60		46.2
Operating Expenses:						
Selling Expenses:						
Advertising Expense		5 1 3 0 20				
Credit Card Fee Expense		5 2 4 4 80				
Depr. Exp.—Store Equip.		9 4 0 00				
Salary Expense—Books		54 0 2 2 20				
Salary Expense—Supplies		50 5 1 0 40				
Supplies Expense—Store		1 1 4 5 80				
Total Selling Expenses			116 9 9 3 40			
Administrative Expenses:						
Depr. Exp.—Office Equip.		8 7 0 00				
Insurance Expense		8 8 0 00				
Miscellaneous Expense		5 3 3 0 20				
Payroll Taxes Expense		15 3 5 4 98				
Rent Expense		14 4 0 0 00				
Salary Expense—Admin.		31 2 3 0 25				
Supplies Exp.—Office		1 5 8 0 20				

1 REINFORCEMENT ACTIVITY (continued)

[16]

Campus Books, Inc.

Income Statement (continued)

For Year Ended December 31, 20--

				% OF NET SALES
Uncollectible Accounts Expense	2 41 2 57			
Total Admin. Expenses		72 0 5 8 20		
Total Operating Expenses			189 0 5 1 60	39.3
Net Income before Fed. Inc. Tax			33 4 2 5 00	6.9
Less Federal Income Tax Expense			5 0 1 3 75	
Net Income after Fed. Inc. Tax			28 4 1 1 25	5.9

[17]

Campus Books, Inc.

Statement of Stockholders' Equity

For Year Ended December 31, 20--

Capital Stock:			
$100.00 Per Share			
January 1, 20--, 3,000 Shares Issued		300 0 0 0 00	
Issued during Current Year, None		-0-	
Balance, December 31, 20--, 3,000 Shares Issued			300 0 0 0 00
Retained Earnings:			
Balance, January 1, 20--		97 5 2 5 70	
Net Income after Federal Income Tax for 20--	28 4 1 1 25		
Less Dividends Declared during 20--	20 0 0 0 00		
Net Increase during 20--		8 4 1 1 25	
Balance, December 31, 20--			105 9 3 6 95
Total Stockholders' Equity, December 31, 20--			405 9 3 6 95

Campus Books, Inc.

Balance Sheet

December 31, 20--

ASSETS														
Current Assets:														
Cash						61	3	9	7	91				
Petty Cash						5	0	0	0	00				
Accounts Receivable	13	4	7	1	50									
Less Allowance for Uncollectible Accounts	2	7	5	2	77	10	7	1	8	73				
Merchandise Inventory—Books						174	4	6	9	25				
Merchandise Inventory—Supplies						151	4	3	9	85				
Supplies—Office						4	6	3	5	00				
Supplies—Store						3	9	6	0	00				
Prepaid Insurance						4	4	0	0	00				
Total Current Assets											411	5	2	0	74
Plant Assets:														
Office Equipment	19	2	1	0	00									
Less Accumulated Depr.—Office Equipment	9	6	3	0	00	9	5	8	0	00				
Store Equipment	21	1	8	0	00									
Less Accumulated Depr.—Store Equipment	14	5	6	0	00	6	6	2	0	00				
Total Plant Assets											16	2	0	0	00
Total Assets											427	7	2	0	74
LIABILITIES														
Current Liabilities:														
Accounts Payable						9	7	5	8	99				
Employee Income Tax Payable—Federal						1	2	0	4	51				
Employee Income Tax Payable—State						1	1	0	3	00				
Federal Income Tax Payable						2	1	3	75					
Social Security Tax Payable						1	4	9	0	18				
Medicare Tax Payable						3	4	3	08					
Sales Tax Payable						4	5	3	5	93				
Unemployment Tax Payable—Federal						3	8	91						
Unemployment Tax Payable—State						2	6	2	64					
Health Insurance Premiums Payable						2	8	3	2	00				
Total Liabilities											21	7	8	3	79

1 REINFORCEMENT ACTIVITY (continued)

[18]

Campus Books, Inc.

Balance Sheet (continued)

December 31, 20--

STOCKHOLDERS' EQUITY			
Capital Stock	300 0 0 0 00		
Retained Earnings	105 9 3 6 95		
Total Stockholders' Equity		405 9 3 6 95	
Total Liabilities and Stockholders' Equity		427 7 2 0 74	

1 REINFORCEMENT ACTIVITY (continued)

[19, 20]

GENERAL JOURNAL   PAGE 13

	DATE		ACCOUNT TITLE	DOC. NO.	POST. REF.	DEBIT	CREDIT	
1			*Adjusting Entries*					1
2	20-- Dec.	31	Uncollectible Accounts Expense	6240		2 41 2 57		2
3			Allowance for Uncollectible Accounts	1120			2 41 2 57	3
4		31	Merchandise Inventory—Books	1125-1		10 30 5 05		4
5			Income Summary—Books	3120-1			10 30 5 05	5
6		31	Merchandise Inventory—Supplies	1125-2		3 59 9 55		6
7			Income Summary—Supplies	3120-2			3 59 9 55	7
8		31	Supplies Expense—Office	6235		1 58 0 20		8
9			Supplies—Office	1130			1 58 0 20	9
10		31	Supplies Expense—Store	6125		1 14 5 80		10
11			Supplies—Store	1135			1 14 5 80	11
12		31	Insurance Expense	6210		8 80 0 00		12
13			Prepaid Insurance	1140			8 80 0 00	13
14		31	Depreciation Expense—Office Equipment	6205		8 70 0 00		14
15			Accum. Depreciation—Office Equipment	1210			8 70 0 00	15
16		31	Depreciation Expense—Store Equipment	6115		9 40 0 00		16
17			Accum. Depreciation—Store Equipment	1220			9 40 0 00	17
18		31	Federal Income Tax Expense	7105		2 13 75		18
19			Federal Income Tax Payable	2120			2 13 75	19
20			*Closing Entries*					20
21		31	Income Summary—Books	3120-1		10 30 5 05		21
22			Income Summary—Supplies	3120-2		3 59 9 55		22
23			Sales—Books	4105-1		245 35 5 90		23
24			Sales—Supplies	4105-2		245 65 0 40		24
25			Purchases Discount—Books	5110-1		3 41 6 36		25
26			Purchases Discount—Supplies	5110-2		3 43 1 61		26
27			Purchases Returns & Allow.—Books	5115-1		5 54 5 00		27
28			Purchases Returns & Allow.—Supplies	5115-2		4 38 5 70		28
29			Income Summary—General	3125			521 68 9 57	29
30								30
31								31

GENERAL JOURNAL   PAGE 14

	DATE		ACCOUNT TITLE	DOC. NO.	POST. REF.	DEBIT	CREDIT	
1	20-- Dec.	31	Income Summary—General		3125	493 27 8 32		1
2			Sales Discount—Books		4110-1		1 69 1 48	2
3			Sales Discount—Supplies		4110-2		1 94 8 70	3
4			Sales Returns & Allow.—Books		4115-1		1 93 5 00	4
5			Sales Returns & Allow.—Supplies		4115-2		3 88 0 20	5
6			Purchases—Books		5105-1		146 18 3 90	6
7			Purchases—Supplies		5105-2		143 57 3 69	7
8			Advertising Expense		6105		5 13 0 20	8
9			Credit Card Fee Expense		6110		5 24 4 80	9
10			Depreciation Expense—Store Equipment		6115		9 4 0 00	10
11			Salary Expense—Books		6120-1		54 02 2 20	11
12			Salary Expense—Supplies		6120-2		50 51 0 40	12
13			Supplies Expense—Store		6125		1 14 5 80	13
14			Depreciation Expense—Office Equipment		6205		8 7 0 00	14
15			Insurance Expense		6210		8 8 0 00	15
16			Miscellaneous Expense		6215		5 33 0 20	16
17			Payroll Taxes Expense		6220		15 35 4 98	17
18			Rent Expense		6225		14 40 0 00	18
19			Salary Expense—Administrative		6230		31 23 0 25	19
20			Supplies Expense—Office		6235		1 58 0 20	20
21			Uncollectible Accounts Expense		6240		2 41 2 57	21
22			Federal Income Tax Expense		7105		5 01 3 75	22
23		31	Income Summary—General		3125	28 41 1 25		23
24			Retained Earnings		3110		28 41 1 25	24
25		31	Retained Earnings		3110	20 00 0 00		25
26			Dividends		3115		20 00 0 00	26
27								27
28								28
29								29
30								30
31								31

1 REINFORCEMENT ACTIVITY (concluded)

Campus Books, Inc.

Post-Closing Trial Balance

December 31, 20--

ACCOUNT TITLE	DEBIT	CREDIT
Cash	61 3 9 7 91	
Petty Cash	5 0 0 00	
Accounts Receivable	13 4 7 1 50	
Allowance for Uncollectible Accounts		2 7 5 2 77
Merchandise Inventory—Books	174 4 6 9 25	
Merchandise Inventory—Supplies	151 4 3 9 85	
Supplies—Office	4 6 3 5 00	
Supplies—Store	3 9 6 0 00	
Prepaid Insurance	4 4 0 0 00	
Office Equipment	19 2 1 0 00	
Accumulated Depreciation—Office Equipment		9 6 3 0 00
Store Equipment	21 1 8 0 00	
Accumulated Depreciation—Store Equipment		14 5 6 0 00
Accounts Payable		9 7 5 8 99
Employee Income Tax Payable—Federal		1 2 0 4 51
Employee Income Tax Payable—State		1 1 0 3 00
Federal Income Tax Payable		2 1 3 75
Social Security Tax Payable		1 4 9 0 18
Medicare Tax Payable		3 4 3 08
Sales Tax Payable		4 5 3 5 93
Unemployment Tax Payable—Federal		3 8 91
Unemployment Tax Payable—State		2 6 2 64
Health Insurance Premiums Payable		2 8 3 2 00
Capital Stock		300 0 0 0 00
Retained Earnings		105 9 3 6 95
Totals	454 6 6 3 51	454 6 6 3 51

5-1 WORK TOGETHER, p. 150

Preparing a voucher and journalizing vouchers in a voucher register

[4]

Vchr. No.	**152**

Date _____ *10/1/--* _____ Due Date _____ *10/10/--* _____ Payment Date _____ *10/8/--*

To _____ *Dickens Company* _____

Address _____ *11200 Irving Street* _____

Street

_____ *Minneapolis,* _____ *MN* _____ *55411* _____

City   State   ZIP

ACCOUNTS DEBITED	AMOUNT
PURCHASES	600 00
SUPPLIES—SALES	
SUPPLIES—ADMIN.	
MISCELLANEOUS EXPENSE—SALES	
MISCELLANEOUS EXPENSE—ADMIN.	
RENT EXPENSE	
SALARY EXPENSE—SALES	
SALARY EXPENSE—ADMIN.	
TOTAL DEBITS	600 00

ACCOUNTS CREDITED	AMOUNT
VOUCHERS PAYABLE	600 00
EMPLOYEE INC. TAX PAY.—FEDERAL	
EMPLOYEE INC. TAX PAY.—STATE	
SOCIAL SECURITY TAX PAY.	
MEDICARE TAX PAY.	
TOTAL CREDITS	600 00

Voucher Approved by _____

Recorded in Voucher Register Page _____ *10* _____ by _____

Paid { Date _____
Check No. _____ Amount $ _____
Approved by _____

5-1 WORK TOGETHER (continued)

[5, 6]

This voucher register is needed to complete Work Together 5-2.

PAGE 10

VOUCHER

	DATE		PAYEE	VCHR. NO.	PAID		VOUCHERS PAYABLE CREDIT	
					DATE	CK. NO.		
1	20-- Oct.	1	Dickens Company	152	Oct. 8	309	6 0 0 00	1
2		2	Land Development Co.	153	Oct. 11	311	1 3 0 0 00	2
3		4	University Supplies	154	Oct. 9	310	3 5 0 00	3
4		8	City Delivery Co.	155			2 5 00	4
5		30	Totals				2 2 7 5 00	5
6								6
7								7
8								8
9								9
10								10

Extra form

PAGE

VOUCHER

	DATE	PAYEE	VCHR. NO.	PAID		VOUCHERS PAYABLE CREDIT	
				DATE	CK. NO.		
1							1
2							2
3							3
4							4
5							5
6							6
7							7
8							8
9							9
10							10

5-1 WORK TOGETHER (concluded)

[5, 6]

REGISTER   PAGE 10

| | PURCHASES DEBIT | SUPPLIES— SALES DEBIT | SUPPLIES— ADMIN. DEBIT | GENERAL | | | |
				ACCOUNT TITLE	POST. REF.	DEBIT	CREDIT	
1	60000							1
2				Rent Expense		130000		2
3		35000						3
4				Delivery Expense		2500		4
5	60000	35000				132500		5
6								6
7								7
8								8
9								9
10								10

Extra form

REGISTER   PAGE

| | PURCHASES DEBIT | SUPPLIES— SALES DEBIT | SUPPLIES— ADMIN. DEBIT | GENERAL | | | |
				ACCOUNT TITLE	POST. REF.	DEBIT	CREDIT	
1								1
2								2
3								3
4								4
5								5
6								6
7								7
8								8
9								9
10								10

5-1 WORK TOGETHER

Extra form

Vchr.
No.

Date_____ Due Date_____ Payment Date_____

To_____

Address_____
Street

_____
City   State   ZIP

ACCOUNTS DEBITED	AMOUNT
PURCHASES	
SUPPLIES—SALES	
SUPPLIES—ADMIN.	
MISCELLANEOUS EXPENSE—SALES	
MISCELLANEOUS EXPENSE—ADMIN.	
RENT EXPENSE	
SALARY EXPENSE—SALES	
SALARY EXPENSE—ADMIN.	
TOTAL DEBITS	

ACCOUNTS CREDITED	AMOUNT
VOUCHERS PAYABLE	
EMPLOYEE INC. TAX PAY.—FEDERAL	
EMPLOYEE INC. TAX PAY.—STATE	
SOCIAL SECURITY TAX PAY.	
MEDICARE TAX PAY.	
TOTAL CREDITS	

Voucher Approved by _____

Recorded in Voucher
Register Page _____ by_____

Paid {
Date _____
Check No. _____ Amount $_____
Approved by _____

5-1 ON YOUR OWN, p. 150

Preparing a voucher and journalizing vouchers in a voucher register [7]

Vchr. No. **89**

Date_____8/1/--_____ Due Date_____8/10/--_____ Payment Date_____8/8/--_____

To_____*Darst Corporation*_____

Address_____*7020 Niles Lane*_____
Street

Centuria,   *WI*   *54824*
City   State   ZIP

ACCOUNTS DEBITED	AMOUNT
PURCHASES	300 00
SUPPLIES—SALES	
SUPPLIES—ADMIN.	
MISCELLANEOUS EXPENSE—SALES	
MISCELLANEOUS EXPENSE—ADMIN.	
RENT EXPENSE	
SALARY EXPENSE—SALES	
SALARY EXPENSE—ADMIN.	
TOTAL DEBITS	300 00

ACCOUNTS CREDITED	AMOUNT
VOUCHERS PAYABLE	300 00
EMPLOYEE INC. TAX PAY.—FEDERAL	
EMPLOYEE INC. TAX PAY.—STATE	
SOCIAL SECURITY TAX PAY.	
MEDICARE TAX PAY.	
TOTAL CREDITS	300 00

Voucher Approved by _____

Recorded in Voucher Register Page _____8_____ by_____

Paid { Date _____
      Check No. _____ Amount $_____
      Approved by _____

5-1 ON YOUR OWN (continued)

[8, 9]

This voucher register is needed to complete On Your Own 5-2.

PAGE 8   VOUCHER

	DATE		PAYEE	VCHR. NO.	PAID DATE	PAID CK. NO.	VOUCHERS PAYABLE CREDIT	
1	20-- Aug.	1	Darst Corporation	89	Aug. 8	222	3 0 0 00	1
2		3	C & G Company	90	Aug. 11	224	7 5 00	2
3		5	Heartland Supplies	91	Aug. 9	223	2 0 0 00	3
4		8	City News	92			2 2 5 00	4
5		31	Totals				8 0 0 00	5
6								6
7								7
8								8
9								9
10								10

(OYO 5-2 header above PAID / VOUCHERS PAYABLE CREDIT columns; VOUCHER 1)

Extra form

PAGE   VOUCHER

	DATE		PAYEE	VCHR. NO.	PAID DATE	PAID CK. NO.	VOUCHERS PAYABLE CREDIT	
1								1
2								2
3								3
4								4
5								5
6								6
7								7
8								8
9								9
10								10

5-1 ON YOUR OWN (concluded)

[8, 9]

REGISTER

	2 PURCHASES DEBIT	3 SUPPLIES—SALES DEBIT	4 SUPPLIES—ADMIN. DEBIT	GENERAL ACCOUNT TITLE	POST. REF.	5 DEBIT	6 CREDIT	
1	300 00							1
2				Miscellaneous Expense		75 00		2
3			200 00					3
4				Advertising Expense		225 00		4
5	300 00		200 00			300 00		5
6								6
7								7
8								8
9								9
10								10

Extra form

REGISTER

	2 PURCHASES DEBIT	3 SUPPLIES—SALES DEBIT	4 SUPPLIES—ADMIN. DEBIT	GENERAL ACCOUNT TITLE	POST. REF.	5 DEBIT	6 CREDIT	
1								1
2								2
3								3
4								4
5								5
6								6
7								7
8								8
9								9
10								10

5-1 ON YOUR OWN

Extra form

Vchr.
No.

Date_____ Due Date_____ Payment Date_____

To_____

Address_____
                                    Street

_____
City   State   ZIP

ACCOUNTS DEBITED	AMOUNT	
PURCHASES		
SUPPLIES—SALES		
SUPPLIES—ADMIN.		
MISCELLANEOUS EXPENSE—SALES		
MISCELLANEOUS EXPENSE—ADMIN.		
RENT EXPENSE		
SALARY EXPENSE—SALES		
SALARY EXPENSE—ADMIN.		
TOTAL DEBITS		

ACCOUNTS CREDITED	AMOUNT	
VOUCHERS PAYABLE		
EMPLOYEE INC. TAX PAY.—FEDERAL		
EMPLOYEE INC. TAX PAY.—STATE		
SOCIAL SECURITY TAX PAY.		
MEDICARE TAX PAY.		
TOTAL CREDITS		

Voucher Approved by _____

Recorded in Voucher
Register Page _____ by_____

Paid { Date _____
Check No. _____ Amount $_____
Approved by _____

5-2 WORK TOGETHER, p. 154

Journalizing cash payments and deposits in a check register [4–6]

The voucher register completed in Work Together 5-1 is needed to complete this Work Together.

CHECK REGISTER PAGE 10

	DATE		PAYEE	CK. NO.	VCHR. NO.	VOUCHERS PAYABLE DEBIT	PURCHASES DISCOUNT CREDIT	CASH CREDIT	BANK DEPOSITS	BANK BALANCE	
1	20– Oct.	1	Brought Forward		✔					18 765 55	1
2		8	Dickens Company	309	152	600 00	12 00	588 00		18 177 55	2
3		9	University Supplies	310	154	350 00		350 00		17 827 55	3
4		11	Land Development Co.	311	153	1300 00		1300 00		16 527 55	4
5		16	Deposit		✔				3775 09	20 302 64	5
6		31	Totals			2250 00	12 00	2238 00			6
7											7
8											8
9											9
10											10

Extra form

CHECK REGISTER PAGE

	DATE		PAYEE	CK. NO.	VCHR. NO.	VOUCHERS PAYABLE DEBIT	PURCHASES DISCOUNT CREDIT	CASH CREDIT	BANK DEPOSITS	BANK BALANCE	
1											1
2											2
3											3
4											4
5											5
6											6
7											7
8											8
9											9
10											10

Name _____ Date _____ Class _____

Extra form

CHECK REGISTER

PAGE _____

	DATE	PAYEE	CK. NO.	VCHR. NO.	VOUCHERS PAYABLE DEBIT	PURCHASES DISCOUNT CREDIT	CASH CREDIT	BANK DEPOSITS	BANK BALANCE	
1										1
2										2
3										3
4										4
5										5
6										6
7										7
8										8
9										9
10										10
11										11
12										12
13										13
14										14
15										15
16										16
17										17
18										18
19										19
20										20
21										21
22										22
23										23
24										24
25										25
26										26
27										27
28										28
29										29
30										30
31										31

Name _____ Date _____ Class _____

5-2 ON YOUR OWN, p. 154

Journalizing cash payments and deposits in a check register [7–9]

The voucher register completed in On Your Own 5-1 is needed to complete this On Your Own.

CHECK REGISTER — PAGE 8

	DATE		PAYEE	CK. NO.	VCHR. NO.	VOUCHERS PAYABLE DEBIT	PURCHASES DISCOUNT CREDIT	CASH CREDIT	BANK DEPOSITS	BANK BALANCE	
1	Aug. 20–	1	Brought Forward		✔					5 4 2 2 67	1
2		8	Darst Corporation	222	89	3 0 0 00	6 00	2 9 4 00		5 1 2 8 67	2
3		9	Heartland Supplies	223	91	2 0 0 00		2 0 0 00		4 9 2 8 67	3
4		11	C&G Company	224	90	7 5 00		7 5 00		4 8 5 3 67	4
5		15	Deposit		✔				1 3 8 8 12	6 2 4 1 79	5
6		31	Totals			5 7 5 00	6 00	5 6 9 00			6

Extra form

CHECK REGISTER — PAGE

	DATE	PAYEE	CK. NO.	VCHR. NO.	VOUCHERS PAYABLE DEBIT	PURCHASES DISCOUNT CREDIT	CASH CREDIT	BANK DEPOSITS	BANK BALANCE	
1										1
2										2
3										3
4										4
5										5
6										6
7										7
8										8
9										9
10										10

5-2 ON YOUR OWN

Extra form

CHECK REGISTER

	DATE		PAYEE	CK. NO.	VCHR. NO.	VOUCHERS PAYABLE DEBIT	PURCHASES DISCOUNT CREDIT	CASH CREDIT	BANK DEPOSITS	BALANCE	
1											1
2											2
3											3
4											4
5											5
6											6
7											7
8											8
9											9
10											10
11											11
12											12
13											13
14											14
15											15
16											16
17											17
18											18
19											19
20											20
21											21
22											22
23											23
24											24
25											25
26											26
27											27
28											28
29											29
30											30
31											31

5-3 WORK TOGETHER
(Note: The voucher register needed for this problem begins on page 192.)

Extra forms

REGISTER

	PURCHASES DEBIT	SUPPLIES— SALES DEBIT	SUPPLIES— ADMIN. DEBIT	GENERAL			
				ACCOUNT TITLE	POST. REF.	DEBIT	CREDIT
1							
2							
3							
4							
5							
6							
7							
8							
9							
10							

REGISTER

	PURCHASES DEBIT	SUPPLIES— SALES DEBIT	SUPPLIES— ADMIN. DEBIT	GENERAL			
				ACCOUNT TITLE	POST. REF.	DEBIT	CREDIT
1							
2							
3							
4							
5							
6							
7							
8							
9							
10							

5-3 WORK TOGETHER, p. 158

Journalizing purchases returns and allowances and payroll in a voucher register [4]

PAGE 5   VOUCHER

	DATE		PAYEE	VCHR. NO.	PAID DATE	CK. NO.	VOUCHERS PAYABLE CREDIT	
1	20-- May	1	Casey Corporation	75	See Vchr 76		1 5 0 0 00	1
2		4	Casey Corporation	76			1 2 0 0 00	2
3								3
4		15	Payroll	77			3 3 0 8 18	4
5								5
6								6
7								7
8								8
9								9
10								10

Extra form

PAGE   VOUCHER

	DATE		PAYEE	VCHR. NO.	PAID DATE	CK. NO.	VOUCHERS PAYABLE CREDIT	
1								1
2								2
3								3
4								4
5								5
6								6
7								7
8								8
9								9
10								10

5-3 WORK TOGETHER (concluded)

[4]

REGISTER   PAGE 5

	2	3	4			5	6	
	PURCHASES DEBIT	SUPPLIES— SALES DEBIT	SUPPLIES— ADMIN. DEBIT	GENERAL				
				ACCOUNT TITLE	POST. REF.	DEBIT	CREDIT	
1	1 50 00							1
2				Vouchers Payable		1 50 00		2
3				Purchases Returns and Allowances			30 00	3
4				Salary Expense—Sales		2 78 0 52		4
5				Salary Expense—Admin.		1 69 0 00		5
6				Employee Inc. Tax Pay.—Fed.			67 0 58	6
7				Employee Inc. Tax Pay.—State			1 34 12	7
8				Social Security Tax Pay.			29 0 58	8
9				Medicare Tax Pay.			67 06	9
10								10

Extra form

REGISTER   PAGE

	2	3	4			5	6	
	PURCHASES DEBIT	SUPPLIES— SALES DEBIT	SUPPLIES— ADMIN. DEBIT	GENERAL				
				ACCOUNT TITLE	POST. REF.	DEBIT	CREDIT	
1								1
2								2
3								3
4								4
5								5
6								6
7								7
8								8
9								9
10								10

5-3 WORK TOGETHER

Extra forms

PAGE ___   VOUCHER
                                                                    1

	DATE	PAYEE	VCHR. NO.	PAID DATE	CK. NO.	VOUCHERS PAYABLE CREDIT	
1							1
2							2
3							3
4							4
5							5
6							6
7							7
8							8
9							9
10							10

PAGE ___   VOUCHER
                                                                    1

	DATE	PAYEE	VCHR. NO.	PAID DATE	CK. NO.	VOUCHERS PAYABLE CREDIT	
1							1
2							2
3							3
4							4
5							5
6							6
7							7
8							8
9							9
10							10

5-3 ON YOUR OWN
(Note: The voucher register needed for this problem begins on page 196.)

Extra forms

REGISTER   PAGE

	2	3	4	GENERAL		5	6	
	PURCHASES DEBIT	SUPPLIES— SALES DEBIT	SUPPLIES— ADMIN. DEBIT	ACCOUNT TITLE	POST. REF.	DEBIT	CREDIT	
1								1
2								2
3								3
4								4
5								5
6								6
7								7
8								8
9								9
10								10

REGISTER   PAGE

	2	3	4	GENERAL		5	6	
	PURCHASES DEBIT	SUPPLIES— SALES DEBIT	SUPPLIES— ADMIN. DEBIT	ACCOUNT TITLE	POST. REF.	DEBIT	CREDIT	
1								1
2								2
3								3
4								4
5								5
6								6
7								7
8								8
9								9
10								10

5-3 ON YOUR OWN, page 158

Journalizing purchases returns and allowances and payroll in a voucher register [5]

PAGE 6   VOUCHER

	DATE		PAYEE	VCHR. NO.	PAID		VOUCHERS PAYABLE CREDIT	
					DATE	CK. NO.		
1	20– June	1	Prickett Corporation	110	See Vchr 111		9 0 0 00	1
2		4	Prickett Corporation	111			6 0 0 00	2
3								3
4		15	Payroll	112			4 7 7 8 63	4
5								5
6								6
7								7
8								8
9								9
10								10

Extra form

PAGE   VOUCHER

	DATE		PAYEE	VCHR. NO.	PAID		VOUCHERS PAYABLE CREDIT	
					DATE	CK. NO.		
1								1
2								2
3								3
4								4
5								5
6								6
7								7
8								8
9								9
10								10

Name _____ Date _____ Class _____

5-3 ON YOUR OWN (concluded)

[5]

REGISTER

	PURCHASES DEBIT	SUPPLIES—SALES DEBIT	SUPPLIES—ADMIN. DEBIT	GENERAL				
	2	3	4	ACCOUNT TITLE	POST. REF.	5 DEBIT	6 CREDIT	
1	90 00 00							1
2				Vouchers Payable		90 00 00		2
3				Purch. Rets. & Allow.			30 00 00	3
4				Salary Expense—Sales		3 95 7 61		4
5				Salary Expense—Admin.		2 50 0 00		5
6				Employee Inc. Tax Pay.—Fed.			96 8 64	6
7				Employee Inc. Tax Pay.—State			19 3 73	7
8				Social Security Tax Pay.			4 19 75	8
9				Medicare Tax Pay.			96 86	9
10								10

Extra form

REGISTER

PAGE

	PURCHASES DEBIT	SUPPLIES—SALES DEBIT	SUPPLIES—ADMIN. DEBIT	GENERAL				
	2	3	4	ACCOUNT TITLE	POST. REF.	5 DEBIT	6 CREDIT	
1								1
2								2
3								3
4								4
5								5
6								6
7								7
8								8
9								9
10								10

5-3 ON YOUR OWN

Extra forms

PAGE ____

VOUCHER

1

	DATE	PAYEE	VCHR. NO.	PAID DATE	CK. NO.	VOUCHERS PAYABLE CREDIT	
1							1
2							2
3							3
4							4
5							5
6							6
7							7
8							8
9							9
10							10

PAGE ____

VOUCHER

1

	DATE	PAYEE	VCHR. NO.	PAID DATE	CK. NO.	VOUCHERS PAYABLE CREDIT	
1							1
2							2
3							3
4							4
5							5
6							6
7							7
8							8
9							9
10							10

Name _____ Date _____ Class _____

5-1 APPLICATION PROBLEM, p. 160

Preparing a voucher and journalizing vouchers in a voucher register [1]

Vchr. No. **87**

Date **9/1/--** Due Date **9/10/--** Payment Date **9/8/--**

To **Eastern Company**
Address **9424 Denison Pkwy.**
Street
Corning, **NY** **14830**
City State ZIP

ACCOUNTS DEBITED	AMOUNT
PURCHASES	3,100 00
SUPPLIES—SALES	
SUPPLIES—ADMIN.	
MISCELLANEOUS EXPENSE—SALES	
MISCELLANEOUS EXPENSE—ADMIN.	
RENT EXPENSE	
SALARY EXPENSE—SALES	
SALARY EXPENSE—ADMIN.	
TOTAL DEBITS	3,100 00

ACCOUNTS CREDITED	AMOUNT
VOUCHERS PAYABLE	3,100 00
EMPLOYEE INC. TAX PAY.—FEDERAL	
EMPLOYEE INC. TAX PAY.—STATE	
SOCIAL SECURITY TAX PAY.	
MEDICARE TAX PAY.	
TOTAL CREDITS	3,100 00

Voucher Approved by _____

Recorded in Voucher Register Page **9** by _____

Paid { Date _____
Check No. _____ Amount $ _____
Approved by _____

Chapter 5   A Voucher System • **199**

5-1 APPLICATION PROBLEM (continued)

[2, 3]

The voucher register prepared in Application Problem 5-1 is needed to complete Application
Problem 5-2.

PAGE 9   AP 5-2   VOUCHER
                                                                                                                       1

	DATE		PAYEE	VCHR. NO.	PAID DATE	CK. NO.	VOUCHERS PAYABLE CREDIT	
1	Sept.	1	Eastern Company	87	Sept. 9	85	3 1 0 0 00	1
2		2	Post Real Estate Developers	88	Sept. 2	83	1 1 5 0 00	2
3		5	Supra Supply Company	89	Sept. 13	86	2 5 8 00	3
4		8	Newport News	90	Sept. 8	84	8 7 50	4
5		11	Hoyer Company	91	Sept. 19	88	3 3 4 7 75	5
6		18	Rapid Rabbit	92	Sept. 18	87	2 3 5 15	6
7		19	Beggen Company	93			1 9 7 3 00	7
8		23	Syracuse Company	94			1 3 1 5 00	8
9		25	Northside Electric Cooperative	95	Sept. 25	89	1 8 5 00	9
10		29	Northern Supply	96			3 1 7 00	10
11		30	Manley Maintenance Company	97	Sept. 30	90	2 5 00	11
12		30	Totals				11 9 9 3 40	12
13								13
14								14
15								15

Extra form

PAGE _____   VOUCHER
                                                                                                               1

	DATE		PAYEE	VCHR. NO.	PAID DATE	CK. NO.	VOUCHERS PAYABLE CREDIT	
1								1
2								2
3								3
4								4
5								5
6								6

5-1 APPLICATION PROBLEM (concluded)

[2, 3]

The voucher register prepared in Application Problem 5-1 is needed to complete Application Problem 5-2.

REGISTER

PAGE 9

	PURCHASES DEBIT	SUPPLIES—SALES DEBIT	SUPPLIES—ADMIN. DEBIT	GENERAL			
	2	3	4	ACCOUNT TITLE	POST. REF.	DEBIT (5)	CREDIT (6)
1	3100 00						
2				Rent Expense		1150 00	
3		258 00					
4				Advertising Expense		87 50	
5	3347 75						
6				Delivery Expense		235 15	
7	1973 00						
8				Office Equipment		1315 00	
9				Utilities Expense		185 00	
10			317 00				
11				Miscellaneous Expense--Sales		25 00	
12	8420 75	258 00	317 00			2997 65	
13							
14							
15							

Extra form

REGISTER

PAGE

	PURCHASES DEBIT	SUPPLIES—SALES DEBIT	SUPPLIES—ADMIN. DEBIT	GENERAL			
	2	3	4	ACCOUNT TITLE	POST. REF.	DEBIT (5)	CREDIT (6)
1							
2							
3							
4							
5							
6							

5-1 APPLICATION PROBLEM

Extra form

Vchr.
No.

Date_____ Due Date_____ Payment Date_____

To_____

Address_____
                                    Street

_____
City   State   ZIP

_____

ACCOUNTS DEBITED	AMOUNT	
PURCHASES		
SUPPLIES—SALES		
SUPPLIES—ADMIN.		
MISCELLANEOUS EXPENSE—SALES		
MISCELLANEOUS EXPENSE—ADMIN.		
RENT EXPENSE		
SALARY EXPENSE—SALES		
SALARY EXPENSE—ADMIN.		
TOTAL DEBITS		

ACCOUNTS CREDITED	AMOUNT	
VOUCHERS PAYABLE		
EMPLOYEE INC. TAX PAY.—FEDERAL		
EMPLOYEE INC. TAX PAY.—STATE		
SOCIAL SECURITY TAX PAY.		
MEDICARE TAX PAY.		
TOTAL CREDITS		

Voucher Approved by _____

Recorded in Voucher
Register Page _____ by _____

_____

Paid { Date _____
       Check No. _____ Amount $_____
       Approved by _____

5-2 APPLICATION PROBLEM, p. 160

Journalizing cash payments and deposits in a check register [1-3]

The voucher register prepared in Application Problem 5-1 is needed to complete Application Problem 5-2.

CHECK REGISTER PAGE 9

	DATE		PAYEE	CK. NO.	VCHR. NO.	VOUCHERS PAYABLE DEBIT (1)	PURCHASES DISCOUNT CREDIT (2)	CASH CREDIT (3)	BANK DEPOSITS (4)	BANK BALANCE (5)	
1	20-- Sept.	1	Brought Forward		✔					19 443 13	1
2		2	Post Real Estate Developers	83	88	1 150 00		1 150 00		18 293 13	2
3		8	Newport News	84	90	87 50		87 50		18 205 63	3
4		9	Eastern Company	85	87	3 100 00	62 00	3 038 00		15 167 63	4
5		13	Supra Supply Company	86	89	258 00		258 00		14 909 63	5
6		18	Rapid Rabbit	87	92	235 15		235 15		14 674 48	6
7		19	Hoyer Company	88	91	3 347 75	66 96	3 280 79		11 393 69	7
8		24	Deposit		✔				5 684 54	17 078 23	8
9		25	Northside Electric Cooperative	89	95	185 00		185 00		16 893 23	9
10		30	Manley Maintenance Company	90	97	25 00		25 00		16 868 23	10
11		30	Totals			8 388 40	128 96	8 259 44			11
12											12
13											13
14											14
15											15
16											16
17											17
18											18
19											19
20											20
21											21
22											22
23											23
24											24
25											25
26											26
27											27
28											28
29											29

5-2 APPLICATION PROBLEM

Extra form

CHECK REGISTER

PAGE _____

	DATE	PAYEE	CK. NO.	VCHR. NO.	1 VOUCHERS PAYABLE DEBIT	2 PURCHASES DISCOUNT CREDIT	3 CASH CREDIT	4 BANK DEPOSITS	5 BANK BALANCE	
1										1
2										2
3										3
4										4
5										5
6										6
7										7
8										8
9										9
10										10
11										11
12										12
13										13
14										14
15										15
16										16
17										17
18										18
19										19
20										20
21										21
22										22
23										23
24										24
25										25
26										26
27										27
28										28
29										29
30										30
31										31

5-3 APPLICATION PROBLEM
(Note: The voucher register needed to complete this problem begins on page 206.)

Extra forms

REGISTER   PAGE

| | PURCHASES DEBIT | SUPPLIES— SALES DEBIT | SUPPLIES— ADMIN. DEBIT | GENERAL | | | | |
				ACCOUNT TITLE	POST. REF.	DEBIT	CREDIT	
1								1
2								2
3								3
4								4
5								5
6								6
7								7
8								8
9								9
10								10

REGISTER   PAGE

| | PURCHASES DEBIT | SUPPLIES— SALES DEBIT | SUPPLIES— ADMIN. DEBIT | GENERAL | | | | |
				ACCOUNT TITLE	POST. REF.	DEBIT	CREDIT	
1								1
2								2
3								3
4								4
5								5
6								6
7								7
8								8
9								9
10								10

5-3 APPLICATION PROBLEM, page 161

Journalizing purchases returns and allowances in a voucher register

PAGE 2   VOUCHER

	DATE		PAYEE	VCHR. NO.	PAID		VOUCHERS PAYABLE CREDIT	
					DATE	CK. NO.		
1	Feb. 20--	1	Hamline Corporation	10	See Vchr. 11		2 7 0 0 00	1
2		4	Hamline Corporation	11			2 5 0 0 00	2
3								3
4		15	Moorhead, Inc.	12	See Vchr. 13		1 7 7 8 00	4
5		17	Moorhead, Inc.	13			1 4 2 8 00	5
6								6
7								7
8								8
9								9
10								10
11								11
12								12

Extra form

PAGE   VOUCHER

	DATE	PAYEE	VCHR. NO.	PAID		VOUCHERS PAYABLE CREDIT	
				DATE	CK. NO.		
1							1
2							2
3							3
4							4
5							5
6							6
7							7
8							8
9							9
10							10
11							11
12							12

5-3 APPLICATION PROBLEM (concluded)

REGISTER

	PURCHASES DEBIT	SUPPLIES— SALES DEBIT	SUPPLIES— ADMIN. DEBIT	GENERAL				
	2	3	4	ACCOUNT TITLE	POST. REF.	DEBIT (5)	CREDIT (6)	
1	2 700 00							1
2				*Vouchers Payable*		2 700 00		2
3				*Purchases Returns and Allowances*			20 00	3
4	1 778 00							4
5				*Vouchers Payable*		1 778 00		5
6				*Purchases Returns and Allowances*			35 0 00	6
7								7
8								8
9								9
10								10
11								11
12								12

Extra form

REGISTER

	PURCHASES DEBIT	SUPPLIES— SALES DEBIT	SUPPLIES— ADMIN. DEBIT	GENERAL				
	2	3	4	ACCOUNT TITLE	POST. REF.	DEBIT (5)	CREDIT (6)	
1								1
2								2
3								3
4								4
5								5
6								6
7								7
8								8
9								9
10								10
11								11
12								12

Name _____ Date _____ Class _____

5-3 APPLICATION PROBLEM

Extra forms

VOUCHER
1

	DATE	PAYEE	VCHR. NO.	PAID DATE	CK. NO.	VOUCHERS PAYABLE CREDIT	
1							1
2							2
3							3
4							4
5							5
6							6
7							7
8							8
9							9
10							10

PAGE

VOUCHER
1

	DATE	PAYEE	VCHR. NO.	PAID DATE	CK. NO.	VOUCHERS PAYABLE CREDIT	
1							1
2							2
3							3
4							4
5							5
6							6
7							7
8							8
9							9
10							10

5-4 APPLICATION PROBLEM, p. 161

[1, 2]

Preparing and journalizing a voucher for payroll

(Note: The inside of the voucher appears on page 212.)

Vchr.
No. **51**

Date _____5/15/--_____ Due Date _____5/15/--_____ Payment Date _____5/15/--_____

To__*Payroll*_____

Address_____
                                    Street

_____
City   State   ZIP

ACCOUNTS DEBITED	AMOUNT
PURCHASES	
SUPPLIES—SALES	
SUPPLIES—ADMIN.	
MISCELLANEOUS EXPENSE—SALES	
MISCELLANEOUS EXPENSE—ADMIN.	
RENT EXPENSE	
SALARY EXPENSE—SALES	2,530 53
SALARY EXPENSE—ADMIN.	1,687 00
TOTAL DEBITS	4,217 53

ACCOUNTS CREDITED	AMOUNT
VOUCHERS PAYABLE	3,120 97
EMPLOYEE INC. TAX PAY.—FEDERAL	632 63
EMPLOYEE INC. TAX PAY.—STATE	126 53
SOCIAL SECURITY TAX PAY.	274 14
MEDICARE TAX PAY.	63 26
TOTAL CREDITS	4,217 53

Voucher Approved by __*Jason Conway*_____

Recorded in Voucher Register Page _____5_____ by___*J.C.*_____

Paid {
Date _____
Check No. _____ Amount $_____
Approved by _____

5-4 APPLICATION PROBLEM (continued)

[2]

PAGE 5   VOUCHER

	DATE		PAYEE	VCHR. NO.	PAID DATE	CK. NO.	VOUCHERS PAYABLE CREDIT	
1	20-- May	15	Payroll	51			3 1 2 0 97	1
2								2
3								3
4								4
5								5
6								6
7								7
8								8
9								9
10								10

Extra form

PAGE   VOUCHER

	DATE		PAYEE	VCHR. NO.	PAID DATE	CK. NO.	VOUCHERS PAYABLE CREDIT	
1								1
2								2
3								3
4								4
5								5
6								6
7								7
8								8
9								9
10								10

5-4 APPLICATION PROBLEM (continued)

[2]

REGISTER

PAGE 5

	PURCHASES DEBIT	SUPPLIES—SALES DEBIT	SUPPLIES—ADMIN. DEBIT	GENERAL				
				ACCOUNT TITLE	POST. REF.	DEBIT	CREDIT	
1				Salary Expense—Sales		2 5 3 0 53		1
2				Salary Expense—Admin.		1 6 8 7 00		2
3				Employee Inc. Tax Payable—Fed.			6 3 2 63	3
4				Employee Inc. Tax Payable—State			1 2 6 53	4
5				Social Security Tax Payable			2 7 4 14	5
6				Medicare Tax Payable			6 3 26	6
7								7
8								8
9								9
10								10

Extra form

REGISTER

PAGE

	PURCHASES DEBIT	SUPPLIES—SALES DEBIT	SUPPLIES—ADMIN. DEBIT	GENERAL				
				ACCOUNT TITLE	POST. REF.	DEBIT	CREDIT	
1								1
2								2
3								3
4								4
5								5
6								6
7								7
8								8
9								9
10								10

5-4 APPLICATION PROBLEM (concluded)

[1, 2]

			VOUCHER		Vchr. No. **51**

VOUCHER

Vchr. No. **51**

Payment Date _____May 15_____ 20 -- ____

Date _____May 15_____ 20 -- ____ Terms _____

Due _____May 15_____ 20 -- ____

To _Payroll_ _____

Address _____

City _____ State _____ ZIP_____

For the following: Enclose all invoices or other papers.

DATE	VOUCHER DETAILS		AMOUNT
May 15	Payroll for period ended 5/15/--		
	Salary Expense—Sales		$2,530.53
	Salary Expense—Admin.		1,687.00
	Deductions:		
	Employee Inc. Tax Pay.—Federal	$632.63	
	Employee Inc. Tax Pay.—State	126.53	
	Social Security Tax Pay.	274.14	
	Medicare Tax Pay.	63.26	
			1,096.56
	Net cash payment		$3,120.97

5-5 MASTERY PROBLEM, p. 162

Journalizing transactions in a voucher system

[1–3]

CHECK REGISTER

PAGE 20

	DATE		PAYEE	CK. NO.	VCHR. NO.	VOUCHERS PAYABLE DEBIT	PURCHASES DISCOUNT CREDIT	CASH CREDIT	BANK DEPOSITS	BANK BALANCE	
1	20-- Nov.	1	Brought Forward		✔					11676 77	1
2		8	Georgia Company	57	68	975 00	19 50	955 50		10721 27	2
3		10	Deposit		✔				3579 00	14300 27	3
4		14	Quick Delivery	58	72	24 10		24 10		14276 17	4
5		15	North Heights Corporation	59	73	1470 15	29 40	1440 75		12835 42	5
6		16	Payroll	60	74	1459 64		1459 64		11375 78	6
7		22	Supply World	61	69	216 80		216 80		11158 98	7
8		29	Deposit		✔				1170 15	12329 13	8
9		30	Totals			4145 69	48 90	4096 79			9

5-5 MASTERY PROBLEM (continued)

[2, 3]

VOUCHER

1

	DATE		PAYEE	VCHR. NO.	PAID		VOUCHERS PAYABLE CREDIT	
					DATE	CK. NO.		
1	20-- Nov.	1	Georgia Company	68	Nov. 8	57	9 7 5 00	1
2		2	Supply World	69	Nov. 22	61	2 1 6 80	2
3		4	Equipment Plus	70			1 9 9 8 00	3
4		8	North Heights Corporation	71	See Vchr. 73		1 6 9 5 15	4
5		14	Quick Delivery	72	Nov. 14	58	2 4 10	5
6		14	North Heights Corporation	73	Nov. 15	59	1 4 7 0 15	6
7								7
8		16	Payroll	74	Nov. 16	60	1 4 5 9 64	8
9								9
10								10
11								11
12								12
13		25	Fischer Equipment	75			2 3 5 0 00	13
14		30	Georgia Company	76			2 2 5 8 50	14
15		30	Totals				12 4 4 7 34	15
16								16
17								17
18								18
19								19
20								20
21								21
22								22
23								23
24								24
25								25
26								26
27								27
28								28
29								29
30								30
31								31

5-5 MASTERY PROBLEM (concluded)

[2, 3]

REGISTER

	PURCHASES DEBIT (2)	SUPPLIES—SALES DEBIT (3)	SUPPLIES—ADMIN. DEBIT (4)	GENERAL ACCOUNT TITLE	POST. REF.	DEBIT (5)	CREDIT (6)	
1	975 00							1
2			216 80					2
3				Store Equipment		1998 00		3
4	1695 15							4
5				Delivery Expense		24 10		5
6				Vouchers Payable		1695 15		6
7				Purchases Returns and Allowances			225 00	7
8				Salary Expense—Sales		1183 50		8
9				Salary Expense—Admin.		789 00		9
10				Employee Inc. Tax Payable—Fed.			295 88	10
11				Employee Inc. Tax Payable—State			59 18	11
12				Social Security Tax Payable			128 21	12
13				Medicare Tax Payable			29 59	13
14				Office Equipment		2350 00		14
15	2258 50							15
16	4928 65		216 80			8039 75	737 86	16

Name _____ Date _____ Class _____

5-5 MASTERY PROBLEM

Extra form

CHECK REGISTER   PAGE ____

	DATE	PAYEE	CK. NO.	VCHR. NO.	VOUCHERS PAYABLE DEBIT	PURCHASES DISCOUNT CREDIT	CASH CREDIT	BANK DEPOSITS	BANK BALANCE	
					1	2	3	4	5	
1										1
2										2
3										3
4										4
5										5
6										6
7										7
8										8
9										9
10										10
11										11
12										12
13										13
14										14
15										15
16										16
17										17
18										18
19										19
20										20
21										21
22										22
23										23
24										24
25										25
26										26
27										27
28										28
29										29
30										30
31										31

5-6 CHALLENGE PROBLEM, p. 162

Journalizing purchases invoices at the net amount in a voucher system   [1–3]

CHECK REGISTER
PAGE 20

	DATE		PAYEE	CK. NO.	VCHR. NO.	VOUCHERS PAYABLE DEBIT (1)	CASH CREDIT (2)	BANK DEPOSITS (3)	BANK BALANCE (4)	
1	20-- Dec.	11	Brought Forward		✔	1395 00	1395 00		8500 00	1
2		15	Deposit		✔			1000 00	9500 00	2
3		18	Knotts Company	80	109	1960 00	1960 00		7540 00	3
4		22	Deposit		✔			2000 00	9540 00	4
5		25	Hightop Company	81	111	980 00	980 00		8560 00	5
6		26	Fairgate Supply Company	82	113	200 00	200 00		8360 00	6
7		29	Deposit		✔			1000 00	9360 00	7
8		31	Neal Company	83	116	450 00	450 00		8910 00	8
9		31	Totals			4985 00	4985 00			9
10										10
11										11
12										12
13										13
14										14
15										15
16										16
17										17
18										18
19										19
20										20
21										21
22										22
23										23
24										24
25										25
26										26
27										27
28										28
29										29
30										30
31										31

5-6 CHALLENGE PROBLEM (continued)

[2, 3]

VOUCHER

	DATE		PAYEE	VCHR. NO.	PAID		VOUCHERS PAYABLE CREDIT	
					DATE	CK. NO.		
1	Dec.	11	Knotts Company	109	Dec. 18	80	1 9 6 0 00	1
2		15	Fairgate Supply Company	110	See Vchr. 113		1 9 6 00	2
3		18	Hightop Company	111	Dec. 25	81	9 8 0 00	3
4		19	Neal Company	112	See Vchr. 115		4 9 0 00	4
5		26	Fairgate Supply Company	113	Dec. 26	82	2 0 0 00	5
6		28	Peerless Supply Company	114			2 9 4 00	6
7		28	Neal Company	115	See Vchr. 116		4 4 1 00	7
8								8
9		31	Neal Company	116	Dec. 31	83	4 5 0 00	9
10		31	Totals				5 0 1 1 00	10
11								11
12								12
13								13
14								14
15								15
16								16
17								17
18								18
19								19
20								20
21								21
22								22
23								23
24								24
25								25
26								26
27								27
28								28
29								29
30								30
31								31

REGISTER PAGE 25

	PURCHASES DEBIT	DISCOUNTS LOST DEBIT	SUPPLIES DEBIT	ACCOUNT TITLE	POST. REF.	DEBIT	CREDIT	
1	1960 00							1
2			196 00					2
3				Store Equipment		980 00		3
4	490 00							4
5		4 00		Vouchers Payable		196 00		5
6			294 00					6
7				Vouchers Payable		490 00		7
8				Purchases Returns and Allowances			49 00	8
9		9 00		Vouchers Payable		441 00		9
10	2450 00	13 00	490 00			2107 00	49 00	10
11								11
12								12
13								13
14								14
15								15
16								16
17								17
18								18
19								19
20								20
21								21
22								22
23								23
24								24
25								25
26								26
27								27
28								28
29								29
30								30
31								31

Name _____ Date _____ Class _____

5-6 CHALLENGE PROBLEM

Extra form

CHECK REGISTER
PAGE _____

	DATE	PAYEE	CK. NO.	VCHR. NO.	VOUCHERS PAYABLE DEBIT (1)	PURCHASES DISCOUNT CREDIT (2)	CASH CREDIT (3)	BANK DEPOSITS (4)	BANK BALANCE (5)	
1										1
2										2
3										3
4										4
5										5
6										6
7										7
8										8
9										9
10										10
11										11
12										12
13										13
14										14
15										15
16										16
17										17
18										18
19										19
20										20
21										21
22										22
23										23
24										24
25										25
26										26
27										27
28										28
29										29
30										30
31										31

6-1 WORK TOGETHER
ON YOUR OWN, p. 172

Completing a stock record for a perpetual inventory system and comparing it to an inventory record

[4–7]

INVENTORY RECORD

DATE **9/30/--** _____ ITEM **Televisions** _____

1	2	3	4	5
STOCK NUMBER	DESCRIPTION	NO. OF UNITS ON HAND	UNIT PRICE	TOTAL COST
K087	19" color television	85	$175.00	$14,875.00

STOCK RECORD

Description **19" Color Television** _____ Stock No. **K087** _____

Reorder **80** _____ Minimum **20** _____ Location **Bin 12** _____

1	2	3	4	5	6	7
INCREASES			DECREASES			BALANCE
DATE	PURCHASE INVOICE NO.	QUANTITY	DATE	SALES INVOICE NO.	QUANTITY	QUANTITY
Sept. 1						62
			Sept. 12	475	40	22
			Sept. 16	508	8	14
Sept. 17	183	80				94
			Sept. 20	653	15	79
			Sept. 23	714	40	39
			Sept. 25	761	22	17
Sept. 26	255	80				97
			Sept. 30	850	12	85

WT 6-1

OYO 6-1

6-1 **WORK TOGETHER
ON YOUR OWN**

Extra forms

STOCK RECORD

Description _____ Stock No. _____

Reorder _____ Minimum _____ Location _____

1	2	3	4	5	6	7
INCREASES			DECREASES			BALANCE
DATE	PURCHASE INVOICE NO.	QUANTITY	DATE	SALES INVOICE NO.	QUANTITY	QUANTITY

STOCK RECORD

Description _____ Stock No. _____

Reorder _____ Minimum _____ Location _____

1	2	3	4	5	6	7
INCREASES			DECREASES			BALANCE
DATE	PURCHASE INVOICE NO.	QUANTITY	DATE	SALES INVOICE NO.	QUANTITY	QUANTITY

6-2 WORK TOGETHER
ON YOUR OWN, p. 178

Costing ending inventory using fifo, lifo, and weighted average [5]

Fifo:

100 units from October purchase @ $27.60	$ 2,760.00
40 units from July purchase @ $22.00	880.00
Cost of ending inventory	$ 3,640.00

Lifo:

120 units from January inventory @ $20.00	$ 2,400.00
20 units from July purchase @ $22.00	440.00
Cost of ending inventory	$ 2,840.00

Weighted-average:

Total units available for sale	320
Cost of units available for sale	$ 7,360.00
Average cost	$ 23.00

140 units @ $23.00 average cost	$ 3,220.00

[6]

Fifo:

60 units from November purchase @ $5.05	$303.00
15 units from March purchase @ $4.50	67.50
Cost of ending inventory	$370.50

Lifo:

50 units from January inventory @ $4.20	$210.00
25 units from March purchase @ $4.50	112.50
Cost of ending inventory	$322.50

Weighted-average:

Total units available for sale	180
Cost of units available for sale	$828.00
Average cost	$ 4.60

75 units @ $4.60 average cost	$ 345.00

6-2 **WORK TOGETHER**
ON YOUR OWN (concluded)

Extra space for calculations

6-3 WORK TOGETHER, p. 183

Estimating inventory using the gross profit and retail methods

[5]

ESTIMATED MERCHANDISE INVENTORY SHEET
Gross Profit Method

COMPANY _Handy Hardware_   DATE _4/30/--_

1	Beginning inventory, April 1	$ 124,850.00
2	Net purchases to date	73,230.00
3	Merchandise available for sale..................................	$ 198,080.00
4	Net sales to date.......................	$ 138,500.00
5	Less estimated gross profit	51,245.00
	(Net sales × Estimated gross profit _37_ %)	
6	Estimated cost of merchandise sold	87,255.00
7	Estimated ending inventory......................................	$ 110,825.00

[6]

ESTIMATED MERCHANDISE INVENTORY SHEET
Retail Method

COMPANY _Handy Hardware_   DATE _4/30/--_

		Cost	Retail
1			
2	Beginning inventory, April 1	$ 124,850.00	$ 193,400.00
3	Net purchases to date	73,230.00	110,340.00
4	Merchandise available for sale	$ 198,080.00	$ 303,740.00
5	Net sales to date..................................		138,500.00
	Estimated ending inventory at retail		$ 165,240.00
6	Estimated ending inventory at cost	$ 107,736.48	
7	(Inventory at Retail × percentage _65.2_ %)		

6-3 WORK TOGETHER

Extra forms

ESTIMATED MERCHANDISE INVENTORY SHEET
Gross Profit Method

COMPANY _____ DATE _____

1	Beginning inventory, April 1	$_____
2	Net purchases to date	_____
3	Merchandise available for sale	$_____
4	Net sales to date . . . . $ _____	
5	Less estimated gross profit . . . . _____	
	(Net sales × Estimated gross profit _____ %)	
6	Estimated cost of merchandise sold	_____
7	Estimated ending inventory	$_____

ESTIMATED MERCHANDISE INVENTORY SHEET
Retail Method

COMPANY _____ DATE _____

		Cost	Retail
1			
2	Beginning inventory, April 1	$_____	$_____
3	Net purchases to date	_____	_____
4	Merchandise available for sale	$_____	$_____
5	Net sales to date		_____
	Estimated ending inventory at retail		$_____
6	Estimated ending inventory at cost	$_____	
7	(Inventory at Retail × percentage _____ %)		

6-3 ON YOUR OWN, p. 183

Estimating inventory using the gross profit and retail methods [7]

ESTIMATED MERCHANDISE INVENTORY SHEET
Gross Profit Method

COMPANY *Handy Hardware*   DATE *10/31/--*

1	Beginning inventory, October 1.	$	182,570.00
2	Net purchases to date		115,440.00
3	Merchandise available for sale	$	298,010.00
4	Net sales to date. $ 204,340.00		
5	Less estimated gross profit 75,605.80		
	(Net sales × Estimated gross profit *37*%)		
6	Estimated cost of merchandise sold		128,734.20
7	Estimated ending inventory.	$	169,275.80

[8]

ESTIMATED MERCHANDISE INVENTORY SHEET
Retail Method

COMPANY *Handy Hardware*   DATE *10/31/--*

		Cost	Retail
1		Cost	Retail
2	Beginning inventory, October 1.	$ 182,570.00	$ 276,380.00
3	Net purchases to date	115,440.00	190,730.00
4	Merchandise available for sale	$ 298,010.00	$ 467,110.00
5	Net sales to date.		204,340.00
	Estimated ending inventory at retail		$ 262,770.00
6	Estimated ending inventory at cost.	$ 167,647.26	
7	(Inventory at Retail × percentage *63.8*%)		

6-3 ON YOUR OWN

Extra forms

ESTIMATED MERCHANDISE INVENTORY SHEET
Gross Profit Method

COMPANY _____ DATE _____

1	Beginning inventory, October 1	$ _____
2	Net purchases to date	_____
3	Merchandise available for sale	$ _____
4	Net sales to date . . . . $ _____	
5	Less estimated gross profit . . . . _____	
	(Net sales × Estimated gross profit _____%)	
6	Estimated cost of merchandise sold	_____
7	Estimated ending inventory	$ _____

ESTIMATED MERCHANDISE INVENTORY SHEET
Retail Method

COMPANY _____ DATE _____

		Cost	Retail
1			
2	Beginning inventory, October 1	$ _____	$ _____
3	Net purchases to date	_____	_____
4	Merchandise available for sale	$ _____	$ _____
5	Net sales to date		_____
	Estimated ending inventory at retail		$ _____
6	Estimated ending inventory at cost	$ _____	
7	(Inventory at Retail × percentage _____%)		

6-1 APPLICATION PROBLEM, p. 185

Keeping perpetual inventory records

[1, 2]

STOCK RECORD

Description _Lawn Mower_ Stock No. _R263_

Reorder _60_ Minimum _15_ Location _Bin 41_

	1	2	3	4	5	6	7
	INCREASES			DECREASES			BALANCE
	DATE	PURCHASE INVOICE NO.	QUANTITY	DATE	SALES INVOICE NO.	QUANTITY	QUANTITY
20--	Apr. 1						32
				Apr. 2	211	9	23
				Apr. 6	213	6	17
				Apr. 15	215	5	12
	Apr. 16	743	60				72
				Apr. 19	216	30	42
				Apr. 20	217	20	22
				Apr. 24	218	12	10
	Apr. 25	744	60				70
				Apr. 30	220	7	63

STOCK RECORD

Description _Hedge Trimmer_ Stock No. _J184_

Reorder _35_ Minimum _8_ Location _Bin 49_

	1	2	3	4	5	6	7
	INCREASES			DECREASES			BALANCE
	DATE	PURCHASE INVOICE NO.	QUANTITY	DATE	SALES INVOICE NO.	QUANTITY	QUANTITY
20--	Apr. 1						17
				Apr. 3	212	5	12
				Apr. 6	213	6	6
	Apr. 10	742	35				41
				Apr. 11	214	10	31
				Apr. 20	217	15	16
				Apr. 28	219	10	6
	Apr. 29	745	35				41

6-1 APPLICATION PROBLEM

Extra forms

STOCK RECORD

Description _____ Stock No. _____

Reorder _____ Minimum _____ Location _____

1	2	3	4	5	6	7
	INCREASES			DECREASES		BALANCE
DATE	PURCHASE INVOICE NO.	QUANTITY	DATE	SALES INVOICE NO.	QUANTITY	QUANTITY

STOCK RECORD

Description _____ Stock No. _____

Reorder _____ Minimum _____ Location _____

1	2	3	4	5	6	7
	INCREASES			DECREASES		BALANCE
DATE	PURCHASE INVOICE NO.	QUANTITY	DATE	SALES INVOICE NO.	QUANTITY	QUANTITY

6-2 APPLICATION PROBLEM, p. 186

Determining inventory cost using fifo, lifo, weighted average, and lower of cost or market [1–3]

Inventory Costing Method

Stock No.	Dec. 31 Inventory	Market Price	Fifo Unit Price	Fifo Total Cost	Fifo Lower of Cost or Market	Lifo Unit Price	Lifo Total Cost	Lifo Lower of Cost or Market	Weighted Average Unit Price	Weighted Average Total Cost	Weighted Average Lower of Cost or Market
A30	35	35@$12.00 = $420.00	20@$10.00 15@$14.00	$410.00	$410.00	15@$8.00 15@$10.00 5@$12.00	$330.00	$330.00	35@$10.94	$382.90	$382.90
B18	30	30@$7.50 = $225.00	12@$8.00 12@$8.00 6@$9.00	$246.00	$225.00	10@$9.00 10@$9.00 10@$9.00	$270.00	$225.00	30@$8.57	$257.10	$225.00
C45	64	64@$8.00 = $512.00	30@$8.00 30@$7.00 4@$6.00	$474.00	$474.00	22@$5.00 30@$6.00 12@$6.00	$362.00	$362.00	64@$6.48	$414.72	$414.72
D12	20	20@$7.50 = $150.00	5@$7.00 10@$8.00 5@$9.00	$160.00	$150.00	12@$7.00 5@$7.00 3@$9.00	$146.00	$146.00	20@$7.54	$150.80	$150.00
					$1,259.00			$1,063.00			$1,172.62

Highest Method: ___ Fifo ___

Lowest Method: ___ Lifo ___

6-2 APPLICATION PROBLEM

Extra form

Inventory Costing Method

Stock No.	Dec. 31 Inventory	Market Price	Fifo			Lifo			Weighted Average		
			Unit Price	Total Cost	Lower of Cost or Market	Unit Price	Total Cost	Lower of Cost or Market	Unit Price	Total Cost	Lower of Cost or Market

Highest Method: _____

Lowest Method: _____

6-3 APPLICATION PROBLEM, p. 186

Estimating cost of merchandise inventory using estimating methods [1]

ESTIMATED MERCHANDISE INVENTORY SHEET
Gross Profit Method

COMPANY ___Walker, Inc.___   DATE _12/31/--_

1	Beginning inventory, January 1..............................	$	42,400.00
2	Net purchases to date.......................................		136,000.00
3	Merchandise available for sale..............................	$	178,400.00
4	Net sales to date.................................... $ 208,800.00		
5	Less estimated gross profit 83,520.00		
	(Net sales × Estimated gross profit __40_%)		
6	Estimated cost of merchandise sold		125,280.00
7	Estimated ending inventory.................................	$	53,120.00

Extra form

ESTIMATED MERCHANDISE INVENTORY SHEET
Gross Profit Method

COMPANY _____   DATE _____

1	Beginning inventory, January 1..............................	$	
2	Net purchases to date.......................................		
3	Merchandise available for sale..............................	$	
4	Net sales to date.................................... $		
5	Less estimated gross profit		
	(Net sales × Estimated gross profit _____%)		
6	Estimated cost of merchandise sold		
7	Estimated ending inventory.................................	$	

6-3 **APPLICATION PROBLEM (continued)**

[2]

ESTIMATED MERCHANDISE INVENTORY SHEET
Retail Method

COMPANY ___*Walker, Inc.*_____   DATE _*12/31/--*____

		Cost	Retail
1			
2	Beginning inventory, January 1	$ 42,400.00	$ 70,000.00
3	Net purchases to date	136,000.00	227,400.00
4	Merchandise available for sale	$ 178,400.00	$ 297,400.00
5	Net sales to date		208,800.00
	Estimated ending inventory at retail		$ 88,600.00
6	Estimated ending inventory at cost	$ 53,160.00	
7	(Inventory at Retail × percentage __60_%)		

Extra form

ESTIMATED MERCHANDISE INVENTORY SHEET
Retail Method

COMPANY _____   DATE _____

		Cost	Retail
1			
2	Beginning inventory, January 1	$ _____	$ _____
3	Net purchases to date	_____	_____
4	Merchandise available for sale	$ _____	$ _____
5	Net sales to date		_____
	Estimated ending inventory at retail		$ _____
6	Estimated ending inventory at cost	$ _____	
7	(Inventory at Retail × percentage _____%)		

6-4 APPLICATION PROBLEM, p. 187

[1]

Calculating merchandise inventory turnover ratio and average number of days' sales in merchandising inventory

Corporation A:

$$\left(\begin{array}{c}\text{Beginning Merchandise}\\ \text{Inventory}\\ (\$15,800.00\end{array} + \begin{array}{c}\text{Ending Merchandise}\\ \text{Inventory}\\ \$21,200.00)\end{array}\right) \begin{array}{c}\div 2\\ \div 2\end{array} \begin{array}{c}=\\ =\end{array} \begin{array}{c}\text{Average Merchandise}\\ \text{Inventory}\\ \$18,500.00\end{array}$$

$$\begin{array}{c}\text{Cost of Merchandise}\\ \text{Sold}\\ \$167,700.00\end{array} \div \begin{array}{c}\text{Average Merchandise}\\ \text{Inventory}\\ \$18,500.00\end{array} = \begin{array}{c}\text{Merchandise Inventory}\\ \text{Turnover Ratio}\\ \text{9.1 times}\end{array}$$

Corporation B:

$$\left(\begin{array}{c}\text{Beginning Merchandise}\\ \text{Inventory}\\ (\$80,500.00\end{array} + \begin{array}{c}\text{Ending Merchandise}\\ \text{Inventory}\\ \$78,900.00)\end{array}\right) \begin{array}{c}\div 2\\ \div 2\end{array} \begin{array}{c}=\\ =\end{array} \begin{array}{c}\text{Average Merchandise}\\ \text{Inventory}\\ \$79,700.00\end{array}$$

$$\begin{array}{c}\text{Cost of Merchandise}\\ \text{Sold}\\ \$848,000.00\end{array} \div \begin{array}{c}\text{Average Merchandise}\\ \text{Inventory}\\ \$79,700.00\end{array} = \begin{array}{c}\text{Merchandise Inventory}\\ \text{Turnover Ratio}\\ \text{10.6 times}\end{array}$$

Corporation C:

$$\left(\begin{array}{c}\text{Beginning Merchandise}\\ \text{Inventory}\\ (\$64,300.00\end{array} + \begin{array}{c}\text{Ending Merchandise}\\ \text{Inventory}\\ \$54,600.00)\end{array}\right) \begin{array}{c}\div 2\\ \div 2\end{array} \begin{array}{c}=\\ =\end{array} \begin{array}{c}\text{Average Merchandise}\\ \text{Inventory}\\ \$59,450.00\end{array}$$

$$\begin{array}{c}\text{Cost of Merchandise}\\ \text{Sold}\\ \$567,400.00\end{array} \div \begin{array}{c}\text{Average Merchandise}\\ \text{Inventory}\\ \$59,450.00\end{array} = \begin{array}{c}\text{Merchandise Inventory}\\ \text{Turnover Ratio}\\ \text{9.5 times}\end{array}$$

[2]

Corporation A:

Days in a Year	÷	Turnover Ratio	=	Average Number of Days' Sales in Merchandise Inventory
365	÷	9.1 times	=	40 days

Corporation B:

Days in a Year	÷	Turnover Ratio	=	Average Number of Days' Sales in Merchandise Inventory
365	÷	10.6 times	=	34 days

Corporation C:

Days in a Year	÷	Turnover Ratio	=	Average Number of Days' Sales in Merchandise Inventory
365	÷	9.5 times	=	38 days

[3]

Best Turnover Ratio: _Corporation B_

6-4 APPLICATION PROBLEM (concluded)

Extra space for calculations

Name _____ Date _____ Class _____

6-5 MASTERY PROBLEM, p. 187

Determining cost of merchandise inventory; estimating cost of merchandise
inventory using estimating methods; calculating merchandise inventory turnover
ratio and average number of days' sales in merchandise inventory

[1, 2]

Stock No.	Dec. 31 Inventory	Inventory Costing Method					
		Fifo		Lifo		Weighted Average	
		Unit Price	Total Cost	Unit Price	Total Cost	Unit Price	Total Cost
R46	18	15 @ 9.00 3 @ 8.00	159.00	14 @ 7.00 4 @ 8.00	130.00	8.02	144.36
S10	26	10 @ 8.00 10 @ 5.00 6 @ 5.00	160.00	16 @ 5.00 10 @ 5.00	130.00	5.83	151.58
T76	25	15 @ 11.00 10 @ 11.00	275.00	8 @ 12.00 15 @ 11.00 2 @ 11.00	283.00	11.21	280.25
U92	10	7 @ 8.00 3 @ 8.00	80.00	7 @ 8.00 3 @ 8.00	80.00	8.00	80.00
V17	5	5 @ 7.00	35.00	5 @ 4.00	20.00	6.00	30.00
Total Cost			709.00		643.00		686.19

[3]

Stock No.	Lifo Cost	Market Price			Lower of Cost or Market
		Inventory	Unit Price	Total Cost	
R46	$130.00	18	$9.50	$171.00	$130.00
S10	130.00	26	4.75	123.50	123.50
T76	283.00	25	10.00	250.00	250.00
U92	80.00	10	8.00	80.00	80.00
V17	20.00	5	6.00	30.00	20.00
Total					603.50

[6]

$$\left(\begin{array}{c}\text{Beginning Merchandise Inventory} \\ (\$21,200.00\end{array} + \begin{array}{c}\text{Ending Merchandise Inventory} \\ \$26,980.00)\end{array}\right) \begin{array}{c}\div 2 \\ \div 2\end{array} \begin{array}{c}= \\ =\end{array} \begin{array}{c}\text{Average Merchandise Inventory} \\ \$24,090.00\end{array}$$

$$\begin{array}{c}\text{Cost of Merchandise Sold} \\ \$62,220.00\end{array} \begin{array}{c}\div \\ \div\end{array} \begin{array}{c}\text{Average Merchandise Inventory} \\ \$24,090.00\end{array} \begin{array}{c}= \\ =\end{array} \begin{array}{c}\text{Merchandise Inventory Turnover Ratio} \\ 2.6 \text{ times}\end{array}$$

[7]

$$\begin{array}{c}\text{Days in a Year} \\ 365\end{array} \begin{array}{c}\div \\ \div\end{array} \begin{array}{c}\text{Turnover Ratio} \\ 2.6 \text{ times}\end{array} \begin{array}{c}= \\ =\end{array} \begin{array}{c}\text{Average Number of Days' Sales in Merchandise Inventory} \\ 140 \text{ days}\end{array}$$

6-5 MASTERY PROBLEM (concluded)

[4]

ESTIMATED MERCHANDISE INVENTORY SHEET
Gross Profit Method

COMPANY _Sowell, Inc._   DATE _December 31, 20--_

1	Beginning inventory, January 1 . . . . $	21,200.00
2	Net purchases to date	68,000.00
3	Merchandise available for sale . . . . $	89,200.00
4	Net sales to date . . . . $ 103,700.00	
5	Less estimated gross profit 41,480.00	
	(Net sales × Estimated gross profit _40.0_%)	
6	Estimated cost of merchandise sold	62,220.00
7	Estimated ending inventory . . . . $	26,980.00

[5]

ESTIMATED MERCHANDISE INVENTORY SHEET
Retail Method

COMPANY _Sowell, Inc._   DATE _December 31, 20--_

		Cost	Retail
1			
2	Beginning inventory, January 1	$ 21,200.00	$ 35,000.00
3	Net purchases to date	68,000.00	113,700.00
4	Merchandise available for sale	$ 89,200.00	$ 148,700.00
5	Net sales to date		103,700.00
	Estimated ending inventory at retail		$ 45,000.00
6	Estimated ending inventory at cost	$ 27,000.00	
7	(Inventory at Retail × percentage _60.0_%)		

6-6 CHALLENGE PROBLEM, p. 188

Determining the unit price of merchandise inventory purchases   [1]

Total Cost	÷	Subtotal	=	Percentage
$422.30	÷	$410.00	=	103.0%

[2, 3]

Stock No.	Quantity	Unit Price	Total Cost	Adjusted Unit Price	Adjusted Total Cost
A69	50	$2.00	$100.00	$2.06	$103.00
V56	15	6.00	90.00	6.18	92.70
X28	30	4.00	120.00	4.12	123.60
W12	20	3.00	60.00	3.09	61.80
S92	5	8.00	40.00	8.24	41.20

Extra space for calculations

6-6 CHALLENGE PROBLEM (concluded)

Extra space for calculations

7-1 WORK TOGETHER, p. 198

Journalizing entries to write off uncollectible accounts—direct write-off method [4]

GENERAL JOURNAL   PAGE 2

	DATE		ACCOUNT TITLE	DOC. NO.	POST. REF.	DEBIT	CREDIT	
1	20-- Jan.	10	Uncollectible Accounts Expense	M13		261 54		1
2			Accounts Receivable/Melinda Sanford				261 54	2
3	Mar.	12	Uncollectible Accounts Expense	M24		45 00		3
4			Accounts Receivable/Mark Polk				45 00	4
5	Apr.	13	Accounts Receivable/Andrew Leslie	M31		67 42		5
6			Collection of Uncollectible Accounts				67 42	6
7	Nov.	15	Accounts Receivable/Melinda Sanford	M84		261 54		7
8			Collection of Uncollectible Accounts				261 54	8
9								9
10								10
11								11
12								12
13								13
14								14
15								15
16								16
17								17
18								18
19								19
20								20
21								21
22								22
23								23
24								24
25								25
26								26
27								27
28								28
29								29
30								30
31								31

7-1 WORK TOGETHER (concluded)

[4]

CASH RECEIPTS JOURNAL   PAGE 3

	DATE	ACCOUNT TITLE	DOC. NO.	POST. REF.	GENERAL DEBIT (1)	GENERAL CREDIT (2)	ACCOUNTS RECEIVABLE CREDIT (3)	SALES CREDIT (4)	SALES TAX PAYABLE DEBIT (5)	SALES TAX PAYABLE CREDIT (6)	SALES DISCOUNT DEBIT (7)	CASH DEBIT (8)	
1	20-- Apr. 13	Andrew Leslie	R158				6742					6742	1
2	Nov. 15	Melinda Sanford	R313				26154					26154	2
3													3
4													4
5													5
6													6
7													7
8													8
9													9
10													10
11													11
12													12
13													13
14													14
15													15
16													16
17													17
18													18
19													19
20													20
21													21
22													22
23													23
24													24
25													25

7-1 ON YOUR OWN, p. 198

Journalizing entries to write off uncollectible accounts—direct write-off method

[5]

GENERAL JOURNAL   PAGE 2

	DATE		ACCOUNT TITLE	DOC. NO.	POST. REF.	DEBIT	CREDIT	
1	20-- Jan.	20	Uncollectible Accounts Expense	M15		2 6 5 48		1
2			Accounts Receivable/Belinda Rafferty				2 6 5 48	2
3	Feb.	15	Uncollectible Accounts Expense	M21		5 2 00		3
4			Accounts Receivable/Ervin Bond				5 2 00	4
5	Apr.	10	Accounts Receivable/Stephanie Byrd	M34		1 7 8 43		5
6			Collection of Uncollectible Accounts				1 7 8 43	6
7	Oct.	5	Accounts Receivable/Belinda Rafferty	M104		2 6 5 48		7
8			Collection of Uncollectible Accounts				2 6 5 48	8
9								9
10								10
11								11
12								12
13								13
14								14
15								15
16								16
17								17
18								18
19								19
20								20
21								21
22								22
23								23
24								24
25								25
26								26
27								27
28								28
29								29
30								30
31								31

7-1 ON YOUR OWN (concluded)

[5]

CASH RECEIPTS JOURNAL

PAGE 3

	DATE	ACCOUNT TITLE	DOC. NO.	POST. REF.	GENERAL DEBIT	GENERAL CREDIT	ACCOUNTS RECEIVABLE CREDIT	SALES CREDIT	SALES TAX PAYABLE DEBIT	SALES TAX PAYABLE CREDIT	SALES DISCOUNT DEBIT	CASH DEBIT	
1	20-- Apr. 10	Stephanie Byrd	R89				1 7 8 4 3					1 7 8 4 3	1
2	Oct. 5	Belinda Rafferty	R135				2 6 5 4 8					2 6 5 4 8	2
3													3
4													4
5													5
6													6
7													7
8													8
9													9
10													10
11													11
12													12
13													13
14													14
15													15
16													16
17													17
18													18
19													19
20													20
21													21
22													22
23													23
24													24
25													25

7-2 WORK TOGETHER, p. 205

Estimating amount of uncollectible accounts expense; journalizing the adjusting entry [4]

GENERAL JOURNAL

PAGE 12

	DATE		ACCOUNT TITLE	DOC. NO.	POST. REF.	DEBIT	CREDIT	
1			*Adjusting Entries*					1
2	20-- Dec.	31	*Uncollectible Accounts Expense*			1 2 2 6 61		2
3			*Allowance for Uncollectible Accounts*				1 2 2 6 61	3
4								4
5								5
6								6
7								7
8								8
9								9
10								10
11								11
12								12
13								13
14								14
15								15
16								16
17								17
18								18
19								19
20								20
21								21
22								22
23								23
24								24
25								25
26								26
27								27
28								28
29								29
30								30
31								31

7-2 WORK TOGETHER (concluded)

[5]

Age Group	Amount	Percentage	Uncollectible
Not yet due	$ 8,619.18	0.1%	$ 8.62
1–30 days	2,254.83	0.2%	4.51
31–60 days	862.57	0.3%	2.59
61–90 days	2,574.57	0.8%	20.60
Over 90 days	350.90	50.0%	175.45
Totals	$14,662.05		$211.77
Current Balance of Allowance for Uncollectible Accounts			63.24
Estimated Addition to Allowance for Uncollectible Accounts			$148.53

GENERAL JOURNAL   PAGE 14

	DATE		ACCOUNT TITLE	DOC. NO.	POST. REF.	DEBIT	CREDIT	
1			*Adjusting Entries*					1
2	20-- Dec.	31	Uncollectible Accounts Expense			148 53		2
3			Allowance for Uncollectible Accounts				148 53	3
4								4
5								5

7-2 ON YOUR OWN, p. 205

Estimating amount of uncollectible accounts expense; journalizing the adjusting entry [6]

GENERAL JOURNAL   PAGE 18

	DATE		ACCOUNT TITLE	DOC. NO.	POST. REF.	DEBIT	CREDIT	
1			*Adjusting Entries*					1
2	20-- Dec.	31	Uncollectible Accounts Expense			5 4 8 3 28		2
3			*Allowance for Uncollectible Accounts*				5 4 8 3 28	3
4								4
5								5
6								6
7								7
8								8
9								9
10								10
11								11
12								12
13								13
14								14
15								15
16								16
17								17
18								18
19								19
20								20
21								21
22								22
23								23
24								24
25								25
26								26
27								27
28								28
29								29
30								30
31								31

7-2 ON YOUR OWN (concluded)

[7]

Age Group	Amount	Percentage	Uncollectible
Not yet due	$16,453.18	0.1%	$ 16.45
1–30 days	5,354.12	0.5%	26.77
31–60 days	645.15	10.0%	64.52
61–90 days	3,458.01	20.0%	691.60
Over 90 days	894.28	50.0%	447.14
Totals	$26,804.74		$1,246.48
Current Balance of Allowance for Uncollectible Accounts			391.75
Estimated Addition to Allowance for Uncollectible Accounts			$ 854.73

GENERAL JOURNAL

PAGE 16

	DATE		ACCOUNT TITLE	DOC. NO.	POST. REF.	DEBIT	CREDIT	
1			*Adjusting Entries*					1
2	20– Dec.	31	*Uncollectible Accounts Expense*			854 73		2
3			*Allowance for Uncollectible Accounts*				854 73	3
4								4
5								5
6								6
7								7
8								8
9								9
10								10
11								11
12								12
13								13
14								14
15								15
16								16
17								17

7-3 WORK TOGETHER, p. 208

Calculating accounts receivable turnover ratios

[4]

Accounts receivable turnover ratio:

	Accounts Receivable	−	Allowance for Uncollectible Accounts	=	Book Value
Beginning	$264,483.18	−	$ 8,234.22	=	$256,248.96
Ending	$275,486.58	−	$10,723.36	=	$264,763.22

(Beginning Book Value	+	Ending Book Value)	÷ 2	=	Average Book Value
($256,248.96	+	$264,763.22)	÷ 2	=	$260,506.09

Net Sales on Account	÷	Average Book Value	=	Accounts Receivable Turnover Ratio
$2,396,656.10	÷	$260,506.09	=	9.2

[5]

Average number of days for payment:

Days in Year	÷	Accounts Receivable Turnover Ratio	=	Average Number of Days for Payment
365	÷	9.2	=	40

[6]

Is Milliken Industries effective in collecting accounts receivable?

Milliken Industries has reduced the time required to collect the average account

receivable. With n/30 credit terms, Milliken appears to be doing a reasonably good job

in collecting its accounts receivable on a timely basis.

7-3 WORK TOGETHER (concluded)

Extra space for calculations

7-3 ON YOUR OWN, p. 208

Calculating accounts receivable turnover ratios   [7]

Accounts receivable turnover ratio:

	Accounts Receivable	–	Allowance for Uncollectible Accounts	=	Book Value
Beginning	$163,874.05	–	$6,544.83	=	$157,329.22
Ending	$186,383.48	–	$7,745.86	=	$178,637.62

$$(\text{Beginning Book Value} + \text{Ending Book Value}) \div 2 = \text{Average Book Value}$$

$$(\$157,329.22 + \$178,637.62) \div 2 = \$167,983.42$$

$$\text{Net Sales on Account} \div \text{Average Book Value} = \text{Accounts Receivable Turnover Ratio}$$

$$\$872,895.94 \div \$167,983.42 = 5.2$$

[8]

Average number of days for payment:

$$\text{Days in Year} \div \text{Accounts Receivable Turnover Ratio} = \text{Average Number of Days for Payment}$$

$$365 \div 5.2 = 70$$

[9]

Is Stokes Building Supply effective in collecting accounts receivable?

Stokes Building Supply is not effective in collecting its accounts receivable. With n/45 credit terms, Stokes should be able to collect its accounts quicker than 70 days. Because Stokes was more effective collecting its accounts last year, it should reexamine any changes in its collection methods.

7-3 ON YOUR OWN (concluded)

Extra space for calculations

7-1 APPLICATION PROBLEM, p. 210

Journalizing entries to write off uncollectible accounts—direct write-off method

GENERAL JOURNAL | PAGE 3

	DATE		ACCOUNT TITLE	DOC. NO.	POST. REF.	DEBIT	CREDIT	
1	20-- Feb.	16	Uncollectible Accounts Expense	M18		2 1 5 64		1
2			Accounts Receivable/William Rose		/		2 1 5 64	2
3	Mar.	23	Accounts Receivable/Emma Peden	M43	/	1 7 5 00		3
4			Collection of Uncollectible Accounts				1 7 5 00	4
5	May	7	Uncollectible Accounts Expense	M61		1 8 7 32		5
6			Accounts Receivable/Tom Ming		/		1 8 7 32	6
7	Aug.	10	Accounts Receivable/William Rose	M78	/	2 1 5 64		7
8			Collection of Uncollectible Accounts				2 1 5 64	8
9								9
10								10
11								11
12								12
13								13
14								14
15								15
16								16
17								17
18								18
19								19
20								20
21								21
22								22
23								23
24								24
25								25
26								26
27								27
28								28
29								29
30								30
31								31

7-1 APPLICATION PROBLEM (concluded)

CASH RECEIPTS JOURNAL

PAGE 4

	DATE	ACCOUNT TITLE	DOC. NO.	POST. REF.	GENERAL DEBIT	GENERAL CREDIT	ACCOUNTS RECEIVABLE CREDIT	SALES CREDIT	SALES TAX PAYABLE DEBIT	SALES TAX PAYABLE CREDIT	SALES DISCOUNT DEBIT	CASH DEBIT	
1	20-- Mar. 23	Emma Peden	R215				17500					17500	1
2	Aug. 10	William Rose	R341				21564					21564	2
3													3
4													4
5													5
6													6
7													7
8													8
9													9
10													10
11													11
12													12
13													13
14													14
15													15
16													16
17													17
18													18
19													19
20													20
21													21
22													22
23													23
24													24
25													25

7-2 APPLICATION PROBLEM, p. 210

Estimating amount of uncollectible accounts expense by using a percentage of net sales—allowance method; journalizing the adjusting entry

GENERAL JOURNAL　　　　　　　　　　PAGE 24

	DATE	ACCOUNT TITLE	DOC. NO.	POST. REF.	DEBIT	CREDIT	
1		*Adjusting Entries*					1
2	20-- Dec. 31	Uncollectible Accounts Expense			5 1 7 9 47		2
3		*Allowance for Uncollectible Accounts*				5 1 7 9 47	3
4							4
5							5
6							6
7							7
8							8
9							9
10							10
11							11
12							12

Extra space for calculations

Name _____ Date _____ Class _____

Extra form

GENERAL JOURNAL

PAGE _____

	DATE	ACCOUNT TITLE	DOC. NO.	POST. REF.	DEBIT	CREDIT	
1							1
2							2
3							3
4							4
5							5
6							6
7							7
8							8
9							9
10							10
11							11
12							12
13							13
14							14
15							15
16							16
17							17
18							18
19							19
20							20
21							21
22							22
23							23
24							24
25							25
26							26
27							27
28							28
29							29
30							30
31							31

7-3 APPLICATION PROBLEM, p. 210

Estimating the balance of Allowance for Uncollectible Accounts by aging accounts receivable—allowance method; journalizing the adjusting entry [1]

Age Group	Amount	Percentage	Uncollectible
Not yet due	$44,434.51	0.2%	$ 88.87
1–30 days	25,623.64	0.5%	128.12
31–60 days	10,535.20	1.0%	105.35
61–90 days	5,235.40	5.0%	261.77
Over 90 days	3,534.70	60.0%	2,120.82
Totals	$89,363.45		$2,704.93
Current Balance of Allowance for Uncollectible Accounts			589.63
Estimated Addition to Allowance for Uncollectible Accounts			$2,115.30

[2]

GENERAL JOURNAL   PAGE 12

	DATE		ACCOUNT TITLE	DOC. NO.	POST. REF.	DEBIT	CREDIT	
1			*Adjusting Entries*					1
2	20-- Dec.	31	Uncollectible Accounts Expense			2 1 1 5 30		2
3			Allowance for Uncollectible Accounts				2 1 1 5 30	3
4								4
5								5
6								6
7								7
8								8
9								9
10								10
11								11
12								12
13								13
14								14
15								15
16								16

7-3 APPLICATION PROBLEM

Extra form

GENERAL JOURNAL

PAGE _____

	DATE		ACCOUNT TITLE	DOC. NO.	POST. REF.	DEBIT	CREDIT	
1								1
2								2
3								3
4								4
5								5
6								6
7								7
8								8
9								9
10								10
11								11
12								12
13								13
14								14
15								15
16								16
17								17
18								18
19								19
20								20
21								21
22								22
23								23
24								24
25								25
26								26
27								27
28								28
29								29
30								30
31								31

Name _____ Date _____ Class _____

7-4 APPLICATION PROBLEM, p. 211

Journalizing entries to write off uncollectible accounts and collect written-off accounts—allowance method

GENERAL JOURNAL   PAGE 3

	DATE		ACCOUNT TITLE	DOC. NO.	POST. REF.	DEBIT	CREDIT	
1	20-- Feb.	14	Allowance for Uncollectible Accounts	M16		3 5 7 00		1
2			Accounts Receivable/Peggy King		/		3 5 7 00	2
3	Apr.	25	Allowance for Uncollectible Accounts	M34		8 4 98		3
4			Accounts Receivable/Mel Kober		/		8 4 98	4
5	May	12	Accounts Receivable/Carolyn Kelly	M43	/	7 4 00		5
6			Allowance for Uncollectible Accounts				7 4 00	6
7	Aug.	2	Allowance for Uncollectible Accounts	M71		7 4 93		7
8			Accounts Receivable/Lynn Hartman		/		7 4 93	8
9	Oct.	6	Accounts Receivable/Peggy King	M92	/	3 5 7 00		9
10			Allowance for Uncollectible Accounts				3 5 7 00	10
11								11
12								12
13								13
14								14
15								15
16								16
17								17
18								18
19								19
20								20
21								21
22								22
23								23
24								24
25								25
26								26
27								27
28								28
29								29
30								30
31								31

7-4 APPLICATION PROBLEM (concluded)

CASH RECEIPTS JOURNAL   PAGE 8

DATE	ACCOUNT TITLE	DOC. NO.	POST. REF.	GENERAL DEBIT 1	GENERAL CREDIT 2	ACCOUNTS RECEIVABLE CREDIT 3	SALES CREDIT 4	SALES TAX PAYABLE DEBIT 5	SALES TAX PAYABLE CREDIT 6	SALES DISCOUNT DEBIT 7	CASH DEBIT 8
20-- May 12	Carolyn Kelly	R264				74 00					74 00
Oct. 6	Peggy King	R484				357 00					357 00

7-5 APPLICATION PROBLEM, p. 211

Calculating the accounts receivable turnover ratio   **[1]**

Accounts receivable turnover ratio:

	Accounts Receivable	−	Allowance for Uncollectible Accounts	=	Book Value
Beginning	$584,348.48	−	$20,153.35	=	$564,195.13
Ending	$604,285.25	−	$23,485.62	=	$580,799.63

(Beginning Book Value	+	Ending Book Value)	÷ 2	=	Average Book Value
($564,195.13	+	$580,799.63)	÷ 2	=	$572,497.38

Net Sales on Account	÷	Average Book Value	=	Accounts Receivable Turnover Ratio
$3,848,348.27	÷	$572,497.38	=	6.7

[2]

Average number of days for payment:

Days in Year	÷	Accounts Receivable Turnover Ratio	=	Average Number of Days for Payment
365	÷	6.7	=	54

[3]

Is Fleming Company effective in collecting its accounts receivable?

Fleming Company has significantly improved its effectiveness in collecting its accounts.

However, Fleming needs to continue to improve its accounts receivable turnover ratio to

reduce it closer to 30 days.

7-5 APPLICATION PROBLEM (concluded)

Extra space for calculations

7-6 APPLICATION PROBLEM, p. 212

Accounts receivable transactions using the allowance method

GENERAL JOURNAL
PAGE 4

	DATE		ACCOUNT TITLE	DOC. NO.	POST. REF.	DEBIT	CREDIT	
1	20-- Mar.	23	Allowance for Uncollectible Accounts	M32		4 00 00		1
2			Accounts Receivable/Wade Supply				4 00 00	2
3	Apr.	4	Accounts Receivable/Creative Decor	M45		3 20 00		3
4			Allowance for Uncollectible Accounts				3 20 00	4
5	May	14	Allowance for Uncollectible Accounts	M54		7 5 00		5
6			Accounts Receivable/Raymond Fisher				7 5 00	6
7	Oct.	10	Accounts Receivable/Wade Supply	M72		8 00 00		7
8			Allowance for Uncollectible Accounts				8 00 00	8
9	Nov.	21	Allowance for Uncollectible Accounts	M89		6 00 00		9
10			Accounts Receivable/Mary Crawford				6 00 00	10
11								11
12								12
13								13
14								14
15								15
16								16
17								17
18								18
19								19
20								20
21								21
22								22
23								23
24								24
25								25
26								26
27								27
28								28
29								29
30								30
31								31

Name _____ Date _____ Class _____

7-6 APPLICATION PROBLEM (concluded)

CASH RECEIPTS JOURNAL — PAGE 10

DATE	ACCOUNT TITLE	DOC. NO.	POST. REF.	GENERAL DEBIT	GENERAL CREDIT	ACCOUNTS RECEIVABLE CREDIT	SALES CREDIT	SALES TAX PAYABLE DEBIT	SALES TAX PAYABLE CREDIT	SALES DISCOUNT DEBIT	CASH DEBIT
20-- Apr. 4	Creative Decor	R156				320000					320000
Oct. 10	Wade Supply	R348				80000					80000

264 • Working Papers

COPYRIGHT © SOUTH-WESTERN EDUCATIONAL PUBLISHING

7-7 MASTERY PROBLEM, p. 212

Journalizing entries for uncollectible accounts—allowance method; calculating and journalizing the adjusting entry for uncollectible accounts expense [1, 2]

GENERAL JOURNAL

PAGE 1

	DATE		ACCOUNT TITLE	DOC. NO.	POST. REF.	DEBIT	CREDIT	
1	20-- Jan.	9	Allowance for Uncollectible Accounts	M20		634 65		1
2			Accounts Receivable/Jane Martinez				634 65	2
3	Mar.	4	Allowance for Uncollectible Accounts	M29		782 50		3
4			Accounts Receivable/Jason Young				782 50	4
5		28	Accounts Receivable/Jane Martinez	M40		634 65		5
6			Allowance for Uncollectible Accounts				634 65	6
7	June	20	Allowance for Uncollectible Accounts	M58		617 16		7
8			Accounts Receivable/Allison Aanerud				617 16	8
9	Oct.	7	Allowance for Uncollectible Accounts	M74		808 15		9
10			Accounts Receivable/Meredith Darst				808 15	10
11	Dec.	11	Accounts Receivable/Jason Young	M82		782 50		11
12			Allowance for Uncollectible Accounts				782 50	12
13			*Adjusting Entries*					13
14		31	Uncollectible Accounts Expense			3775 40		14
15			Allowance for Uncollectible Accounts				3775 40	15
16								16
17								17
18								18
19								19
20								20
21								21
22								22
23								23
24								24

[2]

Net Sales... $377,539.58

Uncollectible Accounts Expense = Net Sales × 1% ($377,539.58 × 1%) .... $ 3,775.40

7-7 MASTERY PROBLEM (concluded)

[1]

CASH RECEIPTS JOURNAL

PAGE 1

	DATE	ACCOUNT TITLE	DOC. NO.	POST. REF.	GENERAL DEBIT	GENERAL CREDIT	ACCOUNTS RECEIVABLE CREDIT	SALES CREDIT	SALES TAX PAYABLE DEBIT	SALES TAX PAYABLE CREDIT	SALES DISCOUNT DEBIT	CASH DEBIT	
1	20-- Mar. 28	Jane Martinez	R24				634 65					634 65	1
2	Dec. 11	Jason Young	R92				782 50					782 50	2
3													3
4													4
5													5
6													6
7													7

[3]

Accounts receivable turnover ratio:

	Accounts Receivable	−	Allowance for Uncollectible Accounts	=	Book Value
Beginning	$49,576.17	−	$1,463.89	=	$48,112.28
Ending	$62,791.30	−	$3,813.98	=	$58,977.32

(Beginning Book Value	+	Ending Book Value)	÷ 2	=	Average Book Value
($48,112.28	+	$58,977.32)	÷ 2	=	$53,544.80

Net Sales on Account	÷	Average Book Value	=	Accounts Receivable Turnover Ratio
$349,562.10	÷	$53,544.80	=	6.5

Average number of days for payment:

Days in Year	÷	Accounts Receivable Turnover Ratio	=	Average Number of Days for Payment
365	÷	6.5	=	56

Name _____ Date _____ Class _____

7-8 CHALLENGE PROBLEM, p. 213

Estimating and journalizing uncollectible accounts expense by aging accounts
receivable—allowance method; calculating and journalizing the adjusting entry for
uncollectible accounts expense

[1]

Customer	Account Balance	Not Yet Due	Days Account Balance Past Due			
			1–30	31–60	61–90	Over 90
Atkins Co.	$ 2,523.64					2,523.64
Bankhead Supply	2,435.75	2,435.75				
Coffman Distributing	943.74		943.74			
Fleet Trucking	2,643.23	2,643.23				
Griffin Industries	7,896.54			7,896.54		
Miskelly & Sons	2,754.48		2,754.48			
Oswalt, Inc.	8,723.54	8,723.54				
Rice Shipping Co.	4,363.27					4,363.27
Smith Stores	1,324.76				1,324.76	
Totals	$33,608.95	13,802.52	3,698.22	7,896.54	1,324.76	6,886.91

[2]

Age Group	Amount	Percentage	Uncollectible
Not yet due	$13,802.52	0.3%	$ 41.41
1–30 days	3,698.22	1.0%	36.98
31–60 days	7,896.54	4.0%	315.86
61–90 days	1,324.76	20.0%	264.95
Over 90 days	6,886.91	60.0%	4,132.15
Totals	$33,608.95		$4,791.35
Current Balance of Allowance for Uncollectible Accounts			(692.16)
Estimated Addition to Allowance for Uncollectible Accounts			$5,483.51

Chapter 7   Accounting for Uncollectible Accounts • 267

7-8 CHALLENGE PROBLEM (concluded)

[3]

GENERAL JOURNAL   PAGE 12

	DATE		ACCOUNT TITLE	DOC. NO.	POST. REF.	DEBIT	CREDIT	
1			*Adjusting Entries*					1
2	20-- Dec.	31	*Uncollectible Accounts Expense*			5 48 3 51		2
3			*Allowance for Uncollectible Accounts*				5 48 3 51	3
4								4
5								5
6								6
7								7
8								8
9								9
10								10
11								11
12								12
13								13
14								14
15								15
16								16
17								17
18								18
19								19
20								20
21								21
22								22
23								23
24								24
25								25
26								26
27								27
28								28
29								29
30								30
31								31

8-1 WORK TOGETHER, p. 221

Journalizing asset purchase and property tax transactions   [4]

CASH PAYMENTS JOURNAL   PAGE 1

	DATE		ACCOUNT TITLE	CK. NO.	POST. REF.	GENERAL DEBIT	GENERAL CREDIT	ACCOUNTS PAYABLE DEBIT	PURCHASES DISCOUNT CREDIT	CASH CREDIT	
1	20X1 Jan.	3	Office Equipment	310		600 00				600 00	1
2	Feb.	27	Property Tax Expense	389		7525 00				7525 00	2
3											3
4											4
5											5
6											6
7											7
8											8
9											9
10											10
11											11
12											12
13											13

[4]

GENERAL JOURNAL   PAGE 1

	DATE		ACCOUNT TITLE	DOC. NO.	POST. REF.	DEBIT	CREDIT	
1	20X1 Jan.	5	Warehouse Equipment	M61		2800 00		1
2			Accounts Payable/Trent, Inc.				2800 00	2
3								3
4								4
5								5
6								6
7								7
8								8
9								9
10								10
11								11
12								12
13								13

Name _____ Date _____ Class _____

8-1 WORK TOGETHER (concluded)

[5]

(Note: These records are needed to complete Work Together 8-2.)

PLANT ASSET RECORD, No. _162_   General Ledger Account No. _1225_

Description _Scanner_   General Ledger Account _Office Equipment_

Date Bought _Jan. 3, 20X1_   Serial Number _V2GR34_   Original Cost _$600.00_

Estimated Useful Life _3 years_   Estimated Salvage Value _none_   Depreciation _Straight line method_

Disposed of: Discarded _✓_   Sold _____   Traded _____

Date _Jan. 3, 20X5_   Disposal Amount _zero_

YEAR	ANNUAL DEPRECIATION EXPENSE	ACCUMULATED DEPRECIATION	ENDING BOOK VALUE
20X1	$200.00	$200.00	$400.00
20X2	200.00	400.00	200.00
20X3	200.00	600.00	0.00

[5]

PLANT ASSET RECORD, No. _163_   General Ledger Account No. _1245_

Description _Freight Scale_   General Ledger Account _Warehouse Equipment_

Date Bought _Jan. 5, 20X1_   Serial Number _GY52232B_   Original Cost _$2,800.00_

Estimated Useful Life _5 years_   Estimated Salvage Value _$400.00_   Depreciation _Straight line method_

Disposed of: Discarded _____   Sold _✓_   Traded _____

Date _Mar. 30, 20X5_   Disposal Amount _$600.00_

YEAR	ANNUAL DEPRECIATION EXPENSE	ACCUMULATED DEPRECIATION	ENDING BOOK VALUE
20X1	$480.00	$ 480.00	$2,320.00
20X2	480.00	960.00	1,840.00
20X3	480.00	1,440.00	1,360.00
20X4	480.00	1,920.00	880.00
20X5	120.00	2,040.00	760.00

Name _____ Date _____ Class _____

8-1 ON YOUR OWN, p. 221

Journalizing asset purchase and property tax transactions [6]

GENERAL JOURNAL PAGE 1

	DATE		ACCOUNT TITLE	DOC. NO.	POST. REF.	DEBIT	CREDIT	
1	20X1 Jan.	2	Store Equipment	M35		800 00		1
2			Accounts Payable/JP Enterprises		/		800 00	2
3								3
4								4
5								5
6								6
7								7
8								8
9								9
10								10
11								11
12								12

[6]

CASH PAYMENTS JOURNAL PAGE 1

	DATE		ACCOUNT TITLE	CK. NO.	POST. REF.	GENERAL DEBIT	GENERAL CREDIT	ACCOUNTS PAYABLE DEBIT	PURCHASES DISCOUNT CREDIT	CASH CREDIT	
1	20X1 Jan.	6	Office Equipment	415		500 00				500 00	1
2	Feb.	26	Property Tax Expense	489		1176 00				1176 00	2
3											3
4											4
5											5
6											6
7											7
8											8
9											9
10											10
11											11
12											12
13											13

Name _____ Date _____ Class _____

8-1 ON YOUR OWN (concluded)

[7]

(Note: These records are needed to complete On Your Own 8-2.)

PLANT ASSET RECORD, No. __416__   General Ledger Account No. __1235__

Description _Cash Register_   General Ledger Account _Store Equipment_

Date Bought _Jan. 2, 20X1_   Serial Number _G3HR644_   Original Cost ___$800.00___

Estimated Useful Life _5 years_   Estimated Salvage Value _$200.00_   Depreciation _Straight line method_

Disposed of: Discarded _____   Sold __✓__   Traded _____

Date _May 28, 20X5_   Disposal Amount _$100.00_

YEAR	ANNUAL DEPRECIATION EXPENSE	ACCUMULATED DEPRECIATION	ENDING BOOK VALUE
20X1	$120.00	$120.00	$680.00
20X2	120.00	240.00	560.00
20X3	120.00	360.00	440.00
20X4	120.00	480.00	320.00
20X5	50.00	530.00	270.00

[7]

PLANT ASSET RECORD, No. __417__   General Ledger Account No. __1225__

Description _Office Chair_   General Ledger Account _Office Equipment_

Date Bought _Jan. 6, 20X1_   Serial Number _FB1523_   Original Cost ___$500.00___

Estimated Useful Life _7 years_   Estimated Salvage Value _$10.00_   Depreciation _Straight line method_

Disposed of: Discarded _✓_   Sold _____   Traded _____

Date _Jan. 4, 20X5_   Disposal Amount _zero_

YEAR	ANNUAL DEPRECIATION EXPENSE	ACCUMULATED DEPRECIATION	ENDING BOOK VALUE
20X1	$70.00	$ 70.00	$430.00
20X2	70.00	140.00	360.00
20X3	70.00	210.00	290.00
20X4	70.00	280.00	220.00

8-2 WORK TOGETHER, p. 226

Calculating and journalizing depreciation   [6]

(Note: The plant asset records from Work Together 8-1 are needed to complete this problem. The records from Work Together 8-2 are needed to complete Work Together 8-3.)

Plant asset: _Scanner_   Original cost: _$600.00_

Depreciation method: _Straight line_   Estimated salvage value: _none_

Estimated useful life: _3 years_

YEAR	BEGINNING BOOK VALUE	ANNUAL DEPRECIATION	ACCUMULATED DEPRECIATION	ENDING BOOK VALUE
1	$600.00	$200.00	$200.00	$100.00
2	400.00	200.00	400.00	200.00
3	200.00	200.00	600.00	0.00
4				
5				
6				
7				
8				
9				

[6]

Plant asset: _Freight Scale_   Original cost: _$2,800.00_

Depreciation method: _Straight line_   Estimated salvage value: _$400.00_

Estimated useful life: _5 years_

YEAR	BEGINNING BOOK VALUE	ANNUAL DEPRECIATION	ACCUMULATED DEPRECIATION	ENDING BOOK VALUE
1	$2,800.00	$480.00	$ 480.00	$2,320.00
2	2,320.00	480.00	960.00	1,840.00
3	1,840.00	480.00	1,440.00	1,360.00
4	1,360.00	480.00	1,920.00	880.00
5				
6				
7				
8				
9				

8-2 WORK TOGETHER (concluded)

[8]

GENERAL JOURNAL
PAGE 6

	DATE		ACCOUNT TITLE	DOC. NO.	POST. REF.	DEBIT	CREDIT	
1			*Adjusting Entries*					1
2	20X1 Dec.	31	*Depreciation Expense—Office Equipment*			20000		2
3			*Accum. Depr.—Office Equipment*				20000	3
4		31	*Depreciation Expense—Warehouse Equipment*			48000		4
5			*Accum. Depr.—Warehouse Equipment*				48000	5
6								6
7								7
8								8
9								9
10								10
11								11
12								12
13								13
14								14
15								15
16								16
17								17
18								18
19								19
20								20
21								21
22								22
23								23
24								24
25								25
26								26
27								27
28								28
29								29
30								30
31								31

8-2 ON YOUR OWN, p. 226

Calculating and journalizing depreciation   [9]

(Note: The plant asset records from On Your Own 8-1 are needed to complete this problem. The records from On Your Own 8-2 are needed to complete On Your Own 8-3.)

Plant asset: _Cash Register_   Original cost: _$800.00_

Depreciation method: _Straight line_   Estimated salvage value: _$200.00_

                                                    Estimated useful life: _5 years_

YEAR	BEGINNING BOOK VALUE	ANNUAL DEPRECIATION	ACCUMULATED DEPRECIATION	ENDING BOOK VALUE
1	$800.00	$120.00	$120.00	$680.00
2	680.00	120.00	240.00	560.00
3	560.00	120.00	360.00	440.00
4	440.00	120.00	480.00	320.00
5				
6				
7				
8				
9				

[9]

Plant asset: _Office Chair_   Original cost: _$500.00_

Depreciation method: _Straight line_   Estimated salvage value: _10.00_

                                                    Estimated useful life: _7 years_

YEAR	BEGINNING BOOK VALUE	ANNUAL DEPRECIATION	ACCUMULATED DEPRECIATION	ENDING BOOK VALUE
1	$500.00	$70.00	$ 70.00	$430.00
2	430.00	70.00	140.00	360.00
3	360.00	70.00	210.00	290.00
4	290.00	70.00	280.00	220.00
5				
6				
7				
8				
9				

Name _____ Date _____ Class _____

GENERAL JOURNAL   PAGE 12

	DATE		ACCOUNT TITLE	DOC. NO.	POST. REF.	DEBIT	CREDIT	
1			*Adjusting Entries*			7 0 00		1
2	20X1 Dec.	31	*Depreciation Expense—Office Equipment*				7 0 00	2
3			*Accum. Depr.—Office Equipment*			1 2 0 00		3
4		31	*Depreciation Expense—Store Equipment*				1 2 0 00	4
5			*Accum. Depr.—Store Equipment*					5
6								6
7								7
8								8
9								9
10								10
11								11
12								12
13								13
14								14
15								15
16								16
17								17
18								18
19								19
20								20
21								21
22								22
23								23
24								24
25								25
26								26
27								27
28								28
29								29
30								30
31								31

8-3 WORK TOGETHER, p. 233

Recording the disposal of plant assets   **[6]**

(Note: The plant asset records from Work Together 8-2 are needed to complete this problem.)

PLANT ASSET RECORD, No. __127__   General Ledger Account No. __1225__

Description __Desk__   General Ledger Account __Office Equipment__

Date Bought __Apr. 4, 20X2__   Serial Number __EF26796__   Original Cost __$700.00__

Estimated Useful Life __5 years__   Estimated Salvage Value __$200.00__   Depreciation __Straight line method__

Disposed of: Discarded _____   Sold __✓__   Traded _____

Date __June 26, 20X5__   Disposal Amount __$500.00__

YEAR	ANNUAL DEPRECIATION EXPENSE	ACCUMULATED DEPRECIATION	ENDING BOOK VALUE
20X2	$ 75.00	$ 75.00	$625.00
20X3	100.00	175.00	525.00
20X4	100.00	275.00	425.00
20X5	50.00	325.00	375.00

[6]

PLANT ASSET RECORD, No. __116__   General Ledger Account No. __1245__

Description __Truck__   General Ledger Account __Warehouse Equipment__

Date Bought __July 3, 20X1__   Serial Number __01E16742XL42__   Original Cost __$38,000.00__

Estimated Useful Life __5 years__   Estimated Salvage Value __$3,000.00__   Depreciation __Straight line method__

Disposed of: Discarded _____   Sold _____   Traded __✓__

Date __Dec. 28, 20X5__   Disposal Amount __No. 172__

YEAR	ANNUAL DEPRECIATION EXPENSE	ACCUMULATED DEPRECIATION	ENDING BOOK VALUE
20X1	$3,500.00	$ 3,500.00	$34,500.00
20X2	7,000.00	10,500.00	27,500.00
20X3	7,000.00	17,500.00	20,500.00
20X4	7,000.00	24,500.00	13,500.00
20X5	7,000.00	31,500.00	6,500.00

8-3 WORK TOGETHER (continued)

[6]

PLANT ASSET RECORD, No. __106__   General Ledger Account No. __1215__

Description __Lansing Store__   General Ledger Account __Building__

Date Bought __Jan. 6, 19X7__   Serial Number __n/a__   Original Cost __$60,000.00__

Estimated Useful Life __25 years__   Estimated Salvage Value __$10,000.00__   Depreciation __Straight line method__

Disposed of: Discarded _____   Sold __✓__   Traded _____

Date __Dec. 30, 20X5__   Disposal Amount __$110,000.00 with No. 105__

YEAR	ANNUAL DEPRECIATION EXPENSE	ACCUMULATED DEPRECIATION	ENDING BOOK VALUE
19X7	$2,000.00	$ 2,000.00	$58,000.00
19X8	2,000.00	4,000.00	56,000.00
19X9	2,000.00	6,000.00	54,000.00
20X0	2,000.00	8,000.00	52,000.00
20X1	2,000.00	10,000.00	50,000.00
20X2	2,000.00	12,000.00	48,000.00
20X3	2,000.00	14,000.00	46,000.00
20X4	2,000.00	16,000.00	44,000.00
20X5	2,000.00	18,000.00	42,000.00

[6]

PLANT ASSET RECORD, No. __105__   General Ledger Account No. __1205__

Description __Lansing Store__   General Ledger Account __Land__

Date Bought __Jan. 6, 19X7__   Serial Number __n/a__   Original Cost __$40,000.00__

Estimated Useful Life __n/a__   Estimated Salvage Value __n/a__   Depreciation __n/a__

Disposed of: Discarded _____   Sold __✓__   Traded _____

Date __Dec. 30, 20X6__   Disposal Amount __$110,000.00 with No. 106__

YEAR	ANNUAL DEPRECIATION EXPENSE	ACCUMULATED DEPRECIATION	ENDING BOOK VALUE

8-3 WORK TOGETHER (continued)

[5]

GENERAL JOURNAL   PAGE 1

	DATE		ACCOUNT TITLE	DOC. NO.	POST. REF.	DEBIT	CREDIT	
1	20X5 Jan.	3	Accum. Depr.—Office Equipment	M65		6 0 0 00		1
2			Office Equipment				6 0 0 00	2
3	Mar.	30	Depreciation Expense—Warehouse Equipment	M125		1 2 0 00		3
4			Accum. Depr.—Warehouse Equipment				1 2 0 00	4
5	June	26	Depreciation Expense—Office Equipment	M151		5 0 00		5
6			Accum. Depr.—Office Equipment				5 0 00	6
7	Dec.	28	Depreciation Expense—Warehouse Equipment	M222		7 0 0 0 00		7
8			Accum. Depr.—Warehouse Equipment				7 0 0 0 00	8
9	Dec.	30	Depreciation Expense—Building	M224		2 0 0 0 00		9
10			Accum. Depr.—Building				2 0 0 0 00	10
11								11
12								12
13								13
14								14
15								15
16								16
17								17
18								18
19								19
20								20
21								21
22								22
23								23
24								24
25								25
26								26
27								27
28								28
29								29
30								30
31								31

8-3 WORK TOGETHER (concluded)

[5]

CASH RECEIPTS JOURNAL
PAGE 3

				GENERAL		ACCOUNTS RECEIVABLE CREDIT	SALES CREDIT	SALES TAX PAYABLE		SALES DISCOUNT DEBIT	CASH DEBIT
DATE	ACCOUNT TITLE	DOC. NO.	POST. REF.	DEBIT	CREDIT			DEBIT	CREDIT		
											1
20X5 Mar. 30	Accum. Depr.--Warehouse Eq.	R145		204000							60000
	Loss on Plant Assets			16000							
	Warehouse Equipment				280000						
June 26	Accum. Depr.--Office Equip.	R273		32500							50000
	Gain on Plant Assets				12500						
	Office Equipment				70000						
Dec. 30	Accum. Depr.--Building	R663		1800000							11000000
	Gain on Plant Assets				2800000						
	Building				6000000						
	Land				4000000						

[5]

CASH PAYMENTS JOURNAL
PAGE 12

				GENERAL		ACCOUNTS PAYABLE DEBIT	PURCHASES DISCOUNT CREDIT	CASH CREDIT
DATE	ACCOUNT TITLE	CK. NO.	POST. REF.	DEBIT	CREDIT			
20X5 Dec. 28	Warehouse Equipment	671		3650000				3000000
	Accum. Depr.--Warehouse Eq.			3150000				
	Warehouse Equipment				3800000			

Name _____ Date _____ Class _____

8-3 ON YOUR OWN, p. 233

Recording the disposal of plant assets [8]

(Note: The plant asset records from On Your Own 8-2 are needed to complete this problem.)

PLANT ASSET RECORD, No. __390__   General Ledger Account No. __1205__

Description __Columbus Warehouse__   General Ledger Account __Land__

Date Bought __Sept. 29, 20X3__   Serial Number __n/a__   Original Cost __$40,000.00__

Estimated Useful Life __n/a__   Estimated Salvage Value __n/a__   Depreciation __n/a__

Disposed of: Discarded _____   Sold __✓__   Traded _____

Date __June 30, 20X5__   Disposal Amount __$106,000.00 with No. 391__

YEAR	ANNUAL DEPRECIATION EXPENSE	ACCUMULATED DEPRECIATION	ENDING BOOK VALUE

[8]

PLANT ASSET RECORD, No. __391__   General Ledger Account No. __1215__

Description __Columbus Warehouse__   General Ledger Account __Building__

Date Bought __Sept. 29, 20X3__   Serial Number __n/a__   Original Cost __$50,000.00__

Estimated Useful Life __25 years__   Estimated Salvage Value __$10,000.00__   Depreciation __Straight line method__

Disposed of: Discarded _____   Sold __✓__   Traded _____

Date __June 30, 20X5__   Disposal Amount __$106,000.00 with No. 390__

YEAR	ANNUAL DEPRECIATION EXPENSE	ACCUMULATED DEPRECIATION	ENDING BOOK VALUE
20X3	$ 400.00	$ 400.00	$49,600.00
20X4	1,600.00	2,000.00	48,000.00
20X5	800.00	2,800.00	47,200.00

8-3 ON YOUR OWN (continued)

[8]

PLANT ASSET RECORD, No. __369__   General Ledger Account No. __1225__

Description Office File Cabinet   General Ledger Account Office Equipment

Date Bought July 6, 20X1   Serial Number 62B7Q76   Original Cost $500.00

Estimated Useful Life 7 years   Estimated Salvage Value $80.00   Depreciation Straight line method

Disposed of: Discarded ✓   Sold _____   Traded _____

Date Oct. 2, 20X5   Disposal Amount zero

YEAR	ANNUAL DEPRECIATION EXPENSE	ACCUMULATED DEPRECIATION	ENDING BOOK VALUE
20X1	$30.00	$ 30.00	$470.00
20X2	60.00	90.00	410.00
20X3	60.00	150.00	350.00
20X4	60.00	210.00	290.00
20X5	45.00	255.00	245.00

[8]

PLANT ASSET RECORD, No. __428__   General Ledger Account No. __1225__

Description Computer   General Ledger Account Office Equipment

Date Bought Jan. 3, 20X4   Serial Number 62B7QX1472   Original Cost $2,000.00

Estimated Useful Life 3 years   Estimated Salvage Value $500.00   Depreciation Straight line method

Disposed of: Discarded _____   Sold _____   Traded ✓

Date Dec. 29, 20X5   Disposal Amount No. 439

YEAR	ANNUAL DEPRECIATION EXPENSE	ACCUMULATED DEPRECIATION	ENDING BOOK VALUE
20X4	$500.00	$ 500.00	$1,500.00
20X5	500.00	1,000.00	1,000.00

8-3 ON YOUR OWN (continued)

[7]

GENERAL JOURNAL   PAGE 1

	DATE		ACCOUNT TITLE	DOC. NO.	POST. REF.	DEBIT	CREDIT	
1	20X5 Jan.	4	Accum. Depr.—Office Equipment	M5		2 8 0 00		1
2			Loss on Plant Asset			2 2 0 00		2
3			Office Equipment				5 0 0 00	3
4	May	28	Depreciation Expense—Store Equipment	M52		5 0 00		4
5			Accum. Depr.—Store Equipment				5 0 00	5
6	June	30	Depreciation Expense—Building	M63		8 0 0 00		6
7			Accum. Depr.—Building				8 0 0 00	7
8	Oct.	2	Depreciation Expense—Office Equipment	M121		4 5 00		8
9			Accum. Depr.—Office Equipment				4 5 00	9
10		2	Accum. Depr.—Office Equipment	M121		2 5 5 00		10
11			Loss on Plant Asset			2 4 5 00		11
12			Office Equipment				5 0 0 00	12
13	Dec.	29	Depreciation Expense—Office Equipment	M153		5 0 0 00		13
14			Accum. Depr.—Office Equipment				5 0 0 00	14
15								15
16								16
17								17
18								18
19								19
20								20
21								21
22								22
23								23
24								24
25								25
26								26
27								27
28								28
29								29
30								30
31								31

8-3 ON YOUR OWN (concluded)

[7]

CASH RECEIPTS JOURNAL
PAGE 2

	DATE	ACCOUNT TITLE	DOC. NO.	POST. REF.	GENERAL DEBIT	GENERAL CREDIT	ACCOUNTS RECEIVABLE CREDIT	SALES CREDIT	SALES TAX PAYABLE DEBIT	SALES TAX PAYABLE CREDIT	SALES DISCOUNT DEBIT	CASH DEBIT
1	20X5 May 28	Accum. Depr.—Store Equip.	R243		5 3000							1 0000
2		Loss on Plant Assets			1 7000							
3		Store Equipment				8 0000						
4	June 30	Accum. Depr.—Building	R283		2 80000							106 000 00
5		Gain on Plant Assets				18 80000						
6		Building				50 00000						
7		Land				40 00000						
8												
9												
10												
11												
12												

[7]

CASH PAYMENTS JOURNAL
PAGE 12

	DATE	ACCOUNT TITLE	CK. NO.	POST. REF.	GENERAL DEBIT	GENERAL CREDIT	ACCOUNTS PAYABLE DEBIT	PURCHASES DISCOUNT CREDIT	CASH CREDIT
1	20X5 Dec. 29	Office Equipment	775		2 20000 0				1 20000 0
2		Accum. Depr.—Office Equip.			1 00000 0				
3		Office Equipment				2 00000 0			
4									
5									
6									
7									

Name _____ Date _____ Class _____

Computing depreciation using various depreciation methods and calculating depletion   [4]

Plant asset: *Truck* _____   Original cost: __$90,000.00__

Depreciation method: Double declining balance   Estimated salvage value: __$ 6,000.00__

Estimated useful life: __3 years__

YEAR	BEGINNING BOOK VALUE	DECLINING-BALANCE RATE	ANNUAL DEPRECIATION	ENDING BOOK VALUE
1	$90,000.00	66.67%	$60,000.00	$30,000.00
2	30,000.00	66.67%	20,000.00	10,000.00
3	10,000.00	66.67%	4,000.00	6,000.00
4				
5				
6				
7				
8				
9				

Plant asset: *Truck* _____   Original cost: __$90,000.00__

Depreciation method: Sum of the year's digits   Estimated salvage value: __$6,000.00__

Estimated useful life: __3 years__

YEAR	BEGINNING BOOK VALUE	FRACTION	ANNUAL DEPRECIATION	ENDING BOOK VALUE
1	$90,000.00	3/6	$42,000.00	$48,000.00
2	48,000.00	2/6	28,000.00	20,000.00
3	20,000.00	1/6	14,000.00	6,000.00
4				
5				
6				
7				
8				
9				

Plant asset: *Truck* _____   Original cost: __$90,000.00__

Depreciation method: Production units   Estimated salvage value: __$6,000.00__

Estimated useful life: __200,000 miles__

Depreciation rate: __$0.42__

YEAR	BEGINNING BOOK VALUE	MILES DRIVEN	ANNUAL DEPRECIATION	ENDING BOOK VALUE
1	$90,000.00	34,600	$14,532.00	$75,468.00
2	75,468.00	47,300	19,866.00	55,602.00
3	55,602.00	52,800	22,176.00	33,426.00
4	33,426.00	36,900	15,498.00	17,928.00
5				
6				
7				
8				
9				

8-4 WORK TOGETHER (concluded)

[4]

Plant asset: _Truck_

Depreciation method: MACRS

Original cost: _$90,000.00_

Property class: _5 year_

	YEAR	DEPRECIATION RATE	ANNUAL DEPRECIATION	
	1	20.00%	$18,000.00	
	2	32.00%	28,800.00	
	3	19.20%	17,280.00	
	4	11.52%	10,368.00	
	5	11.52%	10,368.00	
	6	5.76%	5,184.00	
	7			
	8			
	9			

[5]

Plant asset: _Mineral mine_

Depletion method: Production units

Original cost: _$260,000.00_

Estimated salvage value: _$60,000.00_

Estimated total depletion: _$200,000.00_

Estimated useful life: _60,000 tons_

Depletion rate: _$3.33_

YEAR	BEGINNING BOOK VALUE	TONS RECOVERED	ANNUAL DEPRECIATION	ENDING BOOK VALUE
1	$260,000.00	3,500	$11,666.67	$248,333.33
2	248,333.33	12,500	$41,666.67	206,666.67
3	206,666.67	15,600	$52,000.00	154,666.67
4				
5				
6				
7				
8				
9				

Name _____ Date _____ Class _____

Computing depreciation using various depreciation methods and calculating depletion [6]

Plant asset: *Machine* _____   Original cost: **$13,500.00**

Depreciation method: Double declining balance   Estimated salvage value: **$1,500.00**

Estimated useful life: *5 years*

YEAR	BEGINNING BOOK VALUE	DECLINING-BALANCE RATE	ANNUAL DEPRECIATION	ENDING BOOK VALUE
1	$13,500.00	40.00%	$5,400.00	$8,100.00
2	8,100.00	40.00%	3,240.00	4,860.00
3	4,860.00	40.00%	1,944.00	2,916.00
4	2,916.00	40.00%	1,166.40	1,749.60
5	1,749.60	40.00%	249.60	1,500.00
6				
7				
8				
9				

Plant asset: *Machine* _____   Original cost: **$13,500.00**

Depreciation method: Sum of the year's digits   Estimated salvage value: **$1,500.00**

Estimated useful life: *5 years*

YEAR	BEGINNING BOOK VALUE	FRACTION	ANNUAL DEPRECIATION	ENDING BOOK VALUE
1	$13,500.00	5/15	$4,000.00	$9,500.00
2	9,500.00	4/15	3,200.00	6,300.00
3	6,300.00	3/15	2,400.00	3,900.00
4	3,900.00	2/15	1,600.00	2,300.00
5	2,300.00	1/15	800.00	1,500.00
6				
7				
8				
9				

Plant asset: *Machine* _____   Original cost: **$13,500.00**

Depreciation method: Production units   Estimated salvage value: **$1,500.00**

Estimated useful life: **5,000 hours**

Depreciation rate: **$2.40**

YEAR	BEGINNING BOOK VALUE	PRODUCTION HOURS	ANNUAL DEPRECIATION	ENDING BOOK VALUE
1	$13,500.00	600	$1,440.00	$12,060.00
2	12,060.00	1,200	2,880.00	9,180.00
3	9,180.00	900	2,160.00	7,020.00
4	7,020.00	1,000	2,400.00	4,620.00
5	4,620.00	800	1,920.00	2,700.00
6				
7				
8				
9				

Name _____ Date _____ Class _____

8-4 ON YOUR OWN (concluded)

Plant asset: *Machine* Original cost: **$13,500.00**
Depreciation method: MACRS Property class: *5 year*

	YEAR	DEPRECIATION RATE	ANNUAL DEPRECIATION	
	1	20.00%	$2,700.00	
	2	32.00%	4,320.00	
	3	19.20%	2,592.00	
	4	11.52%	1,555.20	
	5	11.52%	1,555.20	
	6	5.76%	777.60	
	7			
	8			
	9			

[7]

Plant asset: *Gas Well*

Depletion method: Production units Estimated total depletion: **$900,000.00**
Original cost: *$920,000.00* Estimated useful life: *600,000 mcf*
Estimated salvage value: *$20,000.00* Depletion rate: *$1.50*

YEAR	BEGINNING BOOK VALUE	MCF RECOVERED	ANNUAL DEPRECIATION	ENDING BOOK VALUE
1	$920,000.00	30,000	$ 45,000.00	$875,000.00
2	875,000.00	90,000	135,000.00	740,000.00
3	740,000.00	100,000	150,000.00	590,000.00
4	590,000.00	120,000	180,000.00	410,000.00
5				
6				
7				
8				
9				

288 • Working Papers

COPYRIGHT © SOUTH-WESTERN EDUCATIONAL PUBLISHING

8-1 APPLICATION PROBLEM, p. 243

Journalizing entries to record buying plant assets

[1]

GENERAL JOURNAL

PAGE 1

	DATE		ACCOUNT TITLE	DOC. NO.	POST. REF.	DEBIT	CREDIT	
1	20-- Jan.	3	Office Equipment	M11		40000		1
2			Accounts Payable/Darst, Inc.				40000	2
3	Apr.	4	Warehouse Equipment	M24		10000		3
4			Accounts Payable/Boeser, Inc.				10000	4
5								5
6								6
7								7
8								8
9								9
10								10
11								11
12								12

[1]

CASH PAYMENTS JOURNAL

PAGE 1

	DATE		ACCOUNT TITLE	CK. NO.	POST. REF.	GENERAL DEBIT	GENERAL CREDIT	ACCOUNTS PAYABLE DEBIT	PURCHASES DISCOUNT CREDIT	CASH CREDIT	
1	20-- Jan.	2	Office Equipment	130		50000				50000	1
2	May	1	Warehouse Equipment	210		850000				850000	2
3	July	1	Store Equipment	250		50000				50000	3
4											4
5											5
6											6
7											7
8											8
9											9
10											10
11											11
12											12
13											13

8-1 APPLICATION PROBLEM (continued)

[2]

(Note: These plant asset records are needed to complete Application Problems 8-3. 8-4. and 8-5.)

PLANT ASSET RECORD, No. _1_   General Ledger Account No. _1225_

Description _File Cabinet_   General Ledger Account _Office Equipment_

Date Bought _Jan. 2, 20X1_   Serial Number _FC2467_   Original Cost _$500.00_

Estimated Useful Life _5 years_   Estimated Salvage Value _$50.00_   Depreciation _Straight line method_

Disposed of: Discarded _✓_   Sold _____   Traded _____

Date _Jan. 28, 20X5_   Disposal Amount _zero_

YEAR	ANNUAL DEPRECIATION EXPENSE	ACCUMULATED DEPRECIATION	ENDING BOOK VALUE
20X1	$90.00	$ 90.00	$410.00
20X2	90.00	180.00	320.00
20X3	90.00	270.00	230.00
20X4	90.00	360.00	140.00
20X5	7.50	367.50	132.50

PLANT ASSET RECORD, No. _2_   General Ledger Account No. _1225_

Description _Word Processor_   General Ledger Account _Office Equipment_

Date Bought _Jan. 3, 20X1_   Serial Number _X4672Y101_   Original Cost _$400.00_

Estimated Useful Life _5 years_   Estimated Salvage Value _None_   Depreciation _Straight line method_

Disposed of: Discarded _✓_   Sold _____   Traded _____

Date _Jan. 21, 20X5_   Disposal Amount _zero_

YEAR	ANNUAL DEPRECIATION EXPENSE	ACCUMULATED DEPRECIATION	ENDING BOOK VALUE
20X1	$80.00	$ 80.00	$320.00
20X2	80.00	160.00	240.00
20X3	80.00	240.00	160.00
20X4	80.00	320.00	80.00
20X5	6.67	326.67	73.33

8-1 APPLICATION PROBLEM (continued)

[2]

PLANT ASSET RECORD, No. _3_ General Ledger Account No. _1245_

Description _Hand Truck_ General Ledger Account _Warehouse Equipment_

Date Bought _Apr. 4, 20X1_ Serial Number _23D4689_ Original Cost _$100.00_

Estimated Useful Life _5 years_ Estimated Salvage Value _$25.00_ Depreciation _Straight line method_

Disposed of: Discarded _____ Sold _✓_ Traded _____

Date _Mar. 29, 20X6_ Disposal Amount _$10.00_

YEAR	ANNUAL DEPRECIATION EXPENSE	ACCUMULATED DEPRECIATION	ENDING BOOK VALUE
20X1	$11.25	$11.25	$88.75
20X2	15.00	26.25	73.75
20X3	15.00	41.25	58.75
20X4	15.00	56.25	43.75
20X5	15.00	71.25	28.75
20X6	3.75	75.00	25.00

PLANT ASSET RECORD, No. _4_ General Ledger Account No. _1245_

Description _Truck_ General Ledger Account _Warehouse Equipment_

Date Bought _May 1, 20X1_ Serial Number _45J3257XF29_ Original Cost _$8,500.00_

Estimated Useful Life _5 years_ Estimated Salvage Value _$1,000.00_ Depreciation _Straight line method_

Disposed of: Discarded _____ Sold _____ Traded _✓_

Date _Dec. 31, 20X6_ Disposal Amount _No. 29_

YEAR	ANNUAL DEPRECIATION EXPENSE	ACCUMULATED DEPRECIATION	ENDING BOOK VALUE
20X1	$1,000.00	$1,000.00	$7,500.00
20X2	1,500.00	2,500.00	6,000.00
20X3	1,500.00	4,000.00	4,500.00
20X4	1,500.00	5,500.00	3,000.00
20X5	1,500.00	7,000.00	1,500.00
20X6	500.00	7,500.00	1,000.00

Name _____ Date _____ Class _____

PLANT ASSET RECORD, No. _5____   General Ledger Account No. _1235_____

Description _Shelving_____   General Ledger Account _Store Equipment_____

Date
Bought _July 1, 20X1_____   Serial
Number _None_____   Original
Cost ____$500.00____

Estimated
Useful Life _10 years_____   Estimated
Salvage Value _$25.00____   Depreciation _Straight line method_____

Disposed of: Discarded _____   Sold ___✓___   Traded _____

Date ___Dec. 31, 20X6_____   Disposal Amount ___$250.00_____

YEAR	ANNUAL DEPRECIATION EXPENSE	ACCUMULATED DEPRECIATION	ENDING BOOK VALUE
20X1	$23.75	$ 23.75	$476.25
20X2	47.50	71.25	428.75
20X3	47.50	118.75	381.25
20X4	47.50	166.25	333.75
20X5	47.50	213.75	286.25
20X6	47.50	261.25	238.75

Extra form

PLANT ASSET RECORD, No. _____   General Ledger Account No. _____

Description _____   General Ledger Account _____

Date
Bought _____   Serial
Number _____   Original
Cost _____

Estimated
Useful Life _____   Estimated
Salvage Value _____   Depreciation _____

Disposed of: Discarded _____   Sold _____   Traded _____

Date _____   Disposal Amount _____

YEAR	ANNUAL DEPRECIATION EXPENSE	ACCUMULATED DEPRECIATION	ENDING BOOK VALUE

8-2 APPLICATION PROBLEM, p. 243

Calculating and journalizing property tax   [1]

Annual property tax calculation:

Assessed Value	×	Rate	=	Annual Tax
$350,000.00	×	4.5%	=	$15,750.00

Annual Tax	÷	2	=	Each Tax Payment
$15,750.00	÷	2	=	$7,875.00

[2]

CASH PAYMENTS JOURNAL   PAGE 3

	DATE	ACCOUNT TITLE	CK. NO.	POST. REF.	GENERAL DEBIT	GENERAL CREDIT	ACCOUNTS PAYABLE DEBIT	PURCHASES DISCOUNT CREDIT	CASH CREDIT	
1	20-- Feb. 26	Property Tax Expense	124		7875 00				7875 00	1
2										2
3										3
4										4
5										5
6										6
7										7
8										8
9										9
10										10
11										11
12										12
13										13
14										14
15										15

Name _____ Date _____ Class _____

8-2 APPLICATION PROBLEM (concluded)

Extra form

CASH PAYMENTS JOURNAL   PAGE _____

	DATE	ACCOUNT TITLE	CK. NO.	POST. REF.	GENERAL DEBIT	GENERAL CREDIT	ACCOUNTS PAYABLE DEBIT	PURCHASES DISCOUNT CREDIT	CASH CREDIT	
1										1
2										2
3										3
4										4
5										5
6										6
7										7
8										8
9										9
10										10
11										11
12										12
13										13
14										14
15										15
16										16
17										17
18										18
19										19
20										20
21										21
22										22
23										23
24										24
25										25
26										26
27										27
28										28
29										29
30										30
31										31
32										32

8-3 APPLICATION PROBLEM, p. 243

Calculating depreciation using straight-line method

The plant asset records used in Application Problem 8-1 are needed to complete Application Problem 8-3. The depreciation tables completed in Application Problem 8-3 are needed to complete Application Problem 8-4.

Plant asset: File Cabinet
Depreciation method: *Straight line*
Original cost: *$500.00*
Estimated salvage value: *$50.00*
Estimated useful life: *5 years*

YEAR	BEGINNING BOOK VALUE	ANNUAL DEPRECIATION	ACCUMULATED DEPRECIATION	ENDING BOOK VALUE
1	$500.00	$90.00	$ 90.00	$410.00
2	410.00	90.00	180.00	320.00
3	320.00	90.00	270.00	230.00
4	230.00	90.00	360.00	140.00
5	140.00	90.00	450.00	50.00

Plant asset: Word Processor
Depreciation method: *Straight-line*
Original cost: *$400.00*
Estimated salvage value: *None*
Estimated useful life: *5 years*

YEAR	BEGINNING BOOK VALUE	ANNUAL DEPRECIATION	ACCUMULATED DEPRECIATION	ENDING BOOK VALUE
1	$400.00	$80.00	$ 80.00	$320.00
2	320.00	80.00	160.00	240.00
3	240.00	80.00	240.00	160.00
4	160.00	80.00	320.00	80.00
5	80.00	80.00	400.00	—

Plant asset: Hand Truck
Depreciation method: *Straight-line*
Original cost: *$100.00*
Estimated salvage value: *$25.00*
Estimated useful life: *5 years*

YEAR	BEGINNING BOOK VALUE	ANNUAL DEPRECIATION	ACCUMULATED DEPRECIATION	ENDING BOOK VALUE
1	$100.00	$11.25	$11.25	$88.75
2	88.75	15.00	26.25	73.75
3	73.75	15.00	41.25	58.75
4	58.75	15.00	56.25	43.75
5	43.75	15.00	71.25	28.75
6	28.75	3.75	75.00	25.00

Name _____ Date _____ Class _____

8-3 APPLICATION PROBLEM (concluded)

Plant asset: Truck _____ Original cost: **$8,500.00**

Depreciation method: *Straight-line* _____ Estimated salvage value: **$1,000.00**

Estimated useful life: **5 years**

YEAR	BEGINNING BOOK VALUE	ANNUAL DEPRECIATION	ACCUMULATED DEPRECIATION	ENDING BOOK VALUE
1	$8,500.00	$1,000.00	$1,000.00	$7,500.00
2	7,500.00	1,500.00	2,500.00	6,000.00
3	6,000.00	1,500.00	4,000.00	4,500.00
4	4,500.00	1,500.00	5,500.00	3,000.00
5	3,000.00	1,500.00	7,000.00	1,500.00
6	1,500.00	500.00	7,500.00	1,000.00

Plant asset: Shelving _____ Original cost: **$500.00**

Depreciation method: *Straight-line* _____ Estimated salvage value: **$25.00**

Estimated useful life: **10 years**

YEAR	BEGINNING BOOK VALUE	ANNUAL DEPRECIATION	ACCUMULATED DEPRECIATION	ENDING BOOK VALUE
1	$500.00	$23.75	$ 23.75	$476.25
2	476.25	47.50	71.25	428.75
3	428.75	47.50	118.75	381.25
4	381.25	47.50	166.25	333.75
5	333.75	47.50	213.75	286.25
6	286.25	47.50	261.25	238.75
7	238.75	47.50	308.75	191.25
8	191.25	47.50	356.25	143.75
9	143.75	47.50	403.75	96.25
10	96.25	47.50	451.25	48.75
11	48.75	23.75	475.00	25.00

8-4 APPLICATION PROBLEM, p. 244

Journalizing annual depreciation expense [2, 4]

GENERAL JOURNAL PAGE 12

	DATE		ACCOUNT TITLE	DOC. NO.	POST. REF.	DEBIT	CREDIT	
1			*Adjusting Entries*					1
2	20X1 Dec.	31	*Depreciation Expense—Office Equipment*			1 7 0 00		2
3			*Accum. Depr.—Office Equipment*				1 7 0 00	3
4		31	*Depreciation Expense—Store Equipment*			2 3 75		4
5			*Accum. Depr.—Store Equipment*				2 3 75	5
6		31	*Depreciation Expense—Warehouse Equip.*			1 0 1 1 25		6
7			*Accum. Depr.—Warehouse Equipment*				1 0 1 1 25	7
8			*Adjusting Entries*					8
9	Dec.	31	*Depreciation Expense—Office Equipment*			1 7 0 00		9
10			*Accum. Depr.—Office Equipment*				1 7 0 00	10
11		31	*Depreciation Expense—Store Equipment*			4 7 50		11
12			*Accum. Depr.—Store Equipment*				4 7 50	12
13		31	*Depreciation Expense—Warehouse Equip.*			1 5 1 5 00		13
14			*Accum. Depr.—Warehouse Equipment*				1 5 1 5 00	14
15								15
16								16
17								17
18								18
19								19
20								20
21								21
22								22
23								23
24								24
25								25
26								26
27								27
28								28
29								29
30								30
31								31

8-4 APPLICATION PROBLEM

Extra form

GENERAL JOURNAL   PAGE _____

	DATE		ACCOUNT TITLE	DOC. NO.	POST. REF.	DEBIT	CREDIT	
1								1
2								2
3								3
4								4
5								5
6								6
7								7
8								8
9								9
10								10
11								11
12								12
13								13
14								14
15								15
16								16
17								17
18								18
19								19
20								20
21								21
22								22
23								23
24								24
25								25
26								26
27								27
28								28
29								29
30								30
31								31

Name _____ Date _____ Class _____

8-5 APPLICATION PROBLEM, p. 244

Recording disposal of plant assets   [1, 3]

The plant asset records used in Application Problem 8-4 are needed to complete Application Problem 8-5.

GENERAL JOURNAL   PAGE 1

	DATE		ACCOUNT TITLE	DOC. NO.	POST. REF.	DEBIT	CREDIT	
1	20X5 Jan.	21	Depreciation Expense—Office Equipment	M522		6 67		1
2			Accum. Depr.—Office Equipment				6 67	2
3		21	Accum. Depr.—Office Equipment	M522		3 26 67		3
4			Loss on Plant Assets			73 33		4
5			Equipment—Office				4 00 00	5
6		28	Depreciation Expense—Office Equipment	M523		7 50		6
7			Accum. Depr.—Office Equipment				7 50	7
8		28	Accum. Depr.—Office Equipment	M523		3 67 50		8
9			Loss on Plant Assets			1 32 50		9
10			Equipment—Office				5 00 00	10
11	20X6 Mar.	29	Depreciation Expense—Warehouse Equipment	M575		3 75		11
12			Accum. Depr.—Warehouse Equipment				3 75	12
13	Dec.	31	Depreciation Expense—Store Equipment	M631		47 50		13
14			Accum. Depr.—Store Equipment				47 50	14
15		31	Depreciation Expense—Warehouse Equipment	M632		5 00 00		15
16			Accum. Depr.—Warehouse Equipment				5 00 00	16

[1, 3]

PAGE 6

CASH RECEIPTS JOURNAL

	DATE	ACCOUNT TITLE	DOC. NO.	POST. REF.	GENERAL DEBIT	GENERAL CREDIT	ACCOUNTS RECEIVABLE CREDIT	SALES CREDIT	SALES TAX PAYABLE DEBIT	SALES TAX PAYABLE CREDIT	SALES DISCOUNT DEBIT	CASH DEBIT	
1	20X6 Mar. 29	Accum. Depr.—Warehouse Eq.	R645		7500							10000	1
2		Loss on Plant Assets			1500								2
3		Warehouse Equipment				10000							3
4	Dec. 31	Accum. Depr.—Store Equip.	R733		26125							25000	4
5		Gain on Plant Assets				1125							5
6		Store Equipment				50000							6
7													7
8													8
9													9
10													10
11													11
12													12

[1]

PAGE 12

CASH PAYMENTS JOURNAL

	DATE	ACCOUNT TITLE	CK. NO.	POST. REF.	GENERAL DEBIT	GENERAL CREDIT	ACCOUNTS PAYABLE DEBIT	PURCHASES DISCOUNT CREDIT	CASH CREDIT	
1	20X6 Dec. 31	Warehouse Equipment	815		9000000				8000000	1
2		Accum. Depr.—Warehouse Eq.			7500000					2
3		Warehouse Equipment				8500000				3
4										4
5										5
6										6
7										7

8-6 APPLICATION PROBLEM, p. 245

Recording the sale of land and building

[1]

CASH RECEIPTS JOURNAL

PAGE 12

	DATE	ACCOUNT TITLE	DOC. NO.	POST. REF.	GENERAL DEBIT (1)	GENERAL CREDIT (2)	ACCOUNTS RECEIVABLE CREDIT (3)	SALES CREDIT (4)	SALES TAX PAYABLE DEBIT (5)	SALES TAX PAYABLE CREDIT (6)	SALES DISCOUNT DEBIT (7)	CASH DEBIT (8)
1	20X6 Jan. 2	Accum. Depr.—Building	R125		6120000							73000000
2		Land				2000000						
3		Building				10000000						
4		Gain on Plant Assets				1420000						
5												
6												
7												
8												
9												
10												
11												
12												
13												
14												
15												
16												
17												
18												
19												
20												
21												
22												
23												
24												
25												

8-6 APPLICATION PROBLEM (concluded)

[2]

PLANT ASSET RECORD, No. __61__   General Ledger Account No. __1205__

Description __Jackson Warehouse__   General Ledger Account __Land__

Date Bought __Jan. 1, 20--__   Serial Number __n/a__   Original Cost __$20,000.00__

Estimated Useful Life __Indefinite__   Estimated Salvage Value __n/a__   Depreciation __n/a__

Disposed of: Discarded _____   Sold __✓__   Traded _____

Date __1/2/X6__   Disposal Amount __$73,000.00 with No. 62__

YEAR	ANNUAL DEPRECIATION EXPENSE	ACCUMULATED DEPRECIATION	ENDING BOOK VALUE

PLANT ASSET RECORD, No. __62__   General Ledger Account No. __1215__

Description __Jackson Warehouse__   General Ledger Account __Building__

Date Bought __Jan. 1, 20--__   Serial Number __None__   Original Cost __$100,000.00__

Estimated Useful Life __25 years__   Estimated Salvage Value __$10,000.00__   Depreciation __Straight line method__

Disposed of: Discarded _____   Sold __✓__   Traded _____

Date __1/2/X6__   Disposal Amount __$73,000.00 with No. 61__

YEAR	ANNUAL DEPRECIATION EXPENSE	ACCUMULATED DEPRECIATION	ENDING BOOK VALUE
20X5	$3,600.00	$61,200.00	$38,800.00

8-7 APPLICATION PROBLEM, p. 245

Calculating depreciation expense using the straight-line, declining-balance, and sum-of-the-years digits method

Plant asset: *Office Desk* _____   Original cost: *$2,400.00*

Depreciation method: Straight line _____   Estimated salvage value: *$200.00*

                                   Estimated useful life: *4 years*

YEAR	BEGINNING BOOK VALUE	ANNUAL DEPRECIATION	ACCUMULATED DEPRECIATION	ENDING BOOK VALUE
1	$2,400.00	$550.00	$ 550.00	$1,850.00
2	1,850.00	550.00	1,100.00	1,300.00
3	1,300.00	550.00	1,650.00	750.00
4	750.00	550.00	2,200.00	200.00
5				
6				
7				
8				
9				

Plant asset: *Office Desk* _____   Original cost: *$2,400.00*

Depreciation method: Double declining balance _____   Estimated salvage value: *$200.00*

                                   Estimated useful life: *4 years*

YEAR	BEGINNING BOOK VALUE	DECLINING-BALANCE RATE	ANNUAL DEPRECIATION	ENDING BOOK VALUE
1	$2,400.00	50.00%	$1,200.00	$1,200.00
2	1,200.00	50.00%	600.00	600.00
3	600.00	50.00%	300.00	300.00
4	300.00	50.00%	100.00	200.00
5				
6				
7				
8				
9				

Name _____ Date _____ Class _____

8-7 APPLICATION PROBLEM (concluded)

Plant asset: _Office Desk_

Depreciation method: _Sum of the year's digits_

Original cost: _$2,400.00_

Estimated salvage value: _$200.00_

Estimated useful life: _4 years_

YEAR	BEGINNING BOOK VALUE	FRACTION	ANNUAL DEPRECIATION	ENDING BOOK VALUE
1	$2,400.00	4/10	$880.00	$1,520.00
2	1,520.00	3/10	660.00	860.00
3	860.00	2/10	440.00	420.00
4	420.00	1/10	220.00	200.00
5				
6				
7				
8				
9				

Extra form

Plant asset: _____

Depreciation method: _____

Original cost: _____

Estimated salvage value: _____

Estimated useful life: _____

YEAR	BEGINNING BOOK VALUE	ANNUAL DEPRECIATION	ACCUMULATED DEPRECIATION	ENDING BOOK VALUE

8-8 APPLICATION PROBLEM, p. 245

Calculating depreciation expense using the production-unit method [1]

Depreciation rate calculation:

($10,000.00 original cost — $1,000.00 estimated salvage value) ÷ 120,000 miles = $0.075

[2]

Plant asset: _Truck_____

Depreciation method: _Production units_____

Original cost: _$10,000.00_____   Estimated useful life: _120,000 miles_____

Estimated salvage value: _$1,000.00_____   Depreciation rate: _0.075_____ per mile driven

YEAR	BEGINNING BOOK VALUE	MILES DRIVEN	ANNUAL DEPRECIATION	ENDING BOOK VALUE
1	$10,000.00	27,500	$2,062.50	$7,937.50
2	7,937.50	26,000	1,950.00	5,987.50
3	5,987.50	25,000	1,875.00	4,112.50
4	4,112.50	21,000	1,575.00	2,537.50
5	2,537.50	19,000	1,425.00	1,112.50
Totals	—	118,500	$8,887.50	

Name _____ Date _____ Class _____

Extra forms

Plant asset: _____   Original cost: _____

Depreciation method: _____   Estimated salvage value: _____

Estimated useful life: _____

YEAR	BEGINNING BOOK VALUE	ANNUAL DEPRECIATION	ACCUMULATED DEPRECIATION	ENDING BOOK VALUE

Plant asset: _____   Original cost: _____

Depreciation method: _____   Estimated salvage value: _____

Estimated useful life: _____

YEAR	BEGINNING BOOK VALUE	ANNUAL DEPRECIATION	ACCUMULATED DEPRECIATION	ENDING BOOK VALUE

8-9 APPLICATION PROBLEM, p. 246

Calculating depreciation expense using MACRS

Plant asset: _Computer_____   Original cost: _$3,300.00_____

Depreciation method: MACRS_____   Property class: _5 year_____

	YEAR	DEPRECIATION RATE	ANNUAL DEPRECIATION	
	1	20.00%	$ 660.00	
	2	32.00%	1,056.00	
	3	19.20%	633.60	
	4	11.52%	380.16	
	5	11.52%	380.16	
	6	5.76%	190.08	
	Totals	100.00%	$3,300.00	

Extra form

Plant asset: _____   Original cost: _____
Depreciation method: _____   Property class: _____

	YEAR	DEPRECIATION RATE	ANNUAL DEPRECIATION	

Name _____ Date _____ Class _____

8-10 APPLICATION PROBLEM, p. 246

Calculating depletion expense using production-unit method

Plant asset: _Mine_____

Depletion method: _____   Estimated total value of coal: _$44,000.00_____

Original cost: _$45,000.00_____   Estimated tons of recoverable coal: _50,000 tons_____

Estimated salvage value: _$1,000.00_____   Depletion rate: _0.88_____ per ton mined

YEAR	BEGINNING BOOK VALUE	TONS MINED	ANNUAL DEPLETION	ENDING BOOK VALUE
1	$45,000.00	9,000	$ 7,920.00	$37,080.00
2	37,080.00	9,400	8,272.00	28,808.00
3	28,808.00	7,000	6,160.00	22,648.00
4	22,648.00	12,500	11,000.00	11,648.00
5	11,648.00	8,200	7,216.00	4,432.00
Totals	—	46,100	$40,568.00	—

Extra form

Plant asset: _____

Depreciation method: _____   Estimated total value of coal: _____

Original cost: _____   Estimated tons of recoverable coal: _____

Estimated salvage value: _____   Depletion rate: _____ per ton mined

YEAR	BEGINNING BOOK VALUE	TONS MINED	ANNUAL DEPLETION	ENDING BOOK VALUE

8-11 MASTERY PROBLEM, p. 246

Recording entries for plant assets   [1]

GENERAL JOURNAL   PAGE 1

	DATE		ACCOUNT TITLE	DOC. NO.	POST. REF.	DEBIT	CREDIT	
1	20X9 Jan.	2	Accum. Depr.—Office Equipment	M47		6 0 0 00		1
2			Loss on Plant Assets			1 2 0 00		2
3			Equipment—Office				7 2 0 00	3
4	Mar.	29	Depreciation Expense—Office Equipment	M52		2 0 00		4
5			Accum. Depr.—Office Equipment				2 0 00	5
6		29	Accum. Depr.—Office Equipment	M52		4 0 0 00		6
7			Loss on Plant Assets			2 5 00		7
8			Equipment—Office				4 2 5 00	8
9		30	Depreciation Expense—Office Equipment	M54		2 5 00		9
10			Accum. Depr.—Office Equipment				2 5 00	10
11	June	29	Depreciation Expense—Office Equipment	M62		1 7 50		11
12			Accum. Depr.—Office Equipment				1 7 50	12
13	July	2	Depreciation Expense—Office Equipment	M70		7 5 00		13
14			Accum. Depr.—Office Equipment				7 5 00	14
15								15
16								16
17								17
18								18
19								19
20								20
21								21
22								22
23								23
24								24
25								25
26								26
27								27
28								28
29								29
30								30
31								31

Name _____ Date _____ Class _____

8-11 MASTERY PROBLEM (continued)

[1, 3]

CASH RECEIPTS JOURNAL
PAGE 6

DATE	ACCOUNT TITLE	DOC. NO.	POST. REF.	GENERAL DEBIT	GENERAL CREDIT	ACCOUNTS RECEIVABLE CREDIT	SALES CREDIT	SALES TAX PAYABLE DEBIT	SALES TAX PAYABLE CREDIT	SALES DISCOUNT DEBIT	CASH DEBIT
20X9 Mar. 30	Accum. Depr.--Office Equip.	R191		60000							10000
	Loss on Plant Assets			5000							
	Equipment--Office				75000						
	Accum. Depr.--Office Equip.	R224		31500							15000
	Equipment--Office				40000						
	Gain on Plant Assets				6500						

[1]

CASH PAYMENTS JOURNAL
PAGE 8

DATE	ACCOUNT TITLE	CK. NO.	POST. REF.	GENERAL DEBIT	GENERAL CREDIT	ACCOUNTS PAYABLE DEBIT	PURCHASES DISCOUNT CREDIT	CASH CREDIT
20X9 Jan. 2	Equipment--Office	122		190000				190000
July 2	Equipment--Office	239		55000				50000
	Accum. Depr.--Office Equipment				80000			
	Equipment--Office			75000				

8-11 MASTERY PROBLEM (continued)

[2]

PLANT ASSET RECORD, No. __167__   General Ledger Account No. __1230__

Description __Desk__   General Ledger Account __Office Equip.__

Date Bought __Jan. 5, 20X4__   Serial Number __D3481__   Original Cost __$720.00__

Estimated Useful Life __5 years__   Estimated Salvage Value __$120.00__   Depreciation method __Straight line__

Disposed of: Discarded __✓__   Sold _____   Traded _____

Date __Jan. 2, 20X9__   Disposal Amount __zero__

YEAR	ANNUAL DEPRECIATION EXPENSE	ACCUMULATED DEPRECIATION	ENDING BOOK VALUE
20X4	$120.00	$120.00	$600.00
20X5	120.00	240.00	480.00
20X6	120.00	360.00	360.00
20X7	120.00	480.00	240.00
20X8	120.00	600.00	120.00

PLANT ASSET RECORD, No. __168__   General Ledger Account No. __1230__

Description __Table__   General Ledger Account __Office Equip.__

Date Bought __Mar. 29, 20X4__   Serial Number __T3929__   Original Cost __$425.00__

Estimated Useful Life __5 years__   Estimated Salvage Value __$25.00__   Depreciation method __Straight line__

Disposed of: Discarded __✓__   Sold _____   Traded _____

Date __Mar. 29, 20X9__   Disposal Amount __zero__

YEAR	ANNUAL DEPRECIATION EXPENSE	ACCUMULATED DEPRECIATION	ENDING BOOK VALUE
20X4	$60.00	$ 60.00	$365.00
20X5	80.00	140.00	285.00
20X6	80.00	220.00	205.00
20X7	80.00	300.00	125.00
20X8	80.00	380.00	45.00
20X9	20.00	400.00	25.00

8-11 MASTERY PROBLEM (continued)

[2]

PLANT ASSET RECORD, No. __169__   General Ledger Account No. __1230__

Description __Filing Cabinet__   General Ledger Account __Office Equip.__

Date Bought __June 28, 20X0__   Serial Number __FC125__   Original Cost __$400.00__

Estimated Useful Life __10 years__   Estimated Salvage Value __$50.00__   Depreciation method __Straight line__

Disposed of: Discarded _____   Sold __✓__   Traded _____

Date __June 29, 20X9__   Disposal Amount __$150.00__

YEAR	ANNUAL DEPRECIATION EXPENSE	ACCUMULATED DEPRECIATION	ENDING BOOK VALUE
20X0	$17.50	$ 17.50	$382.50
20X1	35.00	52.50	347.50
20X2	35.00	87.50	312.50
20X3	35.00	122.50	277.50
20X4	35.00	157.50	242.50
20X5	35.00	192.50	207.50
20X6	35.00	227.50	172.50
20X7	35.00	262.50	137.50
20X8	35.00	297.50	102.50
20X9	17.50	315.00	85.00

PLANT ASSET RECORD, No. __170__   General Ledger Account No. __1230__

Description __Word Processor__   General Ledger Account __Office Equip.__

Date Bought __Apr. 6, 20X3__   Serial Number __TM48194H32__   Original Cost __$750.00__

Estimated Useful Life __6 years__   Estimated Salvage Value __$150.00__   Depreciation method __Straight line__

Disposed of: Discarded _____   Sold __✓__   Traded _____

Date __Mar. 30, 20X9__   Disposal Amount __$100.00__

YEAR	ANNUAL DEPRECIATION EXPENSE	ACCUMULATED DEPRECIATION	ENDING BOOK VALUE
20X3	$ 75.00	$ 75.00	$675.00
20X4	100.00	175.00	575.00
20X5	100.00	275.00	475.00
20X6	100.00	375.00	375.00
20X7	100.00	475.00	275.00
20X8	100.00	575.00	175.00
20X9	25.00	600.00	150.00

Name _____ Date _____ Class _____

8-11 MASTERY PROBLEM (concluded)

[2]

PLANT ASSET RECORD, No. _171_ General Ledger Account No. _1230_

Description _Copying Machine_ General Ledger Account _Office Equip._

Date Bought _July 1, 20X4_ Serial Number _C56M203_ Original Cost _$800.00_

Estimated Useful Life _5 years_ Estimated Salvage Value _$50.00_ Depreciation _Straight line method_

Disposed of: Discarded _____ Sold _____ Traded ___✓___

Date _July 2, 20X9_ Disposal Amount _____

YEAR	ANNUAL DEPRECIATION EXPENSE	ACCUMULATED DEPRECIATION	ENDING BOOK VALUE
20X4	$ 75.00	$ 75.00	$725.00
20X5	150.00	225.00	575.00
20X6	150.00	375.00	425.00
20X7	150.00	525.00	275.00
20X8	150.00	675.00	125.00
20X9	75.00	750.00	50.00

PLANT ASSET RECORD, No. _172_ General Ledger Account No. _1230_

Description _Computer_ General Ledger Account _Office Equipment_

Date Bought _Jan. 2, 20X9_ Serial Number _SD345J267_ Original Cost _$1,900.00_

Estimated Useful Life _5 years_ Estimated Salvage Value _$400.00_ Depreciation _Straight line method_

Disposed of: Discarded _____ Sold _____ Traded _____

Date _____ Disposal Amount _____

YEAR	ANNUAL DEPRECIATION EXPENSE	ACCUMULATED DEPRECIATION	ENDING BOOK VALUE

PLANT ASSET RECORD, No. _173_ General Ledger Account No. _1230_

Description _Copying Machine_ General Ledger Account _Office Equip._

Date Bought _July 2, 20X9_ Serial Number _C35194_ Original Cost _$550.00_

Estimated Useful Life _5 years_ Estimated Salvage Value _$100.00_ Depreciation _Straight line method_

Disposed of: Discarded _____ Sold _____ Traded _____

Date _____ Disposal Amount _____

8-11 MASTERY PROBLEM

Extra forms

PLANT ASSET RECORD, No. _____   General Ledger Account No. _____

Description _____   General Ledger Account _____

Date
Bought _____   Serial
Number _____   Original
Cost _____

Estimated
Useful Life _____   Estimated
Salvage Value _____   Depreciation _____

Disposed of: Discarded _____   Sold _____   Traded _____

Date _____   Disposal Amount _____

YEAR	ANNUAL DEPRECIATION EXPENSE	ACCUMULATED DEPRECIATION	ENDING BOOK VALUE

PLANT ASSET RECORD, No. _____   General Ledger Account No. _____

Description _____   General Ledger Account _____

Date
Bought _____   Serial
Number _____   Original
Cost _____

Estimated
Useful Life _____   Estimated
Salvage Value _____   Depreciation _____

Disposed of: Discarded _____   Sold _____   Traded _____

Date _____   Disposal Amount _____

YEAR	ANNUAL DEPRECIATION EXPENSE	ACCUMULATED DEPRECIATION	ENDING BOOK VALUE

8-12 CHALLENGE PROBLEM, p. 247

Recording entries for plant assets

GENERAL JOURNAL   PAGE 7

	DATE		ACCOUNT TITLE	DOC. NO.	POST. REF.	DEBIT	CREDIT	
1	20X3 July	1	Depreciation Expense—Office Equipment	M66		1 1 50		1
2			Accum. Depr.—Office Equipment				1 1 50	2
3		1	Accum. Depr.—Office Equipment	M66		4 6 00		3
4			Loss on Plant Assets			7 9 00		4
5			Office Equipment				1 2 5 00	5
6	Sept.	1	Depreciation Expense—Delivery Equipment	M70		1 2 0 0 00		6
7			Accum. Depr.—Delivery Equipment				1 2 0 0 00	7

8-12 CHALLENGE PROBLEM (concluded)

CASH PAYMENTS JOURNAL

PAGE 12

	DATE		ACCOUNT TITLE	CK. NO.	POST. REF.	GENERAL DEBIT	GENERAL CREDIT	ACCOUNTS PAYABLE DEBIT	PURCHASES DISCOUNT CREDIT	CASH CREDIT	
1	20X1 Jan.	1	Office Equipment	130		60000				60000	1
2	Mar.	1	Office Equipment	190		70000				70000	2
3	June	30	Office Equipment	200		12500				12500	3
4	July	1	Delivery Equipment	220		1000000				1000000	4
5	20X3 Jan.	2	Office Equipment	300		87500				40000	5
6			Accum. Depr.--Office Equipment			12500					6
7			Office Equipment				60000				7
8	Sept.	1	Delivery Equipment	310		1160000				550000	8
9			Accum. Depr.--Delivery Equipment			390000					9
10			Delivery Equipment				1000000				10
11											11
12											12
13											13
14											14
15											15
16											16
17											17
18											18
19											19
20											20
21											21
22											22
23											23
24											24
25											25
26											26
27											27
28											28
29											29
30											30
31											31

9-1 WORK TOGETHER, p. 255

Journalizing notes payable transactions

[4]

CASH RECEIPTS JOURNAL

PAGE 15

				GENERAL		ACCOUNTS RECEIVABLE CREDIT	SALES CREDIT	SALES TAX PAYABLE		SALES DISCOUNT DEBIT	CASH DEBIT
DATE	ACCOUNT TITLE	DOC. NO.	POST. REF.	DEBIT	CREDIT			DEBIT	CREDIT		
20-- May 14	Notes Payable	R145		500000							500000
June 5	Notes Payable	R213		800000							800000

[6]

CASH PAYMENTS JOURNAL

PAGE 18

				GENERAL		ACCOUNTS PAYABLE DEBIT	PURCHASES DISCOUNT CREDIT	CASH CREDIT
DATE	ACCOUNT TITLE	CK. NO.	POST. REF.	DEBIT	CREDIT			
20-- Aug. 12	Notes Payable	345		500000				515000
	Interest Expense			15000				
Dec. 2	Notes Payable	652		800000				840000
	Interest Expense			40000				

9-1 WORK TOGETHER (concluded)

[5]

Maturity dates:

May 14 – May 31	17
June	30
July	31
August 1 – August 12	12
	90

June 5 – June 30	25
July	31
August	31
September	30
October	31
November	30
December 1 – December 2	2
	180

[5]

Interest due at maturity:

Note signed May 14:

Principal	×	Interest Rate	×	Time	=	Interest Due at Maturity
$5,000.00	×	12%	×	$\frac{90}{360}$	=	$150.00

Note signed June 5:

Principal	×	Interest Rate	×	Time	=	Interest Due at Maturity
$8,000.00	×	10%	×	$\frac{180}{360}$	=	$400.00

9-1 ON YOUR OWN, p. 255

Journalizing notes payable transactions

[7]

CASH RECEIPTS JOURNAL

PAGE 6

				GENERAL	GENERAL	ACCOUNTS RECEIVABLE	SALES	SALES TAX PAYABLE	SALES TAX PAYABLE	SALES DISCOUNT	CASH
DATE	ACCOUNT TITLE	DOC. NO.	POST. REF.	DEBIT	CREDIT	CREDIT	CREDIT	DEBIT	CREDIT	DEBIT	DEBIT
20-- Mar. 23	Notes Payable	R84			600000						600000
July 12	Notes Payable	R151			1200000						1200000

[9]

CASH PAYMENTS JOURNAL

PAGE 14

				GENERAL	GENERAL	ACCOUNTS PAYABLE	PURCHASES DISCOUNT	CASH
DATE	ACCOUNT TITLE	CK. NO.	POST. REF.	DEBIT	CREDIT	DEBIT	CREDIT	CREDIT
20-- Sept. 10	Notes Payable	455		1200000				1224000
	Interest Expense			24000				
19	Notes Payable	464		600000				630000
	Interest Expense			30000				

9-1 ON YOUR OWN (concluded)

[8]

Maturity dates:

March 23 – March 31	*8*
April	*30*
May	*31*
June	*30*
July	*31*
August	*31*
September 1 – September 19	*19*
Total	*180*

July 12 – July 31	*19*
August	*31*
September 1 – September 10	*10*
Total	*60*

[8]

Interest due at maturity:

Note signed March 23:

Principal	×	Interest Rate	×	Time	=	Interest Due at Maturity
$6,000.00	×	10%	×	$\frac{180}{360}$	=	$300.00

Note signed July 12:

Principal	×	Interest Rate	×	Time	=	Interest Due at Maturity
$12,000.00	×	12%	×	$\frac{60}{360}$	=	$240.00

9-2 WORK TOGETHER, p. 261

Journalizing adjusting and reversing entries for prepaid expenses [4]
initially recorded as expenses

GENERAL JOURNAL   PAGE 15

	DATE		ACCOUNT TITLE	DOC. NO.	POST. REF.	DEBIT	CREDIT	
1			*Adjusting Entries*					1
2	20— Dec.	31	Supplies—Administrative			5 0 0 00		2
3			Supplies Expense—Administrative				5 0 0 00	3
4		31	Supplies—Sales			4 0 0 00		4
5			Supplies Expense—Sales				4 0 0 00	5
6		31	Prepaid Insurance			6 0 0 00		6
7			Insurance Expense				6 0 0 00	7
8								8
9								9
10								10
11								11
12								12
13								13
14								14
15								15
16								16
17								17
18								18
19								19
20								20
21								21
22								22
23								23
24								24
25								25
26								26
27								27
28								28
29								29
30								30

Name _____ Date _____ Class _____

GENERAL JOURNAL   PAGE 16

	DATE		ACCOUNT TITLE	DOC. NO.	POST. REF.	DEBIT	CREDIT	
1			*Reversing Entries*					1
2	20-- Jan.	1	Supplies Expense—Administrative			5 0 0 00		2
3			Supplies—Administrative				5 0 0 00	3
4		1	Supplies Expense—Sales			4 0 0 00		4
5			Supplies—Sales				4 0 0 00	5
6		1	Insurance Expense			6 0 0 00		6
7			Prepaid Insurance				6 0 0 00	7
8								8
9								9
10								10
11								11
12								12
13								13
14								14
15								15
16								16
17								17
18								18
19								19
20								20
21								21
22								22
23								23
24								24
25								25
26								26
27								27
28								28
29								29
30								30
31								31

9-2 ON YOUR OWN, p. 261

Journalizing adjusting and reversing entries for prepaid expenses initially recorded as expenses

[6]

GENERAL JOURNAL

PAGE 13

	DATE		ACCOUNT TITLE	DOC. NO.	POST. REF.	DEBIT	CREDIT	
1			*Adjusting Entries*					1
2	20— Dec.	31	*Supplies—Administrative*			8 0 0 00		2
3			*Supplies Expense—Administrative*				8 0 0 00	3
4		31	*Supplies—Sales*			6 0 0 00		4
5			*Supplies Expense—Sales*				6 0 0 00	5
6		31	*Prepaid Insurance*			9 0 0 00		6
7			*Insurance Expense*				9 0 0 00	7
8								8
9								9
10								10
11								11
12								12
13								13
14								14
15								15
16								16
17								17
18								18
19								19
20								20
21								21
22								22
23								23
24								24
25								25
26								26
27								27
28								28
29								29
30								30

9-2 ON YOUR OWN (concluded)

[7]

GENERAL JOURNAL   PAGE 14

	DATE		ACCOUNT TITLE	DOC. NO.	POST. REF.	DEBIT	CREDIT	
1			*Reversing Entries*					1
2	20– Jan.	1	Supplies Expense—Administrative			8 0 0 00		2
3			Supplies—Administrative				8 0 0 00	3
4		1	Supplies Expense—Sales			6 0 0 00		4
5			Supplies—Sales				6 0 0 00	5
6		1	Insurance Expense			9 0 0 00		6
7			Prepaid Insurance				9 0 0 00	7
8								8
9								9
10								10
11								11
12								12
13								13
14								14
15								15
16								16
17								17
18								18
19								19
20								20
21								21
22								22
23								23
24								24
25								25
26								26
27								27
28								28
29								29
30								30
31								31

9-3 WORK TOGETHER, p. 268

Journalizing adjusting and reversing entries for accrued expenses

a. One note payable is outstanding on December 31: 180-day, 12% note with First National Bank, $10,000, dated October 15.

b. Payroll information from the December 31 payroll:

Payroll and Employee Payroll Taxes		Employer Payroll Taxes	
Salaries—administrative	$1,200.00	Social Security tax	$143.00
Salaries—sales	1,000.00	Medicare tax	33.00
Federal income tax withheld	340.00	Federal unemployment tax	17.60
Social Security tax	143.00	State unemployment tax	118.80
Medicare tax	33.00		

c. Estimated federal income tax quarterly payment, $1,500.00.

[4]

GENERAL JOURNAL   PAGE 13

	DATE		ACCOUNT TITLE	DOC. NO.	POST. REF.	DEBIT	CREDIT	
1			*Adjusting Entries*					1
2	20— Dec.	31	*Interest Expense*			256 67		2
3			*Accrued Interest*				256 67	3
4		31	*Salaries Expense—Administrative*			1200 00		4
5			*Salaries Expense—Sales*			1000 00		5
6			*Employee Income Tax Payable*				340 00	6
7			*Social Security Tax Payable*				143 00	7
8			*Medicare Tax Payable*				33 00	8
9			*Salaries Payable*				1684 00	9
10		31	*Payroll Taxes Expense*			312 40		10
11			*Social Security Tax Payable*				143 00	11
12			*Medicare Tax Payable*				33 00	12
13			*Unemployment Tax Payable—Federal*				17 60	13
14			*Unemployment Tax Payable—State*				118 80	14
15		31	*Income Tax Expense*			1500 00		15
16			*Income Tax Payable*				1500 00	16
17								17

9-3 **WORK TOGETHER (concluded)**

GENERAL JOURNAL   PAGE 14

	DATE		ACCOUNT TITLE	DOC. NO.	POST. REF.	DEBIT	CREDIT	
1			*Reversing Entries*					1
2	20-- Jan.	1	Accrued Interest			25667		2
3			Interest Expense				25667	3
4		1	Employee Income Tax Payable			34000		4
5			Social Security Tax Payable			14300		5
6			Medicare Tax Payable			3300		6
7			Salaries Payable			168400		7
8			Salaries Expense—Administrative				120000	8
9			Salaries Expense—Sales				100000	9
10		1	Social Security Tax Payable			14300		10
11			Medicare Tax Payable			3300		11
12			Unemployment Tax Payable—Federal			1760		12
13			Unemployment Tax Payable— State			11880		13
14			Payroll Taxes Expense				31240	14
15								15
16								16
17								17
18								18
19								19
20								20
21								21
22								22
23								23
24								24
25								25
26								26
27								27
28								28
29								29
30								30
31								31

Name _____ Date _____ Class _____

9-3 ON YOUR OWN, p. 268

Journalizing adjusting and reversing entries for accrued expenses

a. One note payable is outstanding on December 31: 90-day, 10% note with American National Bank, $20,000, dated November 29.

b. Payroll information from the December 31 payroll:

Payroll and Employee Payroll Taxes		Employer Payroll Taxes	
Salaries—administrative	$1,500.00	Social Security tax	$214.50
Salaries—sales	1,800.00	Medicare tax	49.50
Federal income tax withheld	740.00	Federal unemployment tax	9.60
Social Security tax	214.50	State unemployment tax	64.80
Medicare tax	49.50		

c. Estimated federal income tax quarterly payment, $1,500.00.

[6]

GENERAL JOURNAL PAGE 13

	DATE	ACCOUNT TITLE	DOC. NO.	POST. REF.	DEBIT	CREDIT	
1		*Adjusting Entries*					1
2	20-- Dec. 31	Interest Expense			177 78		2
3		Accrued Interest				177 78	3
4	31	Salaries Expense—Administrative			1500 00		4
5		Salaries Expense—Sales			1800 00		5
6		Employee Income Tax Payable				740 00	6
7		Social Security Tax Payable				214 50	7
8		Medicare Tax Payable				49 50	8
9		Salaries Payable				2296 00	9
10	31	Payroll Taxes Expense			338 40		10
11		Social Security Tax Payable				214 50	11
12		Medicare Tax Payable				49 50	12
13		Unemployment Tax Payable—Federal				9 60	13
14		Unemployment Tax Payable—State				64 80	14
15	31	Income Tax Expense			1500 00		15
16		Income Tax Payable				1500 00	16
17							17

9-3 ON YOUR OWN (concluded)

[7]

GENERAL JOURNAL   PAGE 14

	DATE		ACCOUNT TITLE	DOC. NO.	POST. REF.	DEBIT	CREDIT	
1			*Reversing Entries*					1
2	20-- Jan.	1	Accrued Interest			1 7 7 78		2
3			Interest Expense				1 7 7 78	3
4		1	Employee Income Tax Payable			7 4 0 00		4
5			Social Security Tax Payable			2 1 4 50		5
6			Medicare Tax Payable			4 9 50		6
7			Salaries Payable			2 2 9 6 00		7
8			Salaries Expense—Administrative				1 5 0 0 00	8
9			Salaries Expense—Sales				1 8 0 0 00	9
10		1	Social Security Tax Payable			2 1 4 50		10
11			Medicare Tax Payable			4 9 50		11
12			Unemployment Tax Payable—Federal			9 60		12
13			Unemployment Tax Payable—State			6 4 80		13
14			Payroll Taxes Expense				3 3 8 40	14
15								15
16								16
17								17
18								18
19								19
20								20
21								21
22								22
23								23
24								24
25								25
26								26
27								27
28								28
29								29
30								30
31								31

9-1 APPLICATION PROBLEM, p. 270

Journalizing notes payable transactions

[1]

CASH RECEIPTS JOURNAL
PAGE 15

DATE	ACCOUNT TITLE	DOC. NO.	POST. REF.	GENERAL DEBIT	GENERAL CREDIT	ACCOUNTS RECEIVABLE CREDIT	SALES CREDIT	SALES TAX PAYABLE DEBIT	SALES TAX PAYABLE CREDIT	SALES DISCOUNT DEBIT	CASH DEBIT
20-- Aug. 1	Notes Payable	R143			1100 00						1100 00
Sept. 12	Notes Payable	R176			1200 00						1200 00
Oct. 21	Notes Payable	R203			800 00						800 00

[4]

CASH PAYMENTS JOURNAL
PAGE 21

DATE	ACCOUNT TITLE	CK. NO.	POST. REF.	GENERAL DEBIT	GENERAL CREDIT	ACCOUNTS PAYABLE DEBIT	PURCHASES DISCOUNT CREDIT	CASH CREDIT
20-- Oct. 30	Notes Payable	245		1100 00				1130 25
	Interest Expense			30 25				
Nov. 11	Notes Payable	352		1200 00				1224 00
	Interest Expense			24 00				
Dec. 20	Notes Payable	459		800 00				813 33
	Interest Expense			13 33				

9-1 APPLICATION PROBLEM (concluded)

[2]

Maturity dates:

August 1 note:

August 1 – August 31	*30*
September	*30*
October 1 – October 30	*30*
Total	*90*

September 12 note:

September 12 – September 30	*18*
October	*31*
November 1 – November 11	*11*
Total	*60*

October 21 note:

October 21 – October 31	*10*
November	*30*
December 1 – December 20	*20*
Total	*60*

[3]

Interest due at maturity:

Note	Interest at Maturity
August 1	*$30.25*
Sept. 12	*24.00*
Oct. 21	*13.33*

Name _____ Date _____ Class _____

9-2 APPLICATION PROBLEM, p. 270

Journalizing adjusting and reversing entries for prepaid expenses
initially recorded as expenses

[1]

GENERAL JOURNAL

PAGE 13

	DATE		ACCOUNT TITLE	DOC. NO.	POST. REF.	DEBIT	CREDIT	
1			*Adjusting Entries*					1
2	20-- Dec.	31	Supplies—Administrative			45000		2
3			Supplies Expense—Administrative				45000	3
4		31	Supplies—Sales			80000		4
5			Supplies Expense—Sales				80000	5
6		31	Prepaid Insurance			72000		6
7			Insurance Expense				72000	7
8								8
9								9
10								10
11								11
12								12
13								13
14								14
15								15
16								16
17								17
18								18
19								19
20								20
21								21
22								22
23								23
24								24
25								25
26								26
27								27
28								28
29								29
30								30

9-2 APPLICATION PROBLEM (concluded)

[2]

GENERAL JOURNAL   PAGE 1

	DATE		ACCOUNT TITLE	DOC. NO.	POST. REF.	DEBIT	CREDIT	
1			*Reversing Entries*					1
2	20— Jan.	1	Supplies Expense—Administrative			4 5 0 00		2
3			Supplies—Administrative				4 5 0 00	3
4		1	Supplies Expense—Sales			8 0 0 00		4
5			Supplies—Sales				8 0 0 00	5
6		1	Insurance Expense			7 2 0 00		6
7			Prepaid Insurance				7 2 0 00	7
8								8
9								9
10								10
11								11
12								12
13								13
14								14
15								15
16								16
17								17
18								18
19								19
20								20
21								21
22								22
23								23
24								24
25								25
26								26
27								27
28								28
29								29
30								30
31								31

Name _____ Date _____ Class _____

9-3 APPLICATION PROBLEM, p. 271

Journalizing adjusting and reversing entries for accrued expenses [1]

	DATE		ACCOUNT TITLE	DOC. NO.	POST. REF.	DEBIT	CREDIT	
1			*Adjusting Entries*					1
2	20-- Dec.	31	*Interest Expense*			3 5 0 00		2
3			*Interest Payable*				3 5 0 00	3
4		31	*Salary Expense—Administrative*			6 0 0 00		4
5			*Salary Expense—Sales*			5 0 0 00		5
6			*Employee Income Tax Payable*				2 4 0 00	6
7			*Social Security Tax Payable*				7 1 50	7
8			*Medicare Tax Payable*				1 6 50	8
9			*Salaries Payable*				7 7 2 00	9
10		31	*Payroll Taxes Expense*			1 5 6 20		10
11			*Social Security Tax Payable*				7 1 50	11
12			*Medicare Tax Payable*				1 6 50	12
13			*Unemployment Tax Payable—Federal*				8 80	13
14			*Unemployment Tax Payable—State*				5 9 40	14
15		31	*Federal Income Tax Expense*			1 3 0 0 00		15
16			*Federal Income Tax Payable*				1 3 0 0 00	16
17								17
18								18
19								19
20								20
21								21
22								22
23								23
24								24
25								25
26								26
27								27
28								28
29								29
30								30
31								31

9-3 APPLICATION PROBLEM (concluded)

[2]

GENERAL JOURNAL   PAGE 1

	DATE		ACCOUNT TITLE	DOC. NO.	POST. REF.	DEBIT	CREDIT	
1			*Reversing Entries*					1
2	20-- Jan.	1	Interest Payable			3 5 0 00		2
3			Interest Expense				3 5 0 00	3
4		1	Employee Income Tax Payable			2 4 0 00		4
5			Social Security Tax Payable			7 1 50		5
6			Medicare Tax Payable			1 6 50		6
7			Salaries Payable			7 7 2 00		7
8			Salary Expense—Administrative				6 0 0 00	8
9			Salary Expense—Sales				5 0 0 00	9
10		1	Social Security Tax Payable			7 1 50		10
11			Medicare Tax Payable			1 6 50		11
12			Unemployment Tax Payable—Federal			8 80		12
13			Unemployment Tax Payable—State			5 9 40		13
14			Payroll Taxes Expense				1 5 6 20	14
15								15
16								16
17								17
18								18
19								19
20								20
21								21
22								22
23								23
24								24
25								25
26								26
27								27
28								28
29								29
30								30
31								31

9-4 MASTERY PROBLEM, p. 271

Journalizing adjusting and reversing entries for prepaid expenses initially recorded as expenses and for accrued expenses

[1]

[3]

[1]

CASH RECEIPTS JOURNAL

PAGE 15

DATE	ACCOUNT TITLE	DOC. NO.	POST. REF.	GENERAL DEBIT	GENERAL CREDIT	ACCOUNTS RECEIVABLE CREDIT	SALES CREDIT	SALES TAX PAYABLE DEBIT	SALES TAX PAYABLE CREDIT	SALES DISCOUNT DEBIT	CASH DEBIT
20-- July 1	Notes Payable	R123			700000						700000
Oct. 10	Notes Payable	R149			150000						150000
Nov. 1	Notes Payable	R152			100000						100000

CASH PAYMENTS JOURNAL

PAGE 21

DATE	ACCOUNT TITLE	CK. NO.	POST. REF.	GENERAL DEBIT	GENERAL CREDIT	ACCOUNTS PAYABLE DEBIT	PURCHASES DISCOUNT CREDIT	CASH CREDIT
20-- Aug. 30	Notes Payable	105		700000				711400
	Interest Expense			1400				
Nov. 24	Notes Payable	195		150000				151875
	Interest Expense			1875				

9-4 MASTERY PROBLEM (continued)

[2]

Maturity dates:

July 1 note:

July 1 – July 31	*30*
August 1 – August 30	*30*
Total	*60*

October 10 note:

October 10 – October 31	*21*
November 1 – November 24	*24*
Total	*45*

November 1 note:

November 1 – November 30	*29*
December	*31*
January 1 – January 30	*30*
Total	*90*

9-4 MASTERY PROBLEM (continued)

[4]

GENERAL JOURNAL   PAGE 13

	DATE		ACCOUNT TITLE	DOC. NO.	POST. REF.	DEBIT	CREDIT	
1			*Adjusting Entries*					1
2	20-- Dec.	31	Supplies—Administrative			2 0 0 00		2
3			Supplies Expense—Administrative				2 0 0 00	3
4		31	Supplies—Sales			3 0 0 00		4
5			Supplies Expense—Sales				3 0 0 00	5
6		31	Prepaid Insurance			3 5 0 00		6
7			Insurance Expense				3 5 0 00	7
8		31	Interest Expense			1 8 33		8
9			Interest Payable				1 8 33	9
10		31	Salary Expense—Administrative			3 5 0 00		10
11			Salary Expense—Sales			4 1 5 00		11
12			Employee Income Tax Payable				1 2 0 00	12
13			Social Security Tax Payable				4 9 73	13
14			Medicare Tax Payable				1 1 47	14
15			Salaries Payable				5 8 3 80	15
16		31	Payroll Taxes Expense			1 0 8 63		16
17			Social Security Tax Payable				4 9 73	17
18			Medicare Tax Payable				1 1 47	18
19			Unemployment Tax Payable—Federal				6 12	19
20			Unemployment Tax Payable—State				4 1 31	20
21		31	Federal Income Tax Expense			8 0 0 00		21
22			Federal Income Tax Payable				8 0 0 00	22
23								23
24								24
25								25
26								26
27								27
28								28
29								29
30								30
31								31

9-4 MASTERY PROBLEM (concluded)

[5]

GENERAL JOURNAL
PAGE 1

	DATE		ACCOUNT TITLE	DOC. NO.	POST. REF.	DEBIT	CREDIT	
1			*Reversing Entries*					1
2	20-- Jan.	1	Supplies Expense—Administrative			2 0 0 00		2
3			Supplies—Administrative				2 0 0 00	3
4		1	Supplies Expense—Sales			3 0 0 00		4
5			Supplies—Sales				3 0 0 00	5
6		1	Insurance Expense			3 5 0 00		6
7			Prepaid Insurance				3 5 0 00	7
8		1	Interest Payable			1 8 33		8
9			Interest Expense				1 8 33	9
10		1	Employee Income Tax Payable			1 2 0 00		10
11			Social Security Tax Payable			4 9 73		11
12			Medicare Tax Payable			1 1 47		12
13			Salaries Payable			5 8 3 80		13
14			Salary Expense—Administrative				3 5 0 00	14
15			Salary Expense—Sales				4 1 5 00	15
16		1	Social Security Tax Payable			4 9 73		16
17			Medicare Tax Payable			1 1 47		17
18			Unemployment Tax Payable—Federal			6 12		18
19			Unemployment Tax Payable—State			4 1 31		19
20			Payroll Taxes Expense				1 0 8 63	20
21								21
22								22
23								23
24								24
25								25
26								26
27								27
28								28
29								29
30								30
31								31

9-5 CHALLENGE PROBLEM, p. 272

Journalizing entries for notes payable and prepaid insurance when no reversing entries are recorded

[1]

Cash			
Nov. 1	10,000.00	Apr. 30	10,600.00

Income Summary			
Dec. 31 Clos.	200.00	Dec. 31 Clos.	200.00

Accrued Interest			
		Dec. 31 Adj.	200.00

Interest Expense			
Dec. 31 Adj.	200.00	Dec. 31 Clos.	200.00
New Bal.	0.00		
Apr. 30	600.00		

Notes Payable			
Apr. 30	10,000.00	Nov. 1	10,000.00

Retained Earnings			
Dec. 31 Clos.	200.00		

Because no reversing entry was recorded, Interest Expense is overstated by $200.00. In addition, a $200.00 liability remains in Accrued Interest even though the note has been paid. An adjusting entry would be required to eliminate the balance in Accrued Interest and reduce the balance in Interest Expense. The adjusting entry would be the same as the correct reversing entry.

[1]

GENERAL JOURNAL   PAGE 13

	DATE		ACCOUNT TITLE	DOC. NO.	POST. REF.	DEBIT	CREDIT	
1			*Adjusting Entries*					1
2	20X1 Dec.	31	*Interest Expense*			2 0 0 00		2
3			*Accrued Interest*				2 0 0 00	3
4			*Closing Entries*					4
5		31	*Interest Expense*			2 0 0 00		5
6			*Income Summary*				2 0 0 00	6
7		31	*Income Summary*			2 0 0 00		7
8			*Retained Earnings*				2 0 0 00	8
9								9
10								10
11								11

9-5 CHALLENGE PROBLEM (continued)

CASH RECEIPTS JOURNAL

[1]   PAGE 11

DATE	ACCOUNT TITLE	DOC. NO.	POST. REF.	GENERAL DEBIT	GENERAL CREDIT	ACCOUNTS RECEIVABLE CREDIT	SALES CREDIT	SALES TAX PAYABLE DEBIT	SALES TAX PAYABLE CREDIT	SALES DISCOUNT DEBIT	CASH DEBIT
20X1 Nov. 1	Note Payable	R142			1000000						1000000

CASH PAYMENTS JOURNAL

[1]   PAGE 4

DATE	ACCOUNT TITLE	CK. NO.	POST. REF.	GENERAL DEBIT	GENERAL CREDIT	ACCOUNTS PAYABLE DEBIT	PURCHASES DISCOUNT CREDIT	CASH CREDIT
20X2 Apr. 30	Notes Payable	154		1000000				1060000
	Interest Expense			60000				

9-5 CHALLENGE PROBLEM (continued)

[2]

Cash			
Nov. 1	10,000.00	Apr. 30	10,600.00

Accrued Interest			
Apr. 30	200.00	Dec. 31 Adj.	200.00

Notes Payable			
Apr. 30	10,000.00	Nov. 1	10,000.00

Income Summary			
Dec. 31 Clos.	200.00	Dec. 31 Clos.	200.00

Interest Expense			
Dec. 31 Adj.	200.00	Dec. 31 Clos.	200.00
New Bal.	0.00		
Apr. 30	400.00		

Retained Earnings		
Dec. 31 Clos.	200.00	

The correct entry on April 30 effectively combines the reversing entry with the entry to record the note payment. Thus, the $600.00 interest payment is offset by the $200.00 credit to Interest Expense of the reversing entry.

[2]

GENERAL JOURNAL   PAGE 13

	DATE		ACCOUNT TITLE	DOC. NO.	POST. REF.	DEBIT	CREDIT	
1			*Adjusting Entries*					1
2	20X1 Dec.	31	Interest Expense			2 0 0 00		2
3			Accrued Interest				2 0 0 00	3
4			*Closing Entries*					4
5		31	Interest Expense			2 0 0 00		5
6			Income Summary				2 0 0 00	6
7		31	Income Summary			2 0 0 00		7
8			Retained Earnings				2 0 0 00	8
9								9
10								10
11								11

9-5 CHALLENGE PROBLEM (concluded)

[2]

CASH RECEIPTS JOURNAL

PAGE 11

DATE	ACCOUNT TITLE	DOC. NO.	POST. REF.	1 GENERAL DEBIT	2 GENERAL CREDIT	3 ACCOUNTS RECEIVABLE CREDIT	4 SALES CREDIT	5 SALES TAX PAYABLE DEBIT	6 SALES TAX PAYABLE CREDIT	7 SALES DISCOUNT DEBIT	8 CASH DEBIT	
20X1 Nov. 1	Notes Payable	R142			1000000						1000000	1
												2
												3
												4
												5
												6
												7
												8
												9
												10
												11
												12

[2]

CASH PAYMENTS JOURNAL

PAGE 4

DATE	ACCOUNT TITLE	CK. NO.	POST. REF.	1 GENERAL DEBIT	2 GENERAL CREDIT	3 ACCOUNTS PAYABLE DEBIT	4 PURCHASES DISCOUNT CREDIT	5 CASH CREDIT	
20X2 Apr. 30	Notes Payable	154		1000000				1060000	1
	Interest Expense			40000					2
	Accrued Expense			20000					3
									4
									5
									6
									7

Name _____ Date _____ Class _____

10-1 WORK TOGETHER, p. 282

Journalizing notes receivable transactions

[4]

GENERAL JOURNAL   PAGE 5

	DATE		ACCOUNT TITLE	DOC. NO.	POST. REF.	DEBIT	CREDIT	
1	20-- May	1	Notes Receivable	NR1		4 0 0 00		1
2			Accounts Receivable/Patrick Sampson		/		4 0 0 00	2
3	June	1	Notes Receivable	NR2		7 0 0 00		3
4			Sales		/		7 0 0 00	4
5		30	Accounts Receivable/Patrick Sampson	M142		4 1 0 00		5
6			Notes Receivable				4 0 0 00	6
7			Interest Income				1 0 00	7
8								8
9								9
10								10
11								11
12								12
13								13
14								14
15								15
16								16
17								17
18								18
19								19
20								20
21								21
22								22
23								23
24								24
25								25
26								26
27								27
28								28
29								29
30								30
31								31

CASH RECEIPTS JOURNAL

PAGE 8

				GENERAL	GENERAL	ACCOUNTS RECEIVABLE	SALES	SALES TAX PAYABLE	SALES TAX PAYABLE	SALES DISCOUNT	CASH
DATE	ACCOUNT TITLE	DOC. NO.	POST. REF.	DEBIT	CREDIT	CREDIT	CREDIT	DEBIT	CREDIT	DEBIT	DEBIT
				1	2	3	4	5	6	7	8
20-- Nov. 28	Notes Receivable	R310			700 00						763 00
	Interest Income				63 00						
Dec. 12	Patrick Sampson	R432				410 00					438 19
	Interest Income				28 19						

10-1 ON YOUR OWN, p. 282

Journalizing notes receivable transactions

[5]

GENERAL JOURNAL

PAGE 6

	DATE		ACCOUNT TITLE	DOC. NO.	POST. REF.	DEBIT	CREDIT	
1	20-- May	14	Notes Receivable	NR19		3 2 0 00		1
2			Accounts Receivable/Pamula Yates		/		3 2 0 00	2
3	June	1	Notes Receivable	NR20		1 5 0 0 00		3
4			Sales				1 5 0 0 00	4
5	Aug.	12	Accounts Receivable/Pamula Yates	M82	/	3 3 4 40		5
6			Notes Receivable				3 2 0 00	6
7			Interest Income				1 4 40	7
8								8
9								9
10								10
11								11
12								12
13								13
14								14
15								15
16								16
17								17
18								18
19								19
20								20
21								21
22								22
23								23
24								24
25								25
26								26
27								27
28								28
29								29
30								30
31								31

10-1 ON YOUR OWN (concluded)

CASH RECEIPTS JOURNAL

PAGE 9

DATE	ACCOUNT TITLE	DOC. NO.	POST. REF.	GENERAL DEBIT	GENERAL CREDIT	ACCOUNTS RECEIVABLE CREDIT	SALES CREDIT	SALES TAX PAYABLE DEBIT	SALES TAX PAYABLE CREDIT	SALES DISCOUNT DEBIT	CASH DEBIT	
20-- Oct. 26	Notes Receivable	R430			150000						159000	1
	Interest Income				9000							2
Dec. 22	Pamula Yates	R753				33440					35647	3
	Interest Income				2207							4
												5
												6
												7
												8
												9
												10
												11
												12
												13
												14
												15
												16
												17
												18
												19
												20
												21
												22
												23
												24
												25

10-2 WORK TOGETHER, p. 287

Journalizing adjusting and reversing entries for unearned revenue   **[6, 8]**
initially recorded as revenue and for accrued revenue

GENERAL JOURNAL   PAGE 13

	DATE		ACCOUNT TITLE	DOC. NO.	POST. REF.	DEBIT	CREDIT	
1			*Adjusting Entries*					1
2	20-- Dec.	31	Rent Income			1 40 0 00		2
3			Unearned Rent				1 40 0 00	3
4		31	Interest Receivable			7 2 50		4
5			Interest Income				7 2 50	5
6								6
7								7
8								8
9								9
10								10
11								11
12								12
13								13
14								14
15								15
16								16
17								17
18								18
19								19
20								20
21								21
22								22
23								23
24								24
25								25
26								26
27								27
28								28
29								29
30								30

10-2 WORK TOGETHER (concluded)

[7, 9]

GENERAL JOURNAL   PAGE 14

	DATE		ACCOUNT TITLE	DOC. NO.	POST. REF.	DEBIT	CREDIT	
1			*Reversing Entries*					1
2	20-- Jan.	1	*Unearned Rent*			1 40 00		2
3			*Rent Income*				1 40 00	3
4		1	*Interest Income*			72 50		4
5			*Interest Receivable*				72 50	5
6								6
7								7
8								8
9								9
10								10
11								11
12								12

Space for calculations:

Note: Calculation not a required part of solution.

Note	Principal	×	Interest Rate	×	Time as Fraction of a Year	=	Accrued Interest
14	$2,000.00	×	15%	×	$\frac{47}{360}$	=	$39.17
15	$3,000.00	×	16%	×	$\frac{25}{360}$	=	33.33
	Total accrued interest income, December 31						$72.50

10-2 ON YOUR OWN, p. 288

Journalizing adjusting and reversing entries for unearned revenue initially recorded as revenue and for accrued revenue

[10, 12]

GENERAL JOURNAL

PAGE 19

	DATE		ACCOUNT TITLE	DOC. NO.	POST. REF.	DEBIT	CREDIT	
1			*Adjusting Entries*					1
2	20-- Dec.	31	Advertising Income			5 0 0 00		2
3			Unearned Advertising				5 0 0 00	3
4		31	Interest Receivable			1 1 8 67		4
5			Interest Income				1 1 8 67	5
6								6
7								7
8								8
9								9
10								10
11								11
12								12
13								13
14								14
15								15
16								16
17								17
18								18
19								19
20								20
21								21
22								22
23								23
24								24
25								25
26								26
27								27
28								28
29								29
30								30

Name _____ Date _____ Class _____

10-2 ON YOUR OWN (concluded)

[11, 13]

GENERAL JOURNAL   PAGE 20

	DATE		ACCOUNT TITLE	DOC. NO.	POST. REF.	DEBIT	CREDIT	
1			*Reversing Entries*					1
2	20-- Jan.	1	Unearned Advertising			500 00		2
3			Advertising Income				500 00	3
4		1	Interest Income			118 67		4
5			Interest Receivable				118 67	5
6								6
7								7
8								8
9								9
10								10
11								11
12								12

Space for calculations:

Note: Calculation not a required part of solution.

Note	Principal	×	Interest Rate	×	Time as Fraction of a Year	=	Accrued Interest
26	$4,000.00	×	18%	×	$\frac{53}{360}$	=	$106.00
29	$1,500.00	×	16%	×	$\frac{19}{360}$	=	12.67
	Total accrued interest income, December 31						$118.67

EXPLORE ACCOUNTING, p. 289

Projection assuming no factoring

Transaction	Week	Cash	Accounts Receivable	Inventory	Sales	Cost of Goods Sold
Balance	1			10,000		
Sales			2,000	(1,000)	2,000	1,000
Collection						
Purchases						
Balance	2	0	2,000	9,000	2,000	1,000
Sales			1,800	(900)	1,800	900
Collection						
Purchases						
Balance	3	0	3,800	8,100	3,800	1,900
Sales			1,620	(810)	1,620	810
Collection						
Purchases						
Balance	4	0	5,420	7,290	5,420	2,710
Sales			1,458	(729)	1,458	729
Collection						
Purchases						
Balance	5	0	6,878	6,561	6,878	3,439
Sales			1,312	(656)	1,312	656
Collection		2,000				
Purchases		(2,000)		2,000		
Balance	6	0	8,190	7,905	8,190	4,095
Sales			1,581	(790)	1,581	790
Collection		1,800				
Purchases		(1,800)		1,800		
Balance	7	0	9,771	8,915	9,771	4,885
Sales			1,783	(891)	1,783	891
Collection		1,620				
Purchases		(1,620)		1,620		
Balance	8	0	11,554	9,644	11,554	5,776
Sales			1,929	(964)	1,929	964
Collection		1,458				
Purchases		(1,320)		1,320		
Balance	9	138	13,483	10,000	13,483	6,740

Sales	13,483
Cost of Goods Sold	6,740
Income	6,743

 **EXPLORE ACCOUNTING (concluded)**

Projection assuming factoring

Transaction	Week	Cash	Accounts Receivable	Inventory	Sales	Cost of Goods Sold	Factoring Expense
Balance	1			(10,000)			
Sales			2,000	(1,000)	2,000	1,000	
Collection							
Factoring		1,800					200
Purchases		(1,000)		1,000			
Balance	2	800	2,000	10,000	2,000	1,000	200
Sales			2,000	(1,000)	2,000	1,000	
Collection							
Factoring		1,800					200
Purchases		(1,000)		1,000			
Balance	3	1,600	4,000	10,000	4,000	2,000	400
Sales			2,000	(1,000)	2,000	1,000	
Collection							
Factoring		1,800					200
Purchases		(1,000)		1,000			
Balance	4	2,400	6,000	10,000	6,000	3,000	600
Sales			2,000	(1,000)	2,000	1,000	
Collection							
Factoring		1,800					200
Purchases		(1,000)		1,000			
Balance	5	3,200	8,000	10,000	8,000	4,000	800
Sales			2,000	(1,000)	2,000	1,000	
Collection							
Factoring		1,800					200
Purchases		(1,000)		1,000			
Balance	6	4,000	10,000	10,000	10,000	5,000	1,000
Sales			2,000	(1,000)	2,000	1,000	
Collection							
Factoring		1,800					200
Purchases		(1,000)		1,000			
Balance	7	4,800	12,000	10,000	12,000	6,000	1,200
Sales			2,000	(1,000)	2,000	1,000	
Collection							
Factoring		1,800					200
Purchases		(1,000)		1,000			
Balance	8	5,600	14,000	10,000	14,000	7,000	1,400
Sales			2,000	(1,000)	2,000	1,000	
Collection							
Factoring		1,800					200
Purchases		(1,000)		1,000			
Balance	9	6,400	16,000	10,000	16,000	8,000	1,600

Sales	16,000
Cost of Goods Sold	(8,000)
Factoring Expense	(1,600)
Income	6,400

Consultant's recommendation:

Although factoring resulted in slightly less income, factoring did result in two positive points. First, the company generated $6,400 of cash that it can use in other areas of the business. Second, the company was never in an out-of-stock situation, thus providing better customer service, which will likely have a positive impact in the long term.

If the company only factored part of their accounts receivable, only enough to fund restocking inventory to $10,000, its net income would increase.

Name _____ Date _____ Class _____

10-1 APPLICATION PROBLEM, p. 290

Journalizing transactions for notes receivable

GENERAL JOURNAL   PAGE 8

	DATE		ACCOUNT TITLE	DOC. NO.	POST. REF.	DEBIT	CREDIT	
1	20-- Aug.	1	Notes Receivable	NR1		20000		1
2			Accounts Receivable/James Huber		/		20000	2
3		1	Notes Receivable	NR2		30000		3
4			Sales				30000	4
5	Sept.	30	Accounts Receivable/James Huber	M12	/	20333		5
6			Notes Receivable				20000	6
7			Interest Income				333	7
8	Sept.	30	Notes Receivable	NR3		50000		8
9			Accounts Receivable/Melissa Carr		/		50000	9
10								10
11								11
12								12
13								13
14								14
15								15
16								16
17								17
18								18
19								19
20								20
21								21
22								22
23								23
24								24
25								25
26								26
27								27
28								28
29								29
30								30
31								31

Chapter 10   Accounting for Notes Receivable, Unearned Revenue, and Accrued Revenue • **353**

10-1 APPLICATION PROBLEM (concluded)

CASH RECEIPTS JOURNAL

PAGE 15

	DATE	ACCOUNT TITLE	DOC. NO.	POST. REF.	GENERAL DEBIT (1)	GENERAL CREDIT (2)	ACCOUNTS RECEIVABLE CREDIT (3)	SALES CREDIT (4)	SALES TAX PAYABLE DEBIT (5)	SALES TAX PAYABLE CREDIT (6)	SALES DISCOUNT DEBIT (7)	CASH DEBIT (8)	
1	20-- Sept. 30	Notes Receivable	R10			30000						30600	1
2		Interest Income				600							2
3	Nov. 30	Notes Receivable	R32			50000						50833	3
4		Interest Income				833							4
5	Dec. 1	James Huber	R33				20333					20683	5
6		Interest Income				350							6
7													7
8													8
9													9
10													10
11													11
12													12
13													13
14													14
15													15
16													16
17													17
18													18
19													19
20													20
21													21
22													22
23													23
24													24
25													25

10-2 APPLICATION PROBLEM, p. 290

Journalizing adjusting and reversing entries for unearned revenue initially recorded as revenue

[1]

GENERAL JOURNAL   PAGE 13

	DATE		ACCOUNT TITLE	DOC. NO.	POST. REF.	DEBIT	CREDIT	
1			*Adjusting Entry*					1
2	20– Dec.	31	Rent Income			1 8 0 0 00		2
3			Unearned Rent				1 8 0 0 00	3
4								4
5								5
6								6
7								7
8								8
9								9
10								10
11								11
12								12
13								13
14								14
15								15
16								16
17								17
18								18
19								19
20								20
21								21
22								22
23								23
24								24
25								25
26								26
27								27
28								28
29								29
30								30

10-2 APPLICATION PROBLEM (concluded)

[2]

GENERAL JOURNAL   PAGE 1

	DATE		ACCOUNT TITLE	DOC. NO.	POST. REF.	DEBIT	CREDIT	
1			*Reversing Entry*					1
2	20-- Jan.	1	Unearned Rent			1 80 0 00		2
3			Rent Income				1 80 0 00	3
4								4
5								5
6								6
7								7
8								8
9								9
10								10
11								11
12								12
13								13
14								14
15								15
16								16
17								17
18								18
19								19
20								20
21								21
22								22
23								23
24								24
25								25
26								26
27								27
28								28
29								29
30								30
31								31

10-3 APPLICATION PROBLEM, p. 290

Journalizing adjusting and reversing entries for accrued revenue [2]

GENERAL JOURNAL   PAGE 13

	DATE		ACCOUNT TITLE	DOC. NO.	POST. REF.	DEBIT	CREDIT	
1			*Adjusting Entry*					1
2	20– Dec.	31	*Interest Receivable*			5 83		2
3			*Interest Income*				5 83	3
4								4
5								5
6								6
7								7
8								8
9								9
10								10
11								11
12								12

[1]

Space for calculations:

Note	Accrued Interest Income
1	$3.33
2	2.50
Total	$5.83

10-3 APPLICATION PROBLEM (concluded)

[3]

GENERAL JOURNAL   PAGE 1

	DATE		ACCOUNT TITLE	DOC. NO.	POST. REF.	DEBIT	CREDIT	
1			*Reversing Entry*					1
2	20-- Jan.	1	Interest Income			5 83		2
3			Interest Receivable				5 83	3
4								4
5								5
6								6
7								7
8								8
9								9
10								10
11								11
12								12
13								13
14								14
15								15
16								16
17								17
18								18
19								19
20								20
21								21
22								22
23								23
24								24
25								25
26								26
27								27
28								28
29								29
30								30
31								31

10-4 MASTERY PROBLEM, p. 291

Journalizing notes receivable, unearned revenue, and accrued revenue initially recorded as revenue transactions [1, 2]

GENERAL JOURNAL   PAGE 7

	DATE		ACCOUNT TITLE	DOC. NO.	POST. REF.	DEBIT	CREDIT	
1	20-- July	1	Notes Receivable	NR12		5 0 0 00		1
2			Sales				5 0 0 00	2
3		5	Notes Receivable	NR13		6 0 0 00		3
4			Accounts Receivable/Gerald Kammer		/		6 0 0 00	4
5	Sept.	29	Accounts Receivable/Timothy Johnson	M32	/	5 1 2 50		5
6			Notes Receivable				5 0 0 00	6
7			Interest Income				1 2 50	7
8	Dec.	4	Notes Receivable			9 0 0 00		8
9			Sales				9 0 0 00	9
10			*Adjusting Entries*					10
11		31	Interest Receivable			8 10		11
12			Interest Income				8 10	12
13		31	Rent Income			5 0 0 00		13
14			Unearned Rent				5 0 0 00	14
15								15
16								16

[3]

GENERAL JOURNAL   PAGE 1

	DATE		ACCOUNT TITLE	DOC. NO.	POST. REF.	DEBIT	CREDIT	
1			*Reversing Entries*					1
2	20-- Jan.	1	Interest Income			8 10		2
3			Interest Receivable				8 10	3
4		1	Unearned Rent			5 0 0 00		4
5			Rent Income				5 0 0 00	5
6								6
7								7
8								8
9								9

10-4 **MASTERY PROBLEM (concluded)**

CASH RECEIPTS JOURNAL

PAGE 19

	DATE	ACCOUNT TITLE	DOC. NO.	POST. REF.	GENERAL DEBIT	GENERAL CREDIT	ACCOUNTS RECEIVABLE CREDIT	SALES CREDIT	SALES TAX PAYABLE DEBIT	SALES TAX PAYABLE CREDIT	SALES DISCOUNT DEBIT	CASH DEBIT	
1	20-- Oct. 3	Notes Receivable	R65			6 0 0 0 0						6 1 8 0 0	1
2		Interest Income				1 8 0 0							2
3	Nov. 1	Rent Income	R70			1 5 0 0 0 0						1 5 0 0 0 0	3
4	Dec. 1	Timothy Johnson	R81				5 1 2 5 0					5 2 1 4 7	4
5		Interest Income				8 9 7							5
6													6
7													7
8													8
9													9
10													10
11													11
12													12
13													13
14													14
15													15
16													16
17													17
18													18
19													19
20													20
21													21
22													22
23													23
24													24
25													25

10-5 CHALLENGE PROBLEM, p. 291

Journalizing accounts and notes receivable

GENERAL JOURNAL   PAGE 7

	DATE		ACCOUNT TITLE	DOC. NO.	POST. REF.	DEBIT	CREDIT	
1	20-- July	4	Notes Receivable	NR26		5 2 2 50		1
2			Accounts Receivable/Steven Bozeman		/		5 0 0 00	2
3			Interest Income				2 2 50	3
4		31	Allowance for Uncollectible Accounts	M46		3 1 56		4
5			Accounts Receivable/Pierre Black		/		2 7 81	5
6			Accounts Receivable/John Hamilton		/		3 75	6
7								7
8								8
9								9
10								10
11								11
12								12
13								13
14								14
15								15
16								16
17								17
18								18
19								19
20								20
21								21
22								22
23								23
24								24
25								25
26								26
27								27
28								28
29								29
30								30
31								31

10-5 CHALLENGE PROBLEM (concluded)

CASH RECEIPTS JOURNAL

PAGE 7

	DATE	ACCOUNT TITLE	DOC. NO.	POST. REF.	GENERAL DEBIT	GENERAL CREDIT	ACCOUNTS RECEIVABLE CREDIT	SALES CREDIT	SALES TAX PAYABLE DEBIT	SALES TAX PAYABLE CREDIT	SALES DISCOUNT DEBIT	CASH DEBIT	
1	July 12	Notes Receivable	R70			62700						61800	1
2		Interest Income				1881							2
3		Accounts Receivable/Pierre Black		/	2781								3
4	15	John Hamilton	R71				25000					25000	4
5		Interest Income				375							5
6		Accounts Receivable/John Hamilton		/	375								6
7													7
8													8
9													9
10													10
11													11
12													12
13													13
14													14
15													15
16													16
17													17
18													18
19													19
20													20
21													21
22													22
23													23
24													24
25													25

Name _____ Date _____ Class _____

Extra form

CASH PAYMENTS JOURNAL   PAGE _____

	DATE	ACCOUNT TITLE	CK. NO.	POST. REF.	GENERAL DEBIT	GENERAL CREDIT	ACCOUNTS PAYABLE DEBIT	PURCHASES DISCOUNT CREDIT	CASH CREDIT	
					1	2	3	4	5	
1										1
2										2
3										3
4										4
5										5
6										6
7										7
8										8
9										9
10										10
11										11
12										12
13										13
14										14
15										15
16										16
17										17
18										18
19										19
20										20
21										21
22										22
23										23
24										24
25										25
26										26
27										27
28										28
29										29
30										30
31										31
32										32

Name _____ Date _____ Class _____

Extra form

Name _____ Date _____ Class _____

Extra form

Extra form

Extra form

GENERAL JOURNAL   PAGE _____

	DATE	ACCOUNT TITLE	DOC. NO.	POST. REF.	DEBIT	CREDIT	
1							1
2							2
3							3
4							4
5							5
6							6
7							7
8							8
9							9
10							10
11							11
12							12
13							13
14							14
15							15
16							16
17							17
18							18
19							19
20							20
21							21
22							22
23							23
24							24
25							25
26							26
27							27
28							28
29							29
30							30
31							31

Extra form

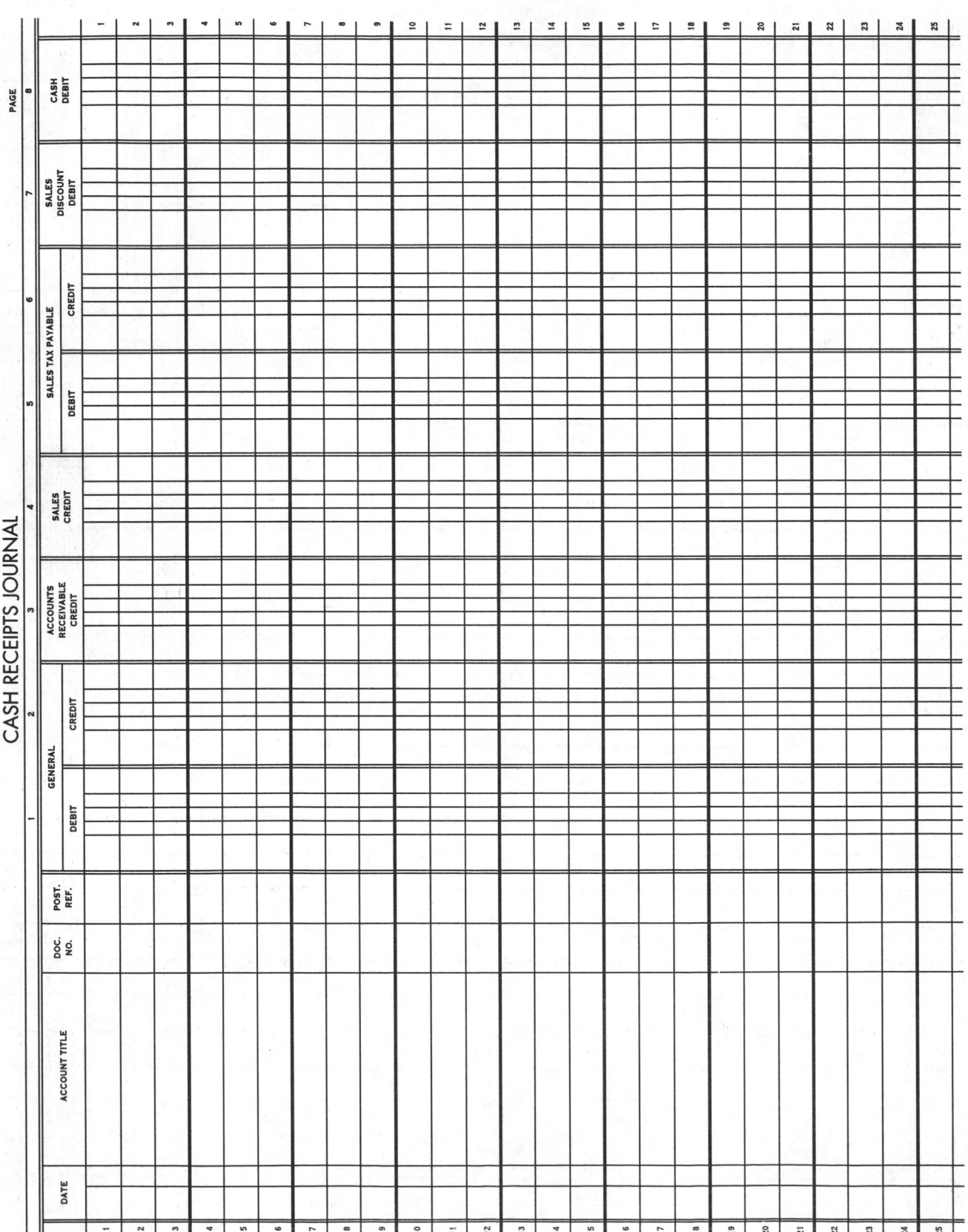

CASH RECEIPTS JOURNAL

PAGE

DATE	ACCOUNT TITLE	DOC. NO.	POST. REF.	GENERAL DEBIT	GENERAL CREDIT	ACCOUNTS RECEIVABLE CREDIT	SALES CREDIT	SALES TAX PAYABLE DEBIT	SALES TAX PAYABLE CREDIT	SALES DISCOUNT DEBIT	CASH DEBIT